ENGINEERING AND WESTERN CIVILIZATION

The Boulder Canyon Dam, 1931–36

Designed by the U.S. Bureau of Reclamation and built by a group of engineering contractors, the Six Companies, this three-million-cubic-yard mass of concrete, 730 ft high, is one of the wonders of this Engineering Age—an outstanding example of the power of engineering know-how, skill, and organization —of mind over matter. (*Courtesy of U.S. Bureau of Reclamation.*)

ENGINEERING

AND WESTERN CIVILIZATION

JAMES KIP FINCH

*Renwick Professor of Civil Engineering
and Dean Emeritus of the School of Engineering
Columbia University*

NEW YORK · TORONTO · LONDON

McGraw-Hill Book Company, Inc.

1951

ENGINEERING AND WESTERN CIVILIZATION

IV

To The
ENGINEERS
Known and Unknown
Whose Contributions To
Technical Knowledge And
Improved Practice Have
Made Possible This
Engineering Age

8131

PREFACE

It is not the technical excellence of an engineering design which alone determines its merit but rather the completeness with which it meets the economic and social needs of its day.

William Barclay Parsons[1]

Some twenty-five or thirty years ago the writer became interested in the history of engineering and accumulated many volumes of detailed notes and references. Much of this material, secured as it was from original sources in various scattered and not too easily available publications, is of interest in revealing the remarkable evolution, through some fifty centuries or more, of one of the oldest of the practical arts. Yet engineering is a constantly growing and developing profession. While important technical principles and a valuable perspective of professional progress can be drawn from such a detailed study of the sequence and development of engineering discoveries and inventions, the methods and practices of yesterday offer little more than curiosity-satisfying value to the engineer of today.

On the other hand, throughout these fifty or more centuries of its history, engineering has been a potent instrumentality in the rise of Western life. It has played an important part in the history of the Western world, and this story has more than merely professional interest. On its proper understanding and interpretation in the light of our present problems and needs the future of Western life will to a major degree depend. For, while engineering in the past has aided in transforming man's dwelling place and also exercised a profound influence on the relationships of men, it has, within the past century or less, become a dominating force in shaping not only the lives of men but the destiny of nations.

Who can deny, for example, that the present position of the United States, now the leading nation of the Western world, has been built largely upon our skill in utilizing technological advances to develop our resources, material and human, for raising our standards of life and living? Obviously, our progress in peace and our strength in defending the rights and principles on which our democracy is built rest to a

[1] Address at the inauguration of the Columbia Student Chapter of the American Society of Civil Engineers, 1927.

major degree on our ability to maintain the technological supremacy and industrial know-how which spring from engineering progress.

Little attempt has been made in this present volume to offer more than a very brief and sketchy outline of the history of engineering, although a selected bibliography is given which will provide suitable references for further study for those who desire to fill out some of the details of this story. Special attention has been given, on the other hand, to an attempt to uncover some of the basic relationships of past engineering advances and economic and social changes. If continued engineering progress is an inescapable essential in our search for the good life for man, to our safety and stability as a nation, and to our power for peace in the world, then it is our responsibility not only to understand how to use technological advances to the optimum advantage but also how to provide those conditions which will foster and maintain such advances. It may be true that ill-considered and short-sighted economic or social legislation cannot prevent scientific research, but that it can so retard or restrict engineering progress as to result in technological stagnation and decay is, unfortunately, only too evident in the records of past civilizations. If the present work aids in some small measure in clarifying this problem of technological-economic-social relationships, the author will have been amply repaid for his efforts.

We have quoted freely in this book from the works of several authors, endeavoring in each case to give proper credit and reference. We are at a loss, however, in giving adequate acknowledgment to the many other writers whose works have influenced our ideas and whose actual words may have—unknowingly, we assure them—found their way into our text. It is surprising how frequently one encounters in his more general reading grist for his mill—even when this mill is supposed to operate on such a specialized subject as engineering. We engineers feel, of course, that this proves that our profession is so much a part of modern life that even our literary friends, as well as our more closely related colleagues in economic, social, and political areas, cannot escape its influences and implications.

To all these authors, known or "unknown," we offer our grateful appreciation. In particular, however, we must express our great debt to Sir Norman Angell, whose apt and penetrating statements, with his most generous permission and that of his publishers, Harper & Brothers, illuminate many pages in this work.

JAMES KIP FINCH

NEW YORK, N.Y.
February, 1951

CONTENTS

ix

CONTENTS

INTRODUCTION

Civilization is, ultimately, the process whereby a human society in search, as Aristotle puts it, of "a good life for man," gradually overcomes the obstacles, material and other, that stand in its way and makes man increasingly master of his environment.

Gilbert Murray, *The Ordeal of This Generation.*

There have been several interpretations of history. In earlier times historians built the story of the past on the lives of great military or political leaders. This was "the great man" theory of history so effectively epitomized in the observation of the great French leader of World War I days, Marshal Foch: "It was not an army that crossed the Alps—it was Hannibal."

More recently we have had the economic interpretation of history, an interpretation which, minimizing those aspirations which man has drawn not from his environment but from his inner spirit, emphasizes the powerful role which economic forces have played in the evolution of Western life.

There has also been what may be termed the ideological theory of history, a theory which attributes the origin and growth of human institutions largely to man's speculations in the realm of philosophic ideals and in attempts to formulate economic and social conceptions. Thus the beginnings of the search for the good life are regarded as stemming from Ancient Greece while the rise of modern free institutions is attributed largely to the revolutionary social thinkers of the 18th century.

The theory advanced in this volume may be regarded as an engineering interpretation of history. It does not deny that there have been great political, military, or even engineering leaders. It attributes, however, the ever-increasing power and importance of engineering in the Western World not to a few men but to the fact that many men of less than extraordinary gifts can and have made worth-while contributions to the ever-accumulating mass of knowledge from which engineering power and progress stem.

1

It recognizes also the engineer's part in meeting the requirements, so clearly stated by a leading Columbia economist of a past generation, Professor Seligman: "Until man had satisfied his major material wants and needs, there was little or no opportunity for the development of what we call 'the higher things of life'." And, further, "No matter how civilized man may become, his material welfare forms the basis on which the whole larger life is erected."

It admits, however, that, for the engineer, brought up in an objective and realistic school, it is difficult to regard philosophic, economic, or social speculations as having exercised a predominating influence in the birth of modern institutions. As Adam Smith, the Father of Modern Economics, pointed out: "Civilization, or the improvement of society, has not been the product of human foresight and calculation, but of the natural propensities of economically active men." To which Dean Inge would add: "The dignified gentlemen in black robes are usually called in after an action has been taken to prove that what has been done is wise and good." The importance of ideological studies in defining and clarifying institutions and movements, in analyzing their consequences and forecasting their possible developments, cannot be questioned, but as prime forces in the birth of such institutions, their direct influence may be questioned.

Certainly, however, all these and other forces and factors in confusing number and complex form have played their part in the rise of Western civilization. In addition to those here noted, increasing attention has been given by historians in recent years to the part played by engineering in what Dr. Osler has characterized as "Man's Redemption of Man."

Engineering is one of the oldest professions. Thirty centuries before Christ—five thousand years ago—the master builders of Ancient Egypt occupied important positions in the life of their day. But there are two quite distinct, quite different periods in the story of this profession which are of quite different importance in the history of man.

Engineering in Ancient times, its revival in the Middle Ages and in those remarkable two centuries or more following the Italian Renaissance, when France carried forward European leadership, was quite a limited and innocuous engineering as compared with the engineering movement which arose in Britain in the 18th century. To a major degree the remarkable French workers whose efforts practically came to an end with the French Revolution of 1789, rather than the Romans, were the last of the Ancient Engineers. As in the case of earlier master builders, they were primarily construction experts and public-works engineers. Like the Romans their major efforts had to do with public, government undertakings, with roads and bridges, and with water supplies. As in earlier times, the materials available for construction were still limited to timber, stone, and brick. Iron and steel were too costly to be used for other than tools and fastenings. Power was limited to the uncertain gifts of wind and water and to the physical efforts of animals and of men. Improvements in machinery had been made, but it was still hand- or animal-operated. French engineers perfected the stone arch and built some of the world's most beautiful bridges. They built some notable canals. They were outstanding construction experts in a pre-metal age. But their engineering played little or no part in aiding the advance of the other old practical arts of industry and manufacturing. These were still largely small rural operations of an agricultural economy and, in urban centers, under the control of the guilds, unprogressive and unpromising. Economic collapse as well as political corruption and injustice was a factor in the French Revolution.

On the other hand, Britain, that tight little isle, built, it was said, on coal and surrounded by fish, had settled her major political problems in the 17th century and, during the 18th, the last century of French leadership, developed a triple alliance of engineering, industry, and individual free enterprise which marked the birth of a new era in the history not only of engineering but of man. The revival of the British iron trade, following the introduction of coal (*i.e.,* coke) for fuel in lieu of charcoal, began about 1740. It was this revival which gave purpose to Newcomen's "atmospheric" mine pump, later improved by Watt and developed into a rotative engine. The mechanization of the British textile industry, beginning with Kay's "fly shuttle" of 1733 and carrying through to Cartwright's mechanical loom of 1785, and the application of Watt's engine in the same year to driving these new machines—these developments marked the birth of a new economy and the creation of new human relationships, the problems and consequences of which we still struggle with today.

From the engineering standpoint, these 18th century years in Britain marked the gradual replacement of the older practical millwright, a skilled worker in wood and iron, by the new engineer—the birth of a new liaison between engineering and the industrial arts. It marked also the rise of an Age of Iron and Steam—the first iron bridge in the world was built at Coalbrookdale in Britain in 1779 and the mine pumps and engines of Boulton and Watt inaugurated the modern Power Era. On the other hand, for almost the first time in history, engineering was brought to the service of private enterprise. British works—not only those noted above but canals, roads, and later railroads—were not government-sponsored projects but were private ventures possible only in an atmosphere of free enterprise.

It was on this new industrialization that Britain's commanding world position of the Victorian Era (1837–1901) was built. Through the export of her manufactures, notably textiles, coal, and iron and its products, through her outstanding maritime position, world-wide trade, and command of capital, Britain and her far-flung empire, "an empire on which the sun never sets," became the industrial and financial leader of the 19th century.

Yet, in spite of this early start, in spite of her commanding position, it became apparent in the earlier years of the 20th century that all was not well with the British economy. The United States was destined to take over the economic-industrial leadership of Western civilization and to lead in further engineering and industrial development.

The 19th century in the United States had been given over largely to the problems connected with the spread of the American people over the North American continent. Transportation dominated the engineering picture and, after earlier experiments with roads and canals, the railroad became king. This is not to say that there were no urban engineering problems and no industrial growth. Even during the 19th century the United States led the world in the development of new, laborsaving machines and the application to her needs of the outstanding inventions and technological skills of her people. Yet all this remarkable progress seems, in the light of the tremendous engineering and industrial expansion which was to follow in the 20th century, to have been merely a making ready of the way.

Many forces and many factors undoubtedly played a part in this phenomenal, unparalleled American advance of the 20th century. Back of it was the progressive, dynamic spirit of the American people, reinforced by a long and continued experience of constantly increasing standards of living and ever more widely distributed material prosperity. As Dave Harum crudely but aptly observed: "It's a sight easier to have faith on meat and potatoes than it is on corn mush." No other people in the world had, to anything approaching those of the United States, this faith and confidence in progress and conviction that, good as life was, there were still better things "just around the corner."

There were also, however, certain basic engineering developments which made this expansion possible. The great American economic and industrial expansion of the 20th century did not stem alone from the exploitation of the unparalleled resources of a most fruitful continent as it had in the past. By 1900 the geographical frontiers of the North American continent had been reached. To a major degree the new era was based on engineering-industrial advances, on technological "know-how."

There had been a rather slow growth in the United States in the utilization of steam power. Even as late as 1876, a century after the advent of the steam engine, New England was still the center of American industrial development, and most of her power needs were still met by the small, isolated water power sites around which the towns of New England had grown up. The advent not only of electric lighting but of electrical means of distributing and utilizing power in the last years of the 19th century was a major factor in the spread of machine and mass manufacturing. The gas engine also furnished a new power source, destined to usher in a new era of motor transport and to revolutionize agricultural methods. Bigger and better engineering became the slogan of the New Era. Playing a vital part in this expansion also was the liaison which had developed during the 19th century between engineering and the natural sciences, especially physics.

In its earlier history, engineering had been almost entirely confined to the practical arts of construction. Through centuries of practice and experience an empirical technique of planning and design, "rules of thumb," had been developed which gave us some of the most notable constructions the world has ever known. Roman, and later French, bridges, medieval castles, and Gothic cathedrals remain, even today, outstanding achievements of an empirical era and the Age of Stone. But there had also been building up within the profession the beginnings of a more fully rationalized mathematical and scientific technique. French engineers of the 18th century made some notable contributions to this development. More practical-minded British workers of the earlier 19th century made marked advances in bridging the gap between this new "theoretical" knowledge and its practical application and use in engineering design. The demand for larger structures, the advent of steam power, and the wider use of more costly materials, notably iron, led to increasing emphasis on a scientific method of design which made safer construction and new economies possible.

What was happening was a gradual drawing together of the common interests in basic physical understandings of natural science and engineering. On the one hand, the reduction of many empirical engineering techniques to a more scientific basis was essential to further engineering progress. On the other, this liaison was helpful and stimulating to further advances in natural science. An important and mutually stimulating tie-up between natural and engineering science, a development which had been discouraged for centuries by the long dominant influence of early Greek thought, was at long last consummated. As the late Professor A. N. Whitehead of Cambridge and Harvard put it: "The history of mankind is yet to be set in its proper relation to the gathering momentum of technological advances. Within the last hundred years, a developed science has wedded itself to a developed technology and a new epoch has opened."[1]

This then is, very briefly, the position in which the United States finds itself today. Through a long series of developments America has become the engineering and industrial heir of the ages. Today she carries forward the leadership of Western civilization, a civilization which has been built primarily upon engineering advances and in the future progress of which continued scientific and engineering progress must play a dominating role. Our institutions and our lives have been created largely through the interplay of engineering advances and the stimulation stemming from free enterprise. We enjoy a widespread if still incompletely realized material prosperity. Our future and our survival as a nation will depend primarily on our ability to continue this progressive growth—so to adjust and adapt our economic and social development to an atmosphere of continued technological change that we may take optimum advantage of the opportunities which such change offers in our search for a good life for man.

In brief, this is the story which we have aimed to develop in this book. It offers an outline of the past history of engineering and the part the engineer has played in the evolution of Western life. It attempts to draw from this history an appraisal of some of the main influences which have, on the one hand, limited engineering activities in the past and, on the other, have been instrumental in bringing

[1] *The Aims of Education,* London, Williams & Norgate, Ltd., 1932, p. 112.

about "the momentum of technological advance" characteristic of our own day. It explores some of the economic, social, and political trends of our times stemming from such advances. It offers, we hope, some suggestions in reference to the problems which America must solve if technology is to play its full part in the continued search for a good life for man.

Chapter 1. ANCIENT ENGINEERING

A vision of a long-past humanity, few in numbers and in dire
peril, the chances all against its survival, fumbling out of a darkness where the beginnings were hidden, and drifting, or impelled
by forces unknown or half guessed, to this discovery and to that,
from land to land, to a partial control of its circumstances.

J. M. Tomlinson, *Galleons Reach.*

EGYPT, GREECE, AND ROME

The beginnings of engineering are undoubtedly hidden in these
earlier ages which were long since dust when the first civilizations of
which we have historical record were developing. We have previously
noted the statement of Professor Gilbert Murray, "Civilization is,
ultimately, the process whereby a human society in search, as Aristotle puts it, of 'a good life for man,' gradually overcomes the obstacles, material and other, that stand in its way and makes man
increasingly master of his environment." The engineer was born
when man first specialized in seeking some mastery of his environment, when, through the practical arts, he first attempted to shape
Nature's gifts and forces to meet his needs and wants.

Engineering is thus as old as civilization. The earliest kings of
Ancient Egypt, five thousand years ago, had their chiefs of works, the
master builders, who not only planned and erected pyramids and
temples but aided in developing an economy which made it possible
to withdraw from productive labor the thousands of workers needed
to build such imposing but, judged by our standards, useless structures as the Great Pyramid. As new nations in turn took up and
carried forward the leadership of Western civilization and culture,
which had its beginnings in these earlier centuries both in the fertile
valley of the Nile in Egypt and in that of the Tigris-Euphrates in
Mesopotamia, these nations in turn became the leaders in engineering. The main stream of engineering history parallels exactly the
evolution of Western life for these two developments have been interdependent, the one fertilizing and stimulating the other.

The story of engineering through these fifty centuries of recorded history offers several clues as to the basic conditions under which it flourishes best and has made its major contributions to human progress. It also clearly reveals that, in its growth and development, engineering has been a powerful force through the centuries, not only in advancing the material welfare of man but in furthering the rise of democratic ideals and institutions. Engineering has, on the one hand, made man increasingly master of his environment but at the same time it has been a vital factor in freeing him from bondage not only to physical labor but to man. It seems desirable, therefore, to review briefly some of the outstanding earlier pages of the history of the profession if we are to evaluate fairly the place of engineering in the world of today.

Egypt. There are notable examples of the flowering of civilized life in isolated areas—the Aztec and Inca civilizations in America and the early Chinese developments, for example—which, for one reason or another, failed to affect our culture and contributed but indirectly, if at all, to the rise of Western life. The main stream of our inheritance in the Western World springs, as we have noted, from Ancient Egypt and Mesopotamia where, some thirty or more centuries before Christ—a period longer than the Christian Era— the beginnings were made in the evolution of a form of life we carry forward today.

It is not difficult to picture the influences which led to this birth of modern life in the valley of the Nile in Egypt or the apparently equally early parallel but independent development in the valley of the Tigris-Euphrates in Mesopotamia. As the ancient saying puts it: Egypt is the Nile and the Nile is Egypt. By scratching up the wonderfully fertile deposits of the great Nile Valley following the annual inundation of the river, quick crops could be grown and man, "fumbling out of a darkness," could, with greater ease and far greater certainty, meet his basic material needs.

There are three elements in the story of Ancient Egypt which cannot fail to impress us as being most extraordinary. First, the rapidity with which this ancient people attained a highly developed government and economy, a stable way of life involving, even in the earliest times, a large population. A great and flourishing nation was, apparently, created almost overnight. We are also, of course, deeply impressed by the magnitude of the works which these people built— accomplishments which become even more remarkable when we discover that the Egyptians had at their command only a few basic mechanical devices, and almost no scientific or technical knowledge.

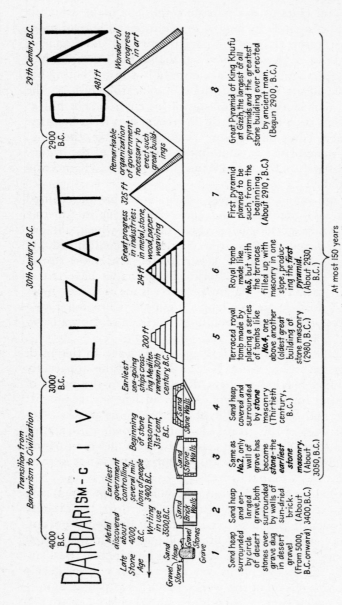

The Concurrent Rise of Civilization and Engineering

(from earliest stone masonry to the Great Pyramid)

The Pyramid Age witnessed the rise in Ancient Egypt, in a brief century and a half, of the art of construction from the earliest cut-stone masonry to the greatest mass of such masonry the world has ever known, the Great Pyramid. This era of remarkably rapid advance also witnessed the first Industrial Revolution, and standards were developed in industry as well as in art, literature, and religion which persisted for many centuries and made this the Golden Age of Ancient Egypt. (*From Breasted's Ancient Times. Courtesy of Ginn and Company.*)

Yet, it seems quite clear that, after the early and remarkable development of the practical arts in the Pyramid Age, which lasted roughly from 3000 to 2500 B.C., an advance unparalleled in human history until modern times, Egyptian technology ceased to progress. A few centuries of tremendously rapid advance were followed by over twenty centuries of struggle and strife, of progressive decline and decay. There was, to be sure, a later great era of military conquest, but engineeringly speaking, Egypt had shot her bolt. She ultimately fell a prey to foreign enemies and in succession came under Persian, Greek, Roman, Turkish, French, and British dominance.

The ancient Egyptian found within easy reach all the essentials for the blossoming of civilized life. In the earliest period, the Pyramid Age or Old Kingdom as it is known, a predominantly agricultural living was supplemented by the products of infant industries and manufacturers. Historians picture the Nile crowded with boats transporting the new industrial products as well as the agricultural needs of a large, self-sufficient, and flourishing economy. The fruits of the economy were, of course, enjoyed only by the limited few who— noble and priest—centered in the court of the king. The Egyptian peasant, or fellah, was simply a human machine of unaltered status, apparently satisfied to exist rather than having ambitions to live. Yet, life could be sustained for century after century, and great numbers of men could be withdrawn from productive labor to build the great works of the king. Herodotus tells us, for example, that a hundred thousand men were employed for twenty years in building the Great Pyramid.

Apparently it is in the almost unlimited human resources of this ancient land that the key to Egypt's remarkable constructions is to be found. Of the six mechanical advantages known to the Ancients —the lever, the inclined plane, the wedge, the roller or wheel, the pulley, and the screw—the Egyptians are known to have used but the first three. No hoists were available, yet the Great Pyramid is estimated to have required the quarrying, transportation, and placing of some $2\frac{1}{4}$ million blocks of stone of an average weight of $2\frac{1}{2}$ tons each. Even the chisel was apparently very sparingly used and Engelbach pictures the quarrying of a huge obelisk at Aswan, by the— to our minds—discouragingly ineffective and laboriously wasteful hand method of simply pounding a channel around and under the granite mass—"bashing," as he calls it, the bedrock by pounding it with even harder balls of dolerite. Yet he estimates that an obelisk could be quarried in this way in some 8 months or thereabouts.

Long, temporary inclines, earth embankments, were also built for construction use and later laboriously removed, undoubtedly by hoards of workers carrying basketfuls of soil like so many ants building an anthill.

The ancient Egyptian was, thus, undoubtedly one of the greatest organizers and directors of labor the world has ever known. And Egyptian labor was not always slave labor nor was life always lightly regarded. The *corvée* system of drafted labor was used, and there are records of an expedition to a desert quarry where the leader bragged that he had not lost a man—not even a mule.

At no time in history has the planner and director of works, the master builder, ever occupied a higher position in life than he did in this early era. The ancient Egyptian chief of works, the ancestor of both the modern architect and the engineer, was a trusted noble of the court and adviser of the king. Under his direction a host of subordinates, superintendents, and foremen, each with his scribes and recorders, formed a highly organized construction force. While the details of many Egyptian construction practices are unknown and while the character and scale of many ancient works have been grossly exaggerated, the modern engineer cannot fail to respect the ability of these ancient workers in marshaling and employing their human resources.

Yet all authorities agree that this remarkable era of advance in the practical arts practically came to an end with the close, about 2500 B.C., of this Golden Age of Egyptian history. It is apparently true that later Egypt produced no essentially new technical procedures or processes. The quality of Egyptian masonry construction, says Engelbach, steadily declined. No important improvements were made in the irrigation system which had always been of the most simple and primitive type. New types of construction—temples and obelisks—came into style, military organization and strategy were developed, but Egypt, Mother of the Practical Arts, failed to care for her offspring. All her remarkable early technological progress and promise ended in stagnation and decay.

It is clearly a mistake to attribute this failure to maintain technological progress to any single factor or group of factors. Early Egyptian history is the story of the rise of civilized life in an almost completely isolated and extremely favorable environment—the long narrow valley of the Nile shut off from contact with the rest of the world by deserts except at its extreme northern end, the Delta or Lower Egypt. But foreign invaders found their way into this land and, after a resurgence in the great period of Egyptian military might in the age of Thutmose III, the Napoleon of Ancient Egypt, about 1500 B.C., foreign hands took control.

Yet there were a number of other factors which contributed to this collapse. A fixed and static political, social, and economic life had been developed at an early date. An all-powerful religious and noble order dominated the land. The peasant multitudes were mere human machines. There was no public demand for continued progress and higher standards of living for there was no public. The ruling class, as always, endeavored, and successfully, to avoid change and maintain their position and the *status quo*. All obvious needs and wants seem to have been satisfied, and there was no pressure for new developments.

From the technical standpoint the conditions also were discouragingly favorable. The Nile served all transportation needs, and ample supplies of construction material, excellent stone of various kinds, were easily available. There was no need for road building and no reason to seek new building materials. Necessity, it is said, is the mother of invention, and of necessity there was none. Engineering in Ancient Egypt was not stillborn but, after a most remarkable, interesting, and promising adolescence, it ceased to grow.

The scientist would, in part at least, attribute this static attitude and decay to what was apparently a complete lack of scientific curiosity on the part of the ancient Egyptian. He was a pure empiricist, quite satisfied to know "how," how to do this or that, and never thinking to ask "why" this or that was true, why it worked. On the other hand, the next great nation to pick up the torch of Western civilization, Greece, never failed to question, never stopped asking "why?"[1]

Greece. Topography deeply influenced Greek development as it had Egyptian. Stretching out like a bony hand into the eastern Aegean, the rocky ribs of Greece prohibited free intercommunication by land between the settlements which developed into city-states in the intervening fertile valleys. The Greeks were, therefore, forced to turn to the sea, and they became the first great harbor builders. In their urban developments they were brought face to face with prob-

[1] In the interest of brevity we omit mention of the various other earlier Near Eastern nations which contributed to the stream of Western civilization. These include, as we have noted, the Babylonian-Assyrian peoples, great military leaders and builders, the first great nation to use iron implements on a large scale, the first to build public water supplies, and as old in their origins as the Egyptians.

lems of city planning and public water supply, and they pioneered in the excavation of tunnels. The remarkable perfection of Greek design and the accuracy of execution of Greek temple building have also long claimed the admiration of later generations. Furthermore, while the modern engineer finds it difficult to place himself in the shoes of the Egyptian builder (until he realizes that Egyptian ideas and construction cannot be understood or judged by modern standards), he immediately recognizes and approves the objectives and methods of the Greek worker. Here he finds an ancient planner of similar interests and ambitions, a fellow worker with an eye to economy of labor and materials, who undertook and solved new problems, especially in surveying, in substantially the same manner we solve them today. Here was a planner whose skill in design, although based on purely qualitative knowledge derived from experience, showed an almost uncanny understanding and structural feeling which produced results approaching modern quantitative methods in accuracy. The Greek was in truth an arch-technician and established technical methods and procedures which were to endure for centuries.[2]

It would appear, therefore, that Greece possessed vital basic requirements for a strong and dynamic engineering development which Egypt had lacked. Yet remaining Greek engineering works constitute but little more than isolated examples of a remarkable technical understanding and skill. The Greek city-state lacked, on the one hand, a completely dominant governing class or, on the other, a representative and organized body of public opinion. A large proportion of the population were slaves.[3] Furthermore, all practical affairs, all activities of craftsmanship and hand labor, were left to menials. The leaders of Greek thought regarded manual work as destructive alike to the bodies and minds of the workers—a viewpoint which still occasionally crops up and which long caused engineering, because of its necessarily close association with the practical arts, to be regarded as a "navvy" profession.

[2] The Greek builder was known as an *architekton,* a title from which the present "architect" is derived. The modern architect, however, is primarily a designer of buildings and monuments, whereas the *architekton* was a true master builder, a general, allround technical expert, and arch-technician, civil or military engineer and mechanician, as occasion might require.

[3] For example, in the age of Pericles, the 5th century B.C., and the great age of Athenian history, out of an Attic population of 315,000 only 43,000 were citizens. Some 115,000 were slaves and there were 28,500 resident aliens. Thus all women, nearly all workingmen, and a great part of the trading class were excluded from the franchise.

Dr. Durant remarks on the difficulty of maintaining an advancing technology under such conditions:

It was in industrial and technical invention that Greece fell farthest below the general standard of its unparalleled achievements. The Greek disdain of manual work kept everybody but the listless slave from direct acquaintance with the processes of production, from that stimulating contact with machinery which reveals defects and prefigures possibilities; technical invention was possible only to those who had no interest in it, and could not derive from it any material reward. Perhaps the very cheapness of the slaves made invention lag; muscle was still less costly than machines.[4]

Even Archimedes (287–212 B.C.), popularly acclaimed for his remarkable mechanical inventions, appears to have been ashamed of his interest in such works. He apologized for them, claiming they were carried out merely for his diversion and amusement. Thus, while great and noble beginnings were made in the development of natural science, practical applications and experimentation were outlawed. Science was held to be a mental exercise, which might sharpen and invigorate the mind but should not be debased by use. Plato regarded even those interested in geometry (*i.e.,* land measurement) as having vulgarized mathematics. This attitude not only, of course, precluded the fertilizing liaison between science and engineering which we know to be so important today, but it also discouraged any attempts to develop the experimental, observational methods basic to the discovery of scientific truths. Science, in fact, became natural philosophy and, as such, both completely divorced from engineering and incapable of further development. As we shall later note, it took the human race close to two thousand years to rectify this Greek error.[5]

Thus in spite of the remarkable advances of Greek mathematics and mechanics, in spite of the notable contributions of Archimedes and others, in spite of those outstanding contributions of the human mind which have stimulated the thoughts and aspirations of Western man through the centuries, in spite of the glory of her art and architecture, technology never became a dominant factor in Greek life. The few great Greek engineering works—water supplies, tunnels,

[4] *The Story of Philosophy,* by Will Durant, New York, Simon and Schuster, Inc., 1926, p. 64.
[5] The last part of Lord Macaulay's famous essay on Lord Bacon (1837) is devoted to an unsparing criticism of the "unprofitable" character of Greek speculation.

harbors, drainage projects, city plans—all exhibit a remarkable advance in technical knowledge and understanding, but they appear, as we have said, to be more or less scattered and isolated examples of a very unusual ability which failed to find in Greek life the essential factors for widespread application and a continued evolution. Furthermore, the Greek city-states were never able to get together and form a strong and stable nation and, in the end, fell easy prey to other more strongly organized foes. Alexander's conquest of the Ancient World brought about but a temporary union, and Rome ultimately took over as mistress of the Mediterranean world.

Rome. The beginnings of Roman engineering antedate the collapse of Greece, but there can be no doubt that much if not most of Roman technical knowledge was imported from Greece. The Romans made the arch, inherited from the Etruscans, a vital form in their constructions. They made a far wider use of natural cement, pozzuolana, than the Greeks had of Santorin earth. They were the first great road builders, and, under the Empire, built roads, bridges, and water supplies all over the Ancient World from Asia Minor to Great Britain. Yet, as far as any continuing addition to technical knowledge is concerned, the Roman *architectus* was disappointing. He lacked the intellectual curiosity of the Greek. Vergil recognized the Roman's limitations in the statement that

> Others, belike, with happier grace
> From bronze or stone shall call the face,
> Plead doubtful causes, map the skies,
> And tell where planets set and rise.

Yet the Roman, in engineering as in architecture, took his inheritance of earlier technical methods and, while adding little in basic understanding or knowledge, applied and used them in developing standards and conveniences of city life which were not to be equaled for at least a thousand years after Rome's collapse as mistress of the Western World. Engineering under Roman rule became a powerful and vital instrument in the building of civilized life. Indeed, the real Roman engineers were the top-ranking government officials, such as Appius Claudius, who was consul about 300 B.C. and directed the construction of both the famous Appian Road and the first water supply for Rome, the Aqua Appia. The letters of Pliny and the Emperor Trajan show clearly that the initiative in public works was in the hands of political leaders, while the details of execution were left to subordinates and to their numerous technical assistants, surveyors, levelers, quantity recorders, and so on. All this was in keeping with an extended public-works program such as the Romans carried out, but it did not lead to a continued evolution of technical knowledge and understanding.

No deeply involved and mathematically complicated technical procedures were, of course, required in planning these earlier engineering undertakings. Engineering was primarily a practical art, and its problems were solved through the exercise of a keen structural sense and practical economic judgment. Under these conditions, government officials were competent to direct such works although they might add little in extending technical competence.

The story of Roman engineering is nevertheless a fascinating one. In the earlier period of the Republic, when the Latin race was overcoming its unruly neighbors and consolidating the Italian peninsula, the major engineering problems had to do with the needs of the growing city of Rome and extending the rule of the Roman state, tying to the Eternal City the newly won provinces by means of roads. This was the period of the substantial stone-masonry construction of early Roman days which culminated in the building of the "high-level" aqueduct Marcia in 140 B.C., the pride of Ancient Rome, and in the erection of the first stone arch bridge, the Pons Aemilius of 142 B.C. These were the days of the simple, sturdy Roman worker, of honest toil, with which the poet Horace so feelingly contrasts the luxury and lack of responsibility of his own time, the early days of the Empire.

Yet, under the Empire, the foreign conquests of Rome, the colonies so ruthlessly taken over and exploited during the Republic, were provided with roads and other important public services. In all, the Romans built some 200 aqueducts and these, with Roman roads and bridges, were scattered all over the Ancient World. One must look, in fact, to Spain and North Africa for the last and some of the most interesting examples of Roman engineering skill. Roman rule provided, as we have said, through notable and widespread public works standards of urban life the world was not to know again for centuries.

While, therefore, we very properly hail the Romans as greatest of ancient engineers, the Roman mind lacked the inventive qualities essential to a continued technological advance. Yet we must not conclude that there was no progress in engineering as a pracitical art during Roman times. Earlier Roman work was impressive because it was solid, massive, and imposing. Roman bridges with their full-centered, semicircular arches and sturdy piers were, in fact, dams with openings rather than bridges. Less than a third of the total area below the floor level was, in many cases, open and thus available for passing floodwaters. The Roman was likewise not always successful with his aqueduct constructions. Numerous patches and repairs are still evident, and it is probable that one or more of the eleven ancient aqueducts, varying in length from 10 to 60 miles, which served Rome, was always cut off for repairs. On the other hand, later works show unmistakable evidence of the teachings of experience, of increased confidence gained through practice and leading to greater skill and daring in construction. Witness the tremendously solid Pont du Gard of about the beginning of the Christian Era and compare it with the startlingly slender stone framework of the aqueduct bridge of Segovia of a century later. In their later constructions, the Romans also turned to a wider use of less expensive brick and concrete. To basic theory they added little or nothing. In construction methods and techniques they established practices which persisted until the advent of modern machinery in the 19th century.

Unfortunately, however, Roman civilization came to an end in the 5th century A.D., and historians have been busy ever since in attempts to explain the decline and fall of the Roman Empire. Although the Roman mind excelled in its capacity for law and administration, Rome was unable to hold together her widely scattered colonies. Social disturbances and food shortages at home played their part in Rome's disintegration. The agricultural areas of the Italian peninsula were insufficient to maintain the city's increasing population. The great, but probably largely ineffective, project of draining Lake Fucinus about A.D. 50 was dictated by the pressing need for added agricultural lands. Egypt became the granary of the Ancient World, and her irrigation system was rehabilitated and improved in the early years of the Empire. But the basic problem seems to have been deeper than that of government or agricultural economics, important as these factors were.

As we have noted, in the first step of her expansion, the consolidation of the Italian peninsula, the Roman roads, all of which, it was said, led to Rome, provided a vital means of communication. But Rome was unable to develop the equally effective communication system which was needed, not only to hold her later vast empire together but to provide the means of transporting essential supplies. As Dean Gauss of Princeton puts it:

The Roman mind remained oriented toward the past and was essentially unimaginative. . . . It failed to recognize that in expanding her

The Roman Aqueduct at Segovia, 100 A.D.

Built to carry the water conduit at grade across a valley for the supply of
this Roman colonial city; the relatively light and daring supporting structure
should be contrasted with such earlier, cumbersome, and massive works as the
similar Pont du Gard in the south of France of a century earlier. (*Courtesy of
Spanish Tourist Office, New York.*)

empire, Rome had altered the nature of her problem. It never dreamed of creating the technological instruments which might have assured Rome's dominion over her over-extended and increasingly impoverished domain. Necessity could not become the mother of invention for a people who remained complacently ignorant even of their needs.

Hindsight is, of course, always easier than foresight. Undoubtedly we are asking too much if we take the Romans to task for not developing Watt's engine or modern means of communication and transportation. The fact remains, however, that these were the developments that Rome needed and, lacking the intellectual curiosity and imagination essential to their birth, the story of Roman civilization ended also in failure and decline as in the case of Egypt and Greece. Having reached a level of civilized life higher than any of her neighbors, Rome fell before the attack of far less cultured barbarian invaders. About A.D. 300 Constantine moved his capitol to the center of the Eastern Roman Empire at Constantinople, thus, in effect, abandoning Rome to its fate. The Visigoths under Alaric captured the city in 410 and the Vandals sacked it in 455. The Dark and Middle Ages followed.

While the progress of Western civilization did not cease completely with the fall of Rome, it had to be reborn during the Middle Ages. Ancient engineering had, after several most interesting and promising developments, come to a close. Western civilization and engineering were to be revived in later centuries under new and quite different conditions.

Chapter 2. THE MIDDLE AGES AND
THE RENAISSANCE

The very use of the names Dark and Middle Ages to describe a group of ten centuries is sufficient evidence that those centuries are neither understood nor appreciated. The student sees in the Middle Ages the mind of modern Europe at school . . . Such an age is not one with which any century since the seventeenth stands in close sympathy, but it is neither a dark age nor a middle age. It witnessed the preparation of the mind of Europe for what was to come.

Nicholas Murray Butler, *Philosophy*.

THE INGENIATOR, STONE MASONRY, AND GUNPOWDER

While it took close to a thousand years for Western civilization again to reach a stage of development even approximating that of Roman times, the new civilization, which was building up in Europe during the thousand years following the fall of Rome (during what is known as the Middle Ages), came into being amid the remains of the material accomplishments of the past. The books of the past were temporarily lost to sight but the bridges, roads, and architecture of Roman days remained as mute reminders, even in ruined form, of what had been and again could be. The Eastern Roman Empire, of course, endured until the 15th century, and ancient learning was conserved and, in certain areas, extended by the scholars of the Near East—was, in fact, to penetrate to Spain where the Moors achieved a great forward step in raising the standards of Western life. It was the Roman Catholic Church, however, which played a most important role throughout these centuries of new growth. This was the age of the rise of the Church to its greatest period of power and authority. It was a powerful, almost the only, organized force for progress during the Middle Ages and held together such of the learning and examples of Ancient Times as survived in this period of uncertainty and strife.

The Middle Ages. In architecture, the new builders secured their inspiration from earlier works and developed first what is known as

21

the Romanesque style. Medieval bridges were also, in large measure, based on Roman works. But one must not assume that the Middle Ages were sterile from the standpoint of new engineering developments. Far from it; this was one of the greatest eras in the history of the profession. It was in the Middle Ages that the engineer received his name, that the most ingenious and daring masonry constructions the world has ever known were built, and this same period also witnessed the rise of a new and revolutionary chemical discovery, gunpowder, which had a profound influence not only on engineering progress but on human relations.

The words "engine" and "engineer" were unknown to the ancients.[1] It was Tertullian, an early father of the Christian Church, who apparently coined the word *ingenium* about A.D. 200. In one of his historical writings describing an attack on the Carthagenians by Roman forces, he notes the consternation of the former when the Romans brought up a new and extraordinary *ingenium*, that is, invention or product of genius. In view of the fact that this device, a battering ram, had been known for centuries, this statement is surprising. But the new name seems to have stuck. Battering rams, catapults, ballista, and similar equipment became known as engines of war. It was another thousand years, however, before the man who devised and directed the operation of these engines was referred to as an *ingeniator,* the origin of our modern title, engineer.

While, in the construction field, the earlier medieval bridges do not indicate any advance on Roman designs, the new builders became the creators of two of the world's masterpieces in stone construction, the medieval castle, and the Gothic cathedral—the most massive of cut-stone buildings and, in sharp contrast, the most daring of "skeleton-stone" constructions.

It has been said that military engineering has been marked by alternating periods in which first defense and then attack secured the upper hand. The medieval castle was the culmination of a long development through the Middle Ages and provided a defense which, evolving from the Roman *castrum* or fortified camp, resulted in the construction of an almost impregnable fortress-home for the independent nobles of this Age of Private Wars. With its solid masonry walls with flanking towers and protected by its moats with its draw-

---

[1] While the title *ingegnere* is used in Italy, even the modern Greek refers to the engineer as a *mechanicos—politicos mechanicos* for civil engineer, *electrologos mechanicos* for electrical engineer, etc. Similarly in Greece an engine is a *mechane.*

The Medieval Ingeniator at Work

The master builder of Medieval Times not only planned and constructed two of man's greatest structures in stone, the medieval castle and the Gothic cathedral, but was the first to be known as an ingeniator, the origin of the present title "engineer." (*After Viollet-le-Duc.*)

bridge and other ingenious devices to repel attack, such a castle was indeed in its day close to impregnable. As a last resort, its forces could retreat to a massive keep where an enemy could be held at bay as long as food, water, and supplies held out.[2]

On the other hand, the Gothic cathedral has, as we have noted, been likened to modern skeleton-steel construction. The great period of cathedral building came in the late 12th and early 13th centuries, again a culmination of an evolution which may be traced back through the ages. Basically, the main hall, or nave, of the cathedral was formed by a series of parallel stone bents, or frameworks, between which stained glass windows formed a major part of the enclosing fabric. Tall and slender columns supported the vaulting, frequently over 100 ft above the floor, while a cleverly designed series of buttresses and buttressing arches (flying buttresses) carried the thrust of the vault safely to earth. The cathedral plan may have evolved from that of the Roman basilica or even earlier temple constructions, but the men who, without the aid of stress analysis or modern structural knowledge, planned and erected these "bird cages in stone" were indeed worthy of the title master builders.

Periods of struggle and strife, "troubled times," appear to force men's minds to turn to invention and, thus, to accelerate technological change. Both World War I and World War II have markedly accelerated technological advances. The strife and the uncertainties of the Middle Ages seem to have likewise had a stimulating effect on invention and design. The most important of all these advances in the Middle Ages was probably the result of an obscure chemical discovery. Known to the alchemists of the 13th century and used in cannon in the 14th century, gunpowder was one of the most potent forces the engineer has ever exploited. It belongs in a group of inventions which, like the steam engine, electric power, and the gas engine, has changed the course of human history—has profoundly influenced the evolution of Western life.

This obscure chemical discovery had a two-part impact. It vitally affected man's position in the world, and it gave new life and interests to engineering. On the one hand, the new cannon which came into use, replacing the older clumsy and ineffective catapults of ancient days, soon eliminated the medieval fortress. Offense again gained

[2] One of the greatest and last of these medieval castles, the Chateau of Coucy, built 1223–1230 near Laon about 60 miles northeast of Paris, had a circular donjon, or keep, almost 100 ft in diameter, 180 ft high, and with lower walls of 18 ft minimum thickness.

supremacy over defense. The noble could no longer retreat in comparative safety to his fortress-home—he became, in fact, in spite of his costly armor, less than a match for the common foot soldier armed with a portable cannon, the blunderbuss. This, of course, spelled the end of the feudal system. As Napoleon observed, "The advent of cannon killed the feudal system." In its first phase it ended the age of petty nobles and, especially in France, led to the rise of a strong central government, the monarchy. The common man was not immediately freed, but a great step forward had been taken in releasing men from the tyranny of man.

Technically, the results were no less important. The use of cannon gave great impetus to the development of both surveying and metallurgy while the provision of new means of defense led to the evolution of a new type of structure, the earthwork fortification which has continued down to modern times. The effective direction and use of cannon raised new problems in the determination of the range and elevation of the target. This gave a new interest to the ancient art of surveying which may, without exaggeration, be said to mark the birth of modern surveying. The earliest printed books on surveying are primarily military works. The casting of cannon similarly posed new and stimulating problems in the metallurgical art. It encouraged a remarkable increase in the scale of metallurgical operations and posed new problems of control and operation which mark the birth of the modern age of metals.

Finally, as has always been the case when new techniques have been introduced in a profession, techniques unrelated to earlier established practices, a breakup in the ranks of the master builder soon began to be evident. Military engineering, taking its name from the ingeniator of earlier days, began to secure recognition as a special profession, the first to bear the title engineering.

These outstanding advances of the Middle Ages were followed by a rediscovery of the past which added old knowledge to the new interests of Western life. It has been the past practice of historians to speak of the culmination of these developments which had been going forward during the Middle Ages as the Renaissance, a "rebirth." Modern workers, however, frown upon this designation of the period between, say, 1450 and 1550, which was marked by a revival of ancient learning and an increased tempo of advance. It was not, they point out, a rebirth but the result of the long period in the rebuilding of Western life during the Middle Ages. In its first phase this new level of accomplishment centered in northern Italy.

The Renaissance. France, which had been a major center of fortress building and of cathedral construction in the later Middle Ages, became a battleground in the 14th and early 15th centuries. The Black Death had fallen heavily on the West in 1348, and the Hundred Years' War between England and France did not come to an end until 1453, following the advent of Joan of Arc. The Moorish surge through Spain had been checked, but Spain also did not rise to the stature of a great power until its consolidation under Ferdinand and Isabella in 1469. To the east, the Turks were still threatening the new civilizations of the West for, following the fall of Constantinople in 1453, this threat was not resolved until the battle of Lepanto over a hundred years later, in 1571.

In between these areas of strife and conflict, the Italian peninsula was, temporarily at least, relatively calm, a center of progress and interest in the further development of Western culture. Southern Italy was still in foreign hands but the grip of the Holy Roman Empire on northern Italy had relaxed—it was ceasing, in the words of Voltaire, to be either holy, Roman, or an empire. From the 12th century onward there had been a revival of town life in Italy, and here in the later 15th and early 16th centuries the major cities of northern Italy —Genoa, Florence, Milan, Venice—became important centers in a revival of classical learning, art, architecture, and in the further progress of engineering.

The outstanding figure in this period was Leonardo da Vinci (1452–1519) but, great genius as he undoubtedly was, his influence, indeed the immediate influence of the new discoveries of this era— classical, scientific, and geographical—on engineering progress, has been greatly exaggerated.

The position of the engineer at this time is clearly revealed in a letter of Leonardo's seeking a new position. Occasionally, the master builder, the combination engineer-architect and military expert of the day, served the assembly of a city republic, such as Florence, on public works—canals, embankments, or bridges. Or he became precariously attached to the retinue of one of the semi-independent military bosses who happened, at the moment, to have the upper hand. The master builder of the Middle Ages had been a remarkably skilled itinerant craftsman, moving from job to job. Leonardo, universal genius—artist, scientist, architect, engineer—likewise had no stable employment. He changed from one patron to another, dying in Paris whither he had gone in the train of the French king, Francis I.

Nevertheless, Leonardo's justly famous notebooks do accurately reflect the tremendous inventive interest and active imagination of his day. One feels that the minds of men had suddenly been freed of past fears and inhibitions, and the vision of a new mechanical era had suddenly been revealed to them. Yet few, very few, of these wonderful mechanical dreams were actually to be realized until centuries later. It is seldom indeed that they reflect the actual accomplishments of the period. Leonardo's notebooks were private, personal records—notes of earlier works which he had seen or of which he had heard, records of suggested plans or devices, memoranda of mechanical speculations, or simple jottings of visionary ideas. They were not available to his engineering brethren; in fact they were, for what they were worth, part of his own stock in trade and were not published until comparatively recent times. Here are mechanical devices of the present day—machine tools, chain drives, the tank of World War I, proposals for airplanes, and a host of other mechanical inventions. But they exercised, perhaps, even less influence on engineering progress than the relatively modern speculations of Jules Verne.

In building construction a major advance was made in this age of Italian leadership in the development of dome construction. The famous Duomo, or cathedral, of Florence of the period of 1420–1434 shows a clear understanding of the hoop tension principle (the outward "bursting" forces) in the construction of its great dome—an advance over that of the great cathedral of St. Sophia in Constantinople of some nine centuries earlier. In bridge-building an important step forward was also made in the adoption of the segmental, and later the elliptical arch, giving far greater free area below the bridge floor for the passage of floodwaters—a vast improvement on the full-centered arch designs invariably used by the Romans. Perhaps, however, the outstanding Italian invention of this period was the canal lock, a device which may possibly also have been independently invented in Holland. Its genesis is clearly shown in early manuscript drawings.

The canalization of rivers was, apparently, first secured in Italy by providing a series of gate dams which could be opened so that boats might be pulled through against the current, and which, when closed, would provide slack-water navigation to the next barrier upstream. The idea of combining two such gates with a lock chamber between would seem to have been an obvious and inevitable development of this earlier clumsy and difficult arrangement. In this connection, it is interesting to note that Leonardo was probably the first to propose the use of two "mitering" lock gates, now the universal practice, instead of the heavy single gate of many earlier designs. This was, perhaps, in addition to his leadership as an outstanding artist-architect-engineer, his major contribution to the progress of the engineering profession.

It is also true that a new form of defense against the new cannon appears to have been first developed in Italy. The earthwork fort of star form was undoubtedly an important milestone in the history of military engineering.

We may, thus, summarize the Renaissance in Italy, as far as its effects on engineering were concerned, by stating that its outstanding contributions were the use of segmental and elliptical arches, the planning and design of river canalizations including, probably, the invention of the canal lock, the design of earthwork fortifications, and advances in the understanding of dome action. The remarkable inventive mechanical speculations of this period had little importance in view of the lack of mechanical power.

On the other hand, whether it is claimed for engineering or for art, the invention in Northern Europe of the technique of printing from type was probably the major mechanical contribution which the Renaissance made to modern life. Releasing, as it did, the written word to millions who could not afford to own manuscript books, it was, as Carlyle remarked, a powerful influence in the spread of democratic ideas. Block printing had been practiced for centuries in China. The first printed book known dates from 868 A.D. The details of the reinvention or development of printing in the West are still in doubt but are ascribed to the German worker, Gutenberg, and to about the year 1450. The books printed in the babyhood of the art, before 1500, the "incunabula," total some 38,000 volumes—many of them, of course, different editions of the same work—and these include both the first printed engineering book, Valturius' *De re militari,* as well as several editions of Vitruvius. Probably, however, the most notable early engineering book was the famous work on mining and metallurgy, Agricola's *De re metallica,* of 1558. This was inspired by the mining revival which had taken place in Saxon Germany, and it remained a standard text for almost two hundred years.

Still another vital contribution of the Renaissance, however, must be noted, for it was to have an outstanding importance some four or five centuries later. The Renaissance was marked not only by a revived interest in the work of the authors of Classical Times but by the beginnings of modern experimental science. Poggio, to whom we are indebted for many discoveries of classical works, searched the monas-

A Great Mine Pump of 1558

Agricola in his famous book on mining and metallurgy, *De re metallica*, describes this pump, driven by a manpower treadwheel and using bored-wood log pipes, as being employed to unwater a mine shaft 66 ft deep.

teries for manuscripts of the Greek and Latin authors, turning up among others, about the year 1400, the earliest known copy of the famous work of Frontinus covering his studies as "Commissioner of Water Supply" of Rome under a reform administration in 97 A.D.

Almost paralleling this turning back to earlier writers who, although pagan, were accepted by the Roman Church as the final authority on nonsecular matters, there were, however, the early discoveries of modern science which, as Sir Norman Angell has put it, "involved turning upside down the intellectual and moral assumptions which had guided man during long centuries and even millenia." Copernicus (1473–1543) was a pioneer of modern astronomical science. Galileo (1564–1642) followed with his upsetting observations on the place of the earth in the solar system and in his pioneer work in experimental mechanics. Kepler (1571–1630) added still another chapter to astronomical knowledge. In 1492 Columbus had discovered a new world, while, in 1519, Magellan had embarrassed the doubters by sailing around this world. Science was beginning, as the Renaissance closed, to become free. Reliance on authority was grudgingly and reluctantly beginning to give way to observation and experiment. Galileo was forced to recant, to give up his "errors," but the steady accumulation of scientific evidence in the end proved to be too much even for the Church.

This change marked the beginning of a separation not only between science and religion but of science from philosophy. For at least four more centuries, natural science was still referred to as natural philosophy, but the Englishman, Sir Francis Bacon, in the first years of the 17th century made it clear that science could and should serve man as well as seek to satisfy his curiosity and stimulate his thoughts. As Sir Norman Angell says,

The triumph of the scientific attitude and method, even in the field of physical science, was no easy conquest, and has never been complete. . . . It was—is—no easy task for men to think inductively, "objectively," to accept conclusions which seemed to demand renunciation of cherished and familiar belief, threatening to cut us adrift from secure anchorages.

This freeing of natural science from the shackles of religion on the one hand and the domination of philosophy on the other ultimately paved the way to a new alignment, a liaison between natural science and engineering, which, however, did not take place for over four hundred years, that is, until the mid-19th century. During the four centuries following the Renaissance, natural science was throwing off the last inhibitions of its earlier days of enslavement and building the foundations of the modern scientific method and understanding. There was little natural science could or did contribute to engineering progress over these intervening centuries. Science and engineering continued to develop independently, each in its own directions and interests. When the wedding of science and engineering did take place, it was thus a developed science which was wedded to a developed technology. Yet we must look back to the Renaissance for the first steps in providing the setting for this event, a liaison so fraught with momentous consequences for the human race. Man began in the Renaissance to correct an error that dates back to Greek days with consequences which, even today, we seek to understand and forecast.

Chapter 3. THE AGE OF FRENCH LEADERSHIP

Along the Paris streets, the death carts rumble, hollow and harsh. The tumbrils carry the day's wine to La Guillotine. And yet there is not in France, with its rich variety of soil and climate, a blade, a leaf, a root, a sprig, which will grow to maturity under conditions more certain than those that have produced this horror. Crush humanity out of shape once more, under similar hammers, and it will twist itself into the same tortured forms. Sow the same seed of rapacious license and oppression over again, and it will surely yield the same fruit according to its kind.

Charles Dickens, *A Tale of Two Cities*.

THE FRENCH ENGINEERS OF THE 17TH AND 18TH CENTURIES

The products and influences of this new advance in Western life which came into being in northern Italy were brought to the attention of French leadership through the Franco-Italian Wars. Northern Italy, first to experience the gathering influences essential to the rebuilding of Western civilization, became, in the late 15th and early 16th centuries, the battleground of Europe. Not only was Italian art carried bodily to France but Italian interests and practices, even Italian artists and engineers, were likewise imported among the spoils of war. Leonardo, as we have noted, died in France in 1519 whither he had gone in the train of Francis I. Other engineers found an outlet for their talents in continuing the Italian development by participating in the birth of what has been known as the French Renaissance. Indeed the debt which engineering owes to France of the 17th and 18th centuries cannot be overemphasized. Under French leadership, engineering was expanded and developed into a modern and effective art and the foundations of engineering science were created. Here, for the first time, engineers were brought together as a group and given professional standing. Vauban, the famous "fortress builder" of the age of Louis XIII, suggested in 1672—an important date in engineering annals—the organization of the engineers of the army, hitherto loosely attached to individual commanders in a semiconsulting capacity, as a Corps du génie. Later, in 1716, under the first chief engineer, Gabriel, a national highway department was created, the famous Corps de ponts et chaussées, which carried the art of bridge and highway building to new levels of accomplishment. Some thirty years later, in 1747, the equally famous École des ponts et chaussées was established—the first civil engineering school—to train men for the corps, a function it still carries forward.

French works, especially bridges, became the models for similar constructions in other countries. Almost two thousand years of evolution of the stone masonry arch were brought to practical perfection in Perronet's famous Pont de la Concorde at Paris, completed in

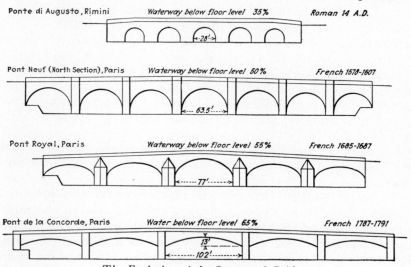

Ponte di Augusto, Rimini   *Waterway below floor level 35%*   *Roman 14 A.D.*

Pont Neuf (North Section), Paris   *Waterway below floor level 50%*   *French 1578-1607*

Pont Royal, Paris   *Waterway below floor level 55%*   *French 1685-1687*

Pont de la Concorde, Paris   *Water below floor level 65%*   *French 1787-1791*

The Evolution of the Stone-arch Bridge

Successive advances in solving the problem of providing a substantially level crossing, the greatest possible free waterway for the passage of floods, and the requisite supporting stone-arch construction.

1791 just as the French Revolution broke on the country. This daring work with its segmental arches of remarkably small rise and its slender piers left almost two-thirds of the area below the floor level free for the passage of floods, thus doubling the usual provisions of the pioneer builders of ancient Rome. With all our modern methods of stress analysis, we could not improve this performance.

In foundation work also, French engineers developed the cofferdam and the open caisson processes although, limited to water wheels and hand pumps in unwatering their excavations, they seldom succeeded in carrying their piers deeper than 8 or 10 feet below the water level.

French engineers were also the first to pass beyond the river canalization stage in the field of inland navigation and to pose and solve the problem of carrying a canal over an intervening height, to handle the problem of a summit water supply. The building of the famous Canal du Midi in 1681, crossing France just north of the Pyrenees from the Atlantic to the Mediterranean, was an undertaking comparable in its day to the Panama Canal in modern times. Topographically, France was especially blessed with opportunities for inland navigation. Great rivers—the Seine, Loire, Rhone, and others—spread out from central France like the arms of a great starfish, affording unparalleled opportunities for river canalizations. One must not lose sight of the fact that the removal of earlier limitations to inland transportation was a major contribution of the later Age of Steam. All great early cities evolved on navigable waters because inland transportation, limited to pack animals or horse-drawn vehicles traveling over poor roads, was prohibitively costly. It cost more, for example, to transport goods the 40 miles overland from Saint-Malo to Rennes than it did to carry them some 350 miles by sea around the entire Brest peninsula to Nantes. It was not the road but the canal that was king in inland transportation before the advent of the railroad.

Between 1738–1742 Belidor's remarkable work on hydraulic engineering, *Architecture hydraulique,* was published in four beautiful volumes. Although Belidor was not the first or greatest of French hydraulicians, his book was widely used as a text, especially by later British workers.[1] Henri Pitot of the same period, builder of the aqueduct of Montpellier and inventor of the Pitot tube, was a pioneer of engineering hydraulics. The outstanding contribution in this field, however, was that of Perronet's famous assistant, Chézy, who proposed about 1775 the remarkable basic equation known the world over for flow in open channels, $V = C\sqrt{RS}$. This empirical formula has been applied to stream flow from the smallest ditches to the Mississippi River, and it is safe to describe it as one of the most outstanding hydraulic generalizations of the ages.

In the birth of modern highway construction also, French engineers were pioneers although the credit has usually gone to the later British workers, McAdam and Telford. The old Roman form of road surfacing—as someone has said, practically a cut-stone masonry wall

[1] The author secured, a number of years ago, the copies of this work which had belonged to the British engineer, John Rennie, and which he had studied at Edinburgh in 1780.

laid on its side—was impossibly costly for extended highway use.[2] Modern highway construction awaited the development of a really practical, low-cost form of highway paving or surfacing. Trésaguet in 1775 proposed a broken-stone construction almost exactly similar to that later known by Telford's name. The French highway budget had reached in fact 7 million livres (approximately $1\frac{1}{2}$ million dollars) just before the Revolution, when there were some 30,000 miles

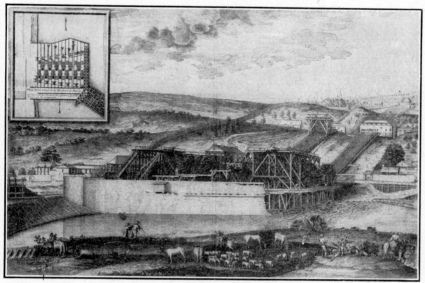

The Machine at Marly, 1686

This "forest of wood and iron," one of the world wonders of its day, pumped water from the river level to the top of the hill where aqueducts carried it to the fountains of the King's gardens at Versailles. The multiple pumps were in three lifts and were mechanically driven by water wheels through operating rods. (*From Les Plans . . . de Versailles, by P. Le Pautre, Paris, 1716.*)

of "constructed" roads, but Trésaguet's method of surfacing came too late to be fully developed before the Revolution ended this era.

French workers also made notable contributions to the development of machines. Current-driven water-wheel pumps were used in the 16th century in Paris, London, and other river cities. The greatest of these, however, was the great French machine at Marly of 1686, "a forest of wood and iron," which, in the reign of Louis

[2] Even the famous Roman roads, such as the Appian Way, so generally thought of and pictured as paved streets, were, in fact, only so surfaced in limited sections in and near towns.

XIV, supplied water for the gardens of Versailles. Diderot's remarkable Encyclopedia of 1751–1772 is filled with illustrations of various mechanical devices from hoisting, pile-driving, and dredging equipment—all, of course, as in Roman times, operated by manpower—through lathes and metalworking tools to looms and other industrial devices.

Finally, we owe to French engineers—such men as Coulomb, Navier, and De Prony—the birth of engineering science. These were the men who began the movement to reduce engineering design to more fully rationalized procedures, to develop a science of engineering which ultimately has replaced many of the older uncertainties of an empirical practice, of engineering which was predominantly an art, with the more exact scientific techniques of the present day. The practical application and use of their efforts were, unfortunately, interrupted by the French Revolution. It may, in fact, be true that their contributions too often lacked the practical, utilitarian turn needed to span the gap which always exists between theoretical knowledge and practical needs and uses. They were, perhaps, ahead of their time. British workers were destined a few years later to make notable contributions in translating such theories into practice. Nevertheless these French masters were the pioneers of modern engineering science.

Through all this period of over two centuries of interesting, continued, and stirring development, however, the economy of France was overloaded with the crushing burden of the French king and court. One able finance minister followed another in efforts to stimulate an impossibly burdened economy—to encourage industries and build up transportation—not primarily with the progress of the people in mind but to create new values which through taxation would aid in supplying funds for the evermounting extravagances of the king. This heavy tax burden was also wastefully administered. Public funds were diverted to maintaining ineffective and burdensome governing and administrative groups. Vauban had offered in his last years suggestions in his *Dixme royale,* or Royal Tenth, on the possibilities of relieving the burdens of the poor through the more efficient administration of taxes but his work displeased the king and his ministers and was banned.[3]

[3] Voltaire, not noted for his compliments, hailed Vauban as "first of engineers and first of citizens." The latter designation refers to the fact that Saint-Simon was said to have coined the word citizen and applied it to Vauban in recognition not only of his devotion to the interests of France but to those of the French people.

Bridge Construction in 1762

Showing the construction of a pier of the Pont d'Orléans. The site is enclosed within a cofferdam which has been excavated to about 10 to 12 ft below river level, where piles are being driven with two drivers operated by manpower. A huge water-wheel pump plus a battery of hand pumps (on the right under the canvas) is used to keep the site clear of water. (*From Perronet's Les Ponts. . . .)*

To this discouraging picture must be added the fact that an agricultural life could no longer maintain the growing population. By the 18th century, the possibilities of a largely agricultural economy had been practically exhausted. While the percentage of land held by the nobility and clergy varied widely in different parts of the country, the amounts were usually relatively small, and this factor apparently was of minor influence. Their holdings were, in fact, largely urban and forest lands, whereas the many, more important, smaller agricultural areas had been so divided and redivided from father to son that the available acreage would no longer maintain a family.

Basically, French life rested on an agricultural economy plus some petty rural industries and a much smaller number of urban manufactures, the latter dominated by the narrow interests and restrictions of the craftsmen of a declining guild system. France needed both political and economic reform. While she had carried forward to new levels of achievement the art of construction in stone, had built roads and canals, had refined earlier machines, and had encouraged the fine arts, little or nothing had been done to bring engineering to the service of the practical arts of manufacturing and industry. French engineering, in scope, character, and methods, was essentially a more refined and fully developed Roman engineering. The same construction equipment as had served in Roman times built her bridges. Earlier lathes, drills, looms, and other machines were improved, but iron and steam, the essentials of a new industrial economy were not available. Mechanical power was lacking, and the surviving guilds resisted every effort toward mechanization and the improvement of manufacturing practices and methods. An industrial revolution might have aided in solving the French economic problems of the 18th century, but a political revolution was essential to a more equitable distribution of the proceeds and burdens of French life and it came first.

On the other hand, Britain had settled her major political difficulties in the 17th century, had been slowly building up her inland communications during the 18th, and had developed steam power and a new iron industry by the close of that century. The Industrial Revolution was well under way before the French Revolution. The stage was thus set, with the close of the Napoleonic Wars which left France in eclipse, for the rapid growth of a new Era of Iron and Power, of modern transportation and industry in Britain. France passed into a long era of retarded progress from which she did not begin to emerge until late in the 19th century.

Chapter 4. EARLY BRITISH ENGINEERING

Britain had turned her face towards the new industry—the wheels of iron and the shriek of escaping steam. In them lay for the future not only her power and wealth but her very existence.

J. H. Clapham, *An Economic History of Modern Britain.*

IRON AND STEAM, TRANSPORTATION AND MANUFACTURES

With the rise of engineering in Britain in the 18th century an entirely new era in human history came into being. In earlier centuries engineering had, as we have seen, been a powerful and effective instrumentality in the evolution of Western civilization. Its interests and activities had, however, been almost entirely confined to public works under government control. Only to a limited extent—as in such fields as mining and metallurgy and to a less degree in the chemical arts—had technology played an important part in the production of consumers' goods, in industry and manufacturing. Engineering had been largely construction engineering, and the civil engineer had relied almost entirely on products available in nature—timber and stone. For almost the first time in the history of the world engineering in this new British era became allied not with government but with private enterprise, and its methods and practices were extended into and, to a major extent, created the great field of modern industrial production of consumers' goods.

Great emphasis has been placed in recent years on the importance of the liaison which has developed since the mid-19th century between natural science and engineering—a wedding of interests from which many new products, processes, and methods spring—in which many elements of "technological change" have their origin. On the other hand, the fact that an earlier wedding, that between technology and industry, has had a more profound effect on man's position in the world and in his relationships to man has been almost completely ignored. It was this earlier wedding of interests, which took place in 18th century Britain and in which natural science played no part, that changed the entire basis of production of consumers' goods and, thus, the means and conditions under which men and women today secure a livelihood. The Industrial Revolution was the immediate product of this union. Its developments, however, occupied the Western nations throughout the entire 19th century. On them Britain's outstanding position and empire of the Victorian Era were built. From them stem the perplexing problems of our social, economic, and political life of which we still seek adequate understanding and an intelligent solution.

In 1798 a young British vicar, Thomas Malthus, became concerned with the limitations of the agricultural home economy, then the predominant way of life of the great majority of people even in the Western World. He argued that, unless constant increases in population were restrained, such an economy would ultimately be unable to sustain life. As we have seen, the division of land holdings from father to son had brought about substantially this situation in France. Britain was obviously even less favorably situated to provide food for an ever-increasing population. Even as Malthus was writing, however, the Industrial Revolution was so increasing the productive power of man that an increase in population in Britain of 100 per cent in the next fifty years was possible; and later it provided higher standards of living for new millions in those nations which adopted what we have come to call industrialization.

Due attention must be given in this story to the fact that the industrial transformation on which Britain embarked at this time was paralleled by—may in large part have been made possible by—a revolutionary change in her agricultural system, by what is known as enclosure.

The origin of the English village, the basic unit of her agricultural economy of the early 18th century, is uncertain. It had evolved, however, from the feudal manor into a communal system in which the three classes of land, arable fields, meadowlands, and the common, or waste, while held by various owners were used in common by all groups from the Lord of the Manor down through the freeholders (yeomen) and tenant farmers to cottagers and squatters. The arable fields were divided into strips, so many furrows, and an owner or tenant might have several scattered strips as these rights were purchased or sold. After harvesting and after hay had been cut from the meadows, all these lands, however, were open to common pasturage. Even the humble cottager or squatter, the farm laborer group, had the opportunity to pasture an animal or two and could, of course, save and purchase other rights. The Lord held ownership of the waste, subject to these common rights, and often increased his ownership in the cultivated fields or meadows through purchase. This was, of course, a great advance from the earlier days of serfdom, though even by the time of Elizabeth the English villein had been a relatively free tenant farmer and could purchase and hold property.

On the other hand, this common use of the land was inefficient and tended to encourage routine, wasteful, and unprogressive practices, and discourage experiment and improvement. The cultivation of land in small, long, narrow, wormlike strips was necessarily uneconomical and ineffective. If standards of living were to be raised and labor was to be released from agriculture for industrial pursuits, it seemed inevitable that these common rights would have to be enclosed and consolidated under individual ownership in larger and more compact holdings. Both the economic trends of the day and the interests of the major landowners favored this change.

The character of English villages varied widely, but enclosure in general resulted in a redistribution of rights which, as is usual in such revolutionary changes, militated against the smaller, less powerful, less articulate farmers and, especially, deprived the tenant farmer and the farm laborer of their common rights. It has been argued that enclosure was largely responsible for the rise of a new class in Britain, the poor. It cannot be denied, however, that it increased the productivity of British agriculture manyfold and was a necessary first step to later improvements and mechanization in farming.

Hindsight is, of course, always easier than foresight. It is easy to criticize the iniquities of the government acts by which enclosure was brought about.[1] Yet we struggle even today to reduce the dislocations and inequalities which are the inevitable accompaniment of economic changes. In Britain, serfdom disappeared much earlier than on the Continent. This change, also, followed a different course. In Britain many of the serf cultivators ended up as wage-earning laborers. In France, Germany, and Denmark a much larger proportion became peasant farm owners. But it may be asked whether the creation of a laboring class was not an essential accompaniment of the Industrial Revolution. The wage earner is still a part of our industrial life and, after all, the Industrial Revolution took place in Britain, not in these other countries. Enclosure acts in the forty years after 1760, that is, in the major earlier era of the Industrial Revolution,

---

[1] See, for example, the scathing denunciation of the part played by the political leaders of the day and the distresses of the laboring groups in *The Village Labourer, 1760–1832*, by J. L. and Barbara Hammond, London, Longmans, Roberts and Green, 4th ed., 1927.

increased tenfold and continued at a high rate throughout the earlier 19th century.[2]

These concurrent changes, agricultural and industrial, which so profoundly affected man's social and economic life did not take place, as we have noted, "all of a sudden." The modernization of British agriculture, the adoption of more scientific methods, and its mechanization did not begin until after 1800, and it never achieved the development it has in the United States. Similarly many major basic engineering advances were 19th century developments. It is also true that there were, even before the Industrial Revolution, important but isolated British engineering works, some of which date back to the period of Queen Elizabeth. The famous New River water supply for London had been built in 1613 under the guidance of Sir Hugh Myddleton (1555–1631), a London goldsmith and capable promoter. Similarly, metal and textile workers had been encouraged to come to Britain, and Queen Elizabeth could brag that she left more iron ordnance than there had been of brass at the beginning of her reign. Clearly also, Britain had established her position as "Mistress of the Seas," a land blessed with ports and harbors, fleets and light-houses, "a hedged and fenced land without forests and of garden-like agriculture," before the new era opened. She had also solved her political problems and had become that peculiarly British institution, a free monarchial democracy. The main problems she faced in the 18th century stemmed from the exhaustion of her fuel resources for the making of iron and the lack of adequate means of power and inland transportation. All through this century British engineers had been working with these problems, and, by the mid-century the iron industry had been revived, a canal and road era established, new textile machinery had been developed, and to these was shortly added the new power of steam. The way was being made ready for the even more rapid growth of the 19th century. With these advantages and the victorious outcome of the Napoleonic Wars, it was inevitable that Britain should forge rapidly ahead.

As in France, the early roads in Britain were atrocious. Even in the late 18th century, it was remarked that it would cost less to make them navigable than to give them a hard surface. Her great cities were inevitably adjacent to coastal waters. She lagged behind France in the development of inland navigation—British engineers, in fact, studied French works and French books. Her early canals, neverthe-

[2] 1700–1760 a total of about 200 acts; 1760–1801, about 2,000; and 1802–1844, about 1,900. See item by Slater in the Bibliography.

less, played an important part in stimulating British life. They brought progress and hope to many of her isolated inland areas.

The Father of the British Canal Era, James Brindley (1716–1772), was a man of little education, a highly skilled and competent millwright and builder, forced to rely on his native abilities and intuitive judgment. The millwright, it should be noted, was the practical designer and highly skilled and resourceful craftsman who had built

Brindley's Barton Aqueduct, 1761

Carrying the Liverpool and Manchester Canal over the Irwell, this work was considered so daring and audacious that people came from far and near to see the canalboats pass over the river using Brindley's "Castle in the Air." (*After Smiles, Lives of the Engineers.*)

the wind and water mills and equipment of earlier days. It was the engineer, replacing this earlier practical worker and bringing new understanding and skills to the service of industry, whose labors brought about the Industrial Revolution. Brindley was capable as a millwright, but he was primarily a pioneer of the transportation industry in this new area of engineering activity.

With the patronage and support of the Duke of Bridgewater, Brindley built two works which, while they posed no problems exceeding those which had already been met in French work, were of pioneer British importance. These private business ventures were also eminently successful from the financial standpoint, and, furthermore, they made possible the birth of industrial life in western England. The Liverpool and Manchester Canal, although bitterly opposed by "the river men," who saw this work ending the transportation monopoly they had long enjoyed, was vital to the rise of Manchester as a great manufacturing center. Seventy years later the canal men were in turn to oppose the railroad which resulted in a further reduction of some 50 per cent in shipping costs. Even later, the present ship canal, which makes Manchester a port, was opposed by the railway interests. The threat of what we now call technological unemployment evidently retarded progress even in those early days. Brindley's other great work, the Grand Trunk Canal, ultimately uniting the Trent with the Mersey and both with the Severn, although likewise strongly opposed, opened up and gave new life to a great area of western England. Involving five tunnels, including the famous Harecastle, it was begun in 1766 with the enthusiastic support of the famous pottery maker, Wedgwood, and was completed in 1777.

The British canal era, initiated by Brindley, continued well into the 19th century when it was destined to fall before the all-conquering steam railway. Many of these early British canals were pure monopolies and paid high dividends. In fact some railroads were built to break down such monopolies and, by 1846, the whole weight of railroad competition fell upon the canals with fatal effect. The toll turnpikes, which came later than the canals, were, in many cases, loaded with debt, badly administered, and suffered a like fate. Yet both of these ventures were of basic importance in the rise of the new era.

While this development of inland navigation was going forward, the textile and iron industries were undergoing vitally important changes. The mechanization of the cotton textile industry in particular, the products of which constituted a major British export throughout the entire Victorian Era (as much as one-third as late as 1887), was of outstanding importance.

There are two major operations in textile manufacturing: the spinning of the yarn from the fibers and the weaving of this yarn into a fabric. For untold centuries spinning had been a hand task performed by women who shaped the fibers into a thread with their fingers at the same time twisting the fibers by means of a whorl attached to a spindle on which the thread was wound. The first improvement was the spinning wheel which came into use in Europe in the 14th century. On the other hand, some crude form of loom had always been essential to weaving, and this device had thus been known from earliest times to primitive people the world over. The British textile development was marked by improvements first in one of these operations then in the other.

The loom was first improved in 1733 by the invention of the fly shuttle by John Kay (b. 1704), an English machinist. Although his device increased the speed of weaving, the weavers, at first, opposed its introduction, demolished everything they could find in his quarters, and forced Kay to flee to France where he later died in poverty. His improvements, however, were stolen from him and came into use.

The agricultural, the spinning, and the weaving steps were all originally carried out in one home, but they now became separate occupations. Kay's device thus resulted in the new weaving communities making a demand for more yarn.

Credit for the invention of a spinning machine to supply this need is usually given to James Hargreaves, an uneducated textile worker (d. 1778). His spinning jenny (named after his daughter) was patented in 1770. This was paralleled by the improvement by Richard Arkwright (1732–1792) of the spinning frame in 1769. To the latter's persistence the British textile industry owes a great debt. Yet these laborsaving devices were regarded as threatening the livelihood of the workers, who destroyed a number of machines in 1779.

Samuel Crompton (1753–1827) best combined these earlier inventions in a new machine, which, because it was a cross between them, became known as the spinning mule. As in the case of the loom, these improvements in turn so increased the output of yarn that it was now a glut on the market and demands grew for increased weaving capacity.

While Arkwright had begun life as a barber, Edward Cartwright (1743–1823) was a minister and an educated man. Although he knew nothing of machines and was a complete stranger to the textile industry, he solved a problem which had baffled all earlier workers. He invented in 1785 a mechanical loom which became the forerunner of the modern power-driven machines. At first driven by animal or water power, by 1790 these new machines had been tied in with Watt's steam engine, and the power age in manufacturing was under way.

In the meantime, the rise of an Iron Age had paved the way for the advent of steam power and the railway. This was an essential and fortunate circumstance, for one of Boulton's and Watt's major problems was that of creating a machine which had to be built largely of metal. They were forced, in fact, in their earlier engines to use wood in all parts in which iron was not absolutely essential.

The production of cast iron had been brought into Britain from Europe at least as early as 1543 and in the 17th century grew rapidly until whole forests were laid waste to meet the needs of "the voracious ironworkers" for the essential fuel, charcoal. By 1640, in fact, it had become necessary to put a stop to this destruction, and blast furnace operations practically came to a standstill. Coal could not be successfully used both because of its sulfur content and because of the difficulty of forcing the furnace blast through the caked mass. This problem was solved by Dud Dudley, son of the Earl of Dudley, by first converting the coal into light and porous coke. Yet, owing to opposition by both the ironmakers and the charcoal workers plus accidents and other difficulties, his efforts resulted only in debt and disaster.

About a century later, however, a famous family of ironmasters, the Darby's, took up the making and casting of iron and, finally, near their works at Coalbrookdale in western England, built the first cast-iron, the first all-metal bridge, in 1779. A new Era of Metal dawned. In 1740 there had been only 59 furnaces in Britain, all using charcoal for fuel. By 1790 there were 106, all but 25 of which were using coke.

A notable advance was also made in steelmaking by a watchmaker, Benjamin Huntsman (1704–1776), who, apparently independently, rediscovered and improved the ancient method of making wrought iron into steel, its alloy with carbon, by the crucible process. The Sheffield steel industry was founded through the theft of Huntsman's secret process.

The next major development followed the work of Henry Cort (1740–1800) who has been referred to as the Father of the British Iron Trade. Wrought iron had, from Ancient Times, been made by hammering out small bars by hand and welding them together. Cort's "puddling process" made it possible to manufacture this tough and resilient metal from cast iron, and it thus became available in relatively large quantities at relatively low cost. Other improvements followed: grooved rolls for rolling iron into bars and shapes, the more economical hot blast introduced by James B. Neilson in 1828, and similar advances.

The Coalbrookdale Iron Bridge of 1779

The ancestor of all modern metal bridges, this cast-iron arch of over 100 ft span crossing the Severn introduced a real Age of Iron Construction and is still in use.

The growth of the British iron industry is illustrated by the fact that in the fifty years of the coal-iron process following 1740 production increased fourfold from about 17,000 to over 68,000 tons annually. Between 1796 and 1820, the era of the steam engine and Cort's process, there was a similar fourfold increase, while after 1828 the increase was even more rapid. Peak production, over 6 million tons, was reached in 1872 after which steel became the principal product. For almost the first three quarters of the 19th century, therefore, iron, cast and wrought, was king. Thomas Telford (1757–1834) and particularly John Rennie (1761–1821) pioneered in the use of the new metals in bridgebuilding, while other workers established a new era of machine tool building, that is, of modern metal tools and working.

It was to this picture of a new textile and iron age that, as the 18th century came to a close, British engineering and inventive skill was to add the new and revolutionary power of steam. We are apt to picture these earlier developments as having followed and resulted from the advent of steam power. It would, perhaps, be nearer the truth to refer to the changes which now took place as a Power Revolution following upon an Industrial Revolution. Even here, however, we must not assume that the results were immediate. It was a long revolution, and it was at least a half century before its full impact on British life became evident.

The history of the steam engine also illustrates the fact that many men usually contribute to a single major development. James Watt (1736–1819) did not invent the steam engine. In fact the first use of steam was not in a direct-acting steam engine but in the operation of an atmospheric mine pump. This device had been first proposed in a practical form by Savery, had been improved by Newcomen, but when Watt entered the picture, still remained prohibitively costly to operate because it was extremely wasteful of fuel.

Although a number of notable engineers attempted to improve Newcomen's pump, it was not until Watt added to it his basic invention, the separate condenser, that it became a really practical device. But even Watt's inventive skill would probably have long remained ineffective had it not been for one of the most fortunate partnerships in history, his association with a practical businessman and progressive manufacturer, Matthew Boulton (1728–1809).

The first Boulton and Watt engine, an atmospheric mine pump, was installed in 1776. Watt later went forward with the design of a rotative engine operated by the direct pressure of steam. He was not alone in this field, but he did build his first rotative engine in 1782, and orders soon began to come to the firm for engines for cotton, silk, paper, and other mills. Watt may be said to have practically perfected the low-pressure condensing reciprocating steam engine which was the standard type for over a century. It remained, however, for others to apply and use the steam engine in both land and water transportation.

A major problem which Boulton and Watt faced was that of making and machining with the necessary accuracy the relatively large iron parts needed for their engines. Watt has been called the Father of Mechanical Engineering but the old millwright, master of the practical art of devising and making machines, was the forerunner of the modern mechanical engineer. He was an expert with hammer, saw, adze, and chisel while blacksmiths forged the few iron parts and fittings he used. His measuring devices were of the simplest—footrule, square, compass, and calipers. Hand- or foot-driven lathes were in use but were not adapted to heavy metal work. Of larger scale power tools there were none. These were the problems Boulton and Watt faced in manufacturing an engine, and British workers were the first to establish the machine tools and standards of an ironworking era. One of the pioneers was John Wilkinson (1728–1808), a cast-iron enthusiast, for whom Boulton and Watt built their first Soho works engine and who, in turn, cast and bored cylinders for the partners. Joseph Bramah (1748–1814) was a pioneer inventor and mechanic, and in his shop Henry Maudsley (1771–1831), generally regarded as Father of the Machine Tool Era, Joseph Whitworth (1803–1887), pioneer of modern measurement, who standardized screw threads, and other founders of the modern machine era were trained.

In the transportation field the Canal Era, initiated by Brindley was continued by such later giants as Telford who was also known, largely because of his Scottish road and bridge work, as "The Colossus of Roads." Telford, and another engineer, John L. McAdam (1756–1836) who gave us a new term, "to macadamize," were in fact the fathers of the modern relatively inexpensive broken-stone highway. By 1829, however, a new method of transportation had been fully demonstrated. The steam locomotive, which was destined practically to render canals obsolete, to retard further highway development until the advent of the motorcar some seventy years later, and thus, to dominate the inland transportation picture more or less completely throughout the remainder of the 19th century, came into use.

Here again the Father of Steam Railroads, George Stephenson (1781–1848), was not the inventor of either the railway or the steam locomotive. Railways had been used for many years—with animal power drawing the "rail waggons." Several earlier inventors had also built steam locomotives. It remained, however, for Stephenson, a lowly mineworker, who was nevertheless, as Emerson said, of such native force of character and vigor of intellect that it was worth crossing the Atlantic merely to meet him, to demonstrate the practical, economic value of steam traction.

Stephenson's first locomotive was built in 1814 for a mine road. The Stockton and Darlington, 22 miles long and opened in 1825, was the first railroad built for public use. But the locomotive first fully demonstrated its power at the famous Rainhill trials of 1829 when Stephenson's *Rocket* attained the unheard of speed of 35 miles per hour and ensured the use of the locomotive on the Liverpool and Manchester Railway, opened in 1830. Other lines followed in rapid succession, and in 1838 the great London and Birmingham line, 112 miles long, was completed.

It should not be forgotten that Stephenson and his associates had to create not only a practical locomotive and new vehicles but the entire specialized technique of railroad surveying and construction. Many of these early lines involved major works, in some cases made necessary by the restrictions of property owners and the necessity of by-passing game preserves. In fact, throughout this period of railroad development the engineer had to face not only strong opposition but widespread misunderstanding. The railroad was denounced as a work of the devil, destructive because of poisonous gases, and dangerous to life and property. Mark Twain tells the story of the problem of securing a franchise from Parliament in an amusing but not exaggerated statement:

There were no railroad men in those Parliaments; the members had to inform themselves through the statements made to them by Stephenson, and they considered him a visionary, a half-lunatic, possibly even ass and poet. Through lack of previous knowledge and experience of railroad matters, they were unable to understand Stephenson. His explanations, so simple to himself, were but a fog to these well-meaning legislators; so far as they were concerned, he was talking riddles, and riddles which seemed also to be dreams and insanities. Still, being gentlemen, and kindly and humane, they listened to Stephenson patiently, benevolently, charitably, until at last, in a burst of irritation, he lost his prudence and proclaimed that he would yet prove to the world that he could

The Liverpool and Manchester Railroad, 1830
Showing the famous Mount Olive Cut on this line, which, although not the first railroad, may be said to have inaugurated the Railroad Era. (*From a famous series of contemporary prints published by Ackerman of London. Courtesy of the William Barclay Parsons Collection of Railroad Prints. Columbia University.*)

drive a steam locomotive over iron rails at the impossible speed of twelve miles an hour! That finished him. After that the lawmakers imposed upon themselves no further polite reserves but called him, frankly, a dreamer, a crank, a lunatic.[3]

It is interesting to note at this point that, while technical developments pass across national boundaries, the engineer has had to re-establish professional status and standing in each new country which has taken up engineering and industrial development. Earlier British power devices, notably wind and water mills, were, as we have said, the creations of a special group of highly skilled practical artisans and craftsmen, the millwrights. It is notable that many of the pioneer British engineers—Brindley, Telford, Rennie, and others—served as millwright assistants. They were, in fact, men of humble family but great ability, who created a new profession. John Smeaton (1724–1792) builder of the Eddystone Lighthouse probably did more than any other man to raise engineering in public esteem in Great Britain. He was a member of a well-to-do family, was admitted to the Royal Society, was the first engineer (c. 1750) to use the designation "civil" to distinguish his work from that of the military engineer, and he brought distinction and recognition to what had previously been regarded as a somewhat "navvy" (i.e., laborer's) calling. Smeaton also organized a famous early engineering society or club. In 1818 the Institution of Civil Engineers of Great Britain was established, of which Telford in 1820 became the first president. This organization adopted the famous definition of engineering, "the art of utilizing the forces of Nature for the use and convenience of man," written by Thomas Tredgold, another contributor to British engineering progress. With the introduction of these new techniques and the rise of mechanical engineering, a new division in the ranks of the civil engineers also began to be recognized and, in 1847, the Institution of Mechanical Engineers was organized with George Stephenson as its first president.

These remarkable advances, marking the birth of modern engineering, the rise of an Engineering Age, also offer some interesting light on the genesis of the early discoveries and inventions. In our brief outline of textile progress, for example, we noted five outstanding contributors none of whom were either scientists or engineers. It is clear that the major inventions of this era which have transformed the modern world did not depend upon discoveries in natural science

[3] *Mark Twain in Eruption,* edited by Bernard DeVoto, New York, Harper & Brothers, 1940, p. 373.

Smeaton's Eddystone Lighthouse of 1759

Built by John Smeaton, the first to use the title civil engineer. This design was followed in many later constructions, and its light served Plymouth for over a century until undermining of the rock on which it was built made a new construction necessary. (*From Smeaton's famous Narrative.*)

and were not the product of organized research. They resulted from the labors of those rare workers, men of inventive genius. Watt, for example, made it clear that his invention of the separate condenser was not influenced by the discoveries of his scientific friend, Dr. Black. As a matter of fact, the modern theory of heat followed the advent of the steam engine. Thus, contrary to modern popular belief, modern engineering did not originate in the discoveries of natural science or natural philosophy, as it was called in these earlier days. It was, as Professor Whitehead has noted, a *developed* technology which became wedded to a developed science about the middle of the 19th century.

Similarly it is a mistake to assume that any great engineering advance has resulted from the labors of one man. Whatever may be true in the realm of military achievement, political ideas, or philosophic concepts, it is clear that the conquests of engineering have almost invariably been brought about through evolution, through the successive efforts of a number of workers each adding his contribution to the development of a device or process.

Finally, it should be noted that we have devoted this chapter to the earlier development of the basic requirements of an industrial age which was building in Britain. It was not until later in the Victorian Era (1837–1901), after the famous Great Exhibition of 1851, that the full implications of the Industrial and Power Revolutions, of the liaison we have outlined between engineering and industry, and the development of adequate means of exchanging goods, the steam railway, were realized. In the furtherance of this evolution the contributions of Blackstone, Adam Smith, and other leaders of economic thought undoubtedly played a part.

Adam Smith (1723–1790), a contemporary of the pioneer British engineers and inventors whose labors we have outlined, published in 1776 his *Wealth of Nations*, "the foundation work of modern economic thought." From the ideological standpoint he is the Father of Free Enterprise and the Prophet of *Laissez Faire*. He did not, as is so often mistakenly assumed, originate the new era. The Industrial Revolution was well under way when he wrote. But, in his great work he "gave order and meaning to the newly emerged world of commerce and the newly merging world of industry." Adam Smith, as we have earlier noted, never missed the opportunity to point out that civilization or the improvement of society had not been the product of human foresight and calculation, but of the natural propensities of economically active men. But, in the late 18th century, certain regulations hindering the free movement of labor from one area to another, stemming from feudal times, certain remnants of the earlier mercantilist era and of guild restrictions, still retarded the full and free development of employment and enterprise. He and his associates were powerful factors in clearing up these difficulties, difficulties which, however, appear to have had little effect in retarding the earlier stages of the Industrial Revolution. Blackstone, whose *Commentaries* appeared about 1765, defended and expounded the legal doctrine of private property, Archdeacon Paley provided a more or less philosophical justification of private ownership, while Adam Smith saw in free enterprise the working out of a natural law which makes all the individual strivings of self-interest in man add up to the social good—the doctrine which has become known as *laissez faire,* or a hands-off attitude by government which leaves this natural law to work out its beneficent ends. As the consequences of the Industrial Revolution later began to clarify, it became apparent that government must at least impose certain controls on individualistic capitalistic enterprise if men are to retain a reasonable degree of freedom and if enterprise is to be stimulated by opportunities for free growth and free competition.

Chapter 5. THE VICTORIAN ERA

> Look yonder where the engines toil
> These England's arms of conquest are . . .
> With these she sails, she weaves, she tills,
> Pierces the everlasting hills,
> And spans the seas.
> W. M. Thackeray, *May-Day Ode,* 1851.

BRITAIN, AN INDUSTRIAL EMPIRE AND WORLD POWER

British engineering did not, of course, cease with the accomplishments which we have outlined in the preceding chapter. Yet, within broad general fields these pioneer advances did set the pattern of British engineering and industrial development which prevailed throughout the 19th century. On these beginnings Britain built an economy which permitted her to achieve, as we have said, her position as the leading industrial nation and world power, the leading nation of the world, in the 19th century. It has been not only because of the social problems and difficulties resulting from this development and because of the limitations imposed by her natural resources, but also because of too great faith in and reliance on these remarkable early advances, that Britain faces today major problems in seeking post-World War II recovery.

Britain's railroad development was carried forward by George Stephenson's son and helper, Robert (1803–1859), who also became an outstanding British engineer. The railroad problem naturally involved a new era of bridgebuilding, and in this field the younger Stephenson built such great structures as the High Level Bridge over the Tyne at Newcastle (1849) and the Britannia Tubular Bridge which crossed the Menai Strait on the route to Ireland (1850) near Telford's famous suspension bridge of a quarter century earlier. Smiles declared the former "a perfect specimen of modern [1859] constructive skill." The latter was a novel structure, essentially a huge wrought iron box girder through which the train crossed to the Isle of Angelsey, but it was a bridge form which has long since passed

56

into history, although it did mark a milestone in the evolution of iron construction.

In connection with these works Stephenson secured the services of two pioneers of modern bridge analysis and materials testing—Sir William Fairbairn (1789–1874) and Professor Eaton Hodgkinson (1789–1861). For almost the first time in the history of bridgebuilding designs were checked as far as was then possible, stresses were estimated by the use of analytical mechanics, materials tested, and

The Britannia Tubular Bridge, 1846–1850
This was the bridge that Lewis Carroll mentioned in *Alice in Wonderland,* with the suggestion that it be kept from rust "by boiling it in wine."

parts proportioned accordingly. An era of scientific bridge design was in process of development.

Also, in building the foundations of the High Level Bridge, the piles were driven not by the ancient Roman type of driver with thirty or forty men pulling up the driving weight (tup) then still in use in French work, but by a steam engine—a development from Nasmyth's steam forging hammer invented in 1839.

Stephenson's great rival was Isambard Kingdom Brunel (1806–1859), son of Marc I. Brunel (1769–1849), whose persistence put through the first subaqueous tunnel in the world, the great double-brick Thames tube of 1825–1842, a feat unparalleled for over a quarter century. The older Brunel had also devised, about 1800, the first sequence of process machines for building pulley blocks for the British Navy, then still in the age of sailing ships. This was an important step in the evolution of modern manufacturing processes. His son was also interested in naval work and designed the three greatest ocean steamships of the day—the *Great Western,* a 2,300-ton giant of 1838, the *Great Britain* of 3,000 tons, the first ocean-going vessel to use a screw propeller (1840), and the *Great Eastern* of 1853–1859 of 18,915 tons—long the world's largest vessel, which later took a spectacular part in the laying of the Atlantic cable.

The younger Brunel's most famous bridge was the Royal Albert or Saltash Bridge in the southwest of England near Plymouth. Notable for its two main spans, 455 ft each, for the peculiar tubular form of the single huge upper compression chord which formed each of the two bowstring trusses, it also marks the first use on a large scale of the compressed-air process in foundation building. Earlier engineers had been plagued with the problem of building adequately deep and secure bridge foundations under water. Brunel carried his central pier down to rock, 86½ ft below water level, by using the pressure of air to balance that of the water in a pneumatic caisson.[1]

These structures seem to have been influenced by one of the major interests of British industry, namely shipbuilding. Britain not only owned by the '80's five-eighths of the world's ocean-going steamers— one-third of the world's ocean-going tonnage—but sold her older ships to and built new ones for all countries of the globe. These iron bridges of the mid-century appear to reflect this preoccupation with the methods and forms of shipbuilding. British engineers favored tubular forms of construction built up from curved plates. Even in the great Firth of Forth Cantilever of 1883–1890, still one of the wonders of the modern world, the compression members were erected in place, piece by piece, in the same way one would build the hull of an iron ship. The unit member, truss type of bridge of modern days was largely an American development.

Space will not permit an adequate review of British engineering of the Victorian Era. We must pass the remarkable work of Sir John Fowler (1817–1899) not only of Forth Bridge fame but pioneer of

[1] The compressed-air process was one of the by-products of that remarkable naval genius and adventurer Thomas, Lord Cochrane, who had received a patent in 1830.

modern subway building, engineer of the first London "underground" of 1860–1863. Also that of his famous partner, Sir Benjamin Baker (1840–1907) who engineered the great Aswan Dam in Egypt. The growth of urban problems and the work of Sir Joseph William Bazalgette (1819–1891) in building the sewer system of London and of other pioneers of sanitary and municipal engineering must also be

The Firth of Forth Cantilever, 1883–1890

Still one of the wonders of modern engineering, this huge work with its two great spans of 1,710 ft each is of a unique tubular form of construction, each member built up in place from curved plates and reflecting, perhaps, British shipbuilding techniques. (*After The Forth Bridge in Its Various Stages of Construction, by Philip Phillips, 1885.*)

left untold. Any adequate treatment of the history of engineering must include the notable contributions of that great pioneer of modern irrigation, Colonel Sir Arthur Thomas Cotton (1803–1899) whose labors in India opened a new era in the service of engineering to colonial areas and led to notable advances in the design and construction of great dams for water supply and irrigation.

In the manufacturing industries the steam engine replaced the old water, horse, or hand-power equipment although as late as 1830 some of these earlier devices were still in use. Watt had practically perfected the low-pressure, condensing reciprocating engine, and it was this engine which turned the wheels of British industry throughout the Victorian Era. British industry continued to expand—coal, iron and its products, textiles, machinery, and ships, plus the income of shipping and trade were the activities which replenished the British pocketbook.

As manufacturing expanded and the population increased, British agriculture declined and she turned to imports to meet not only her raw material needs, such as cotton for her textile industries, but, increasingly, her basic food requirements. British ships sailed the Seven Seas maintaining communication with her colonial possessions scattered all over the globe. It was largely from this colonial empire that she imported her basic materials and food, and to which she exported her manufactured products and found investment opportunities for her surplus capital. This, in brief, was the British economy on which her outstanding world position of the 19th century rested. It is difficult to imagine any other plan which would have met her needs. It seems fortunate for Britain beyond words that this small island, "built on coal and surrounded by fish," should have been the birthplace of a new form of life, an industrialized economy.

One would think that a global economy such as this would be sensitive to the vagaries of the economic weather of the entire world. Yet British industrial and business life was remarkably stable. After our Civil War our high tariffs prevented an increase in her exports to America. She simply turned to other markets. Of competition there was little, and Britain continued on a free-trade basis confident that she could meet all competition in her special export fields. America was not only fully occupied with her own economic development but naturally assumed a position of isolation from world economy, as well as from world politics, for she had all her needs within her own borders. Even the so-called "American invasion" of Britain after 1900 was more of a myth than a fact. France's exports were of the non-competitive luxury type, and only Germany and Japan later came to exercise an influence on the British position.

The maximum British birth rate was reached in 1871–1875, but of the period after 1900—just before World War I—it can be said "Britain was as fully occupied with work as any country could hope to be although it was not stirring industrially as were America and

Germany." As had happened in each preceding nation in the long stream of Western civilization, weaknesses were developing in the British picture which, brought clearly to light by World War II, have made it extremely doubtful whether Britain will be able again to attain her former position in Western life. These weaknesses began to appear before World War I. In the interwar period they were obscured by the lavish flow of American dollars abroad—a total sum comparable to what Britain had lent during the entire 19th century when she was the creditor nation of the world. Today they have become of such vital importance that the British situation has been characterized as one of technological stagnation and decay. This situation has been reflected primarily in a failure of the British economy to provide improving standards of living for her working groups —the major factor in the rise of a Labor government to power in Britain and her turning to socialization of a number of major services and activities.

The economic status of the British worker had improved but slowly in the earlier years of the 19th century. The period up to 1850 was necessarily one of adjustment to new conditions and was marked by the shameful exploitation of men, women, and children by the new entrepreneur group which was struggling to make the most of the opportunities for money gain provided by the Industrial Revolution. It took most of the 19th century to bring about the legal and other reforms which have resulted in the work standards of the present day.

The money wages of the British worker remained practically stationary from 1830 to 1850. His position did improve somewhat, however, because there was a slight decline in the price of the essential necessities of life. The Factory Act of 1850 established the 60-hour week, the *semaine anglaise* which ended the week's labors at 2 P.M. on Saturdays. During the period 1850–1890 money wages increased an average of 50 per cent while prices continued to decline. It is estimated that the purchasing power, the real wages, of the British worker increased 2½ to 3 times during the 19th century.

Adam Smith had pointed out in his *Wealth of Nations,* published in 1776 but in part based on lectures prepared some twenty-five years earlier, that a major factor in production was the division, or specialization, of labor. "The greatest improvement in the productive process of labor," he noted, "seems to have been the effect of the division of labor." This leads to increased dexterity on the part of the worker and to saving time by not continuously passing from one task to another. These advantages he illustrates with an interesting observation:

> A common smith . . . who has never been used to make nails . . . will scarce be able to make above two or three hundred nails in a day, and those too very bad ones. A smith who has been accustomed to make nails, but whose sole or principal business has not been that of a nailor, can seldom with his utmost diligence make more than eight hundred or a thousand nails in a day. I have seen several boys under twenty years of age who have never exercised any other trade but that of making nails, and who, when they exerted themselves, could make, each of them, upwards of two thousand three hundred nails in a day.

This was, of course, not a discovery of the 18th century; it was, in fact, a well-developed procedure as early as the 5th century B.C. when, in Greece, some shoemakers, for example, made only men's or women's shoes or even concentrated on making the uppers or the soles. The division of labor had long been a practice in earlier shops and factories. But while Smith wrote before steam power had been applied to turning the wheels of industry, he was familiar with the current development of textile machines. Specialization, he noted, inevitably leads "to the invention of a great number of machines which facilitate and abridge labor, and enable one man to do the work of many."

Britain led in the earlier development of these machines and in manufacturing processes but, in later years, seems to have lacked the interest and initiative to continue their development—to improve and perfect them. "There was little if any net change in the efficiency of the British cotton and pig iron industries from 1885 to 1910," notes Clapham. In coal mining, stagnant since before 1900, there was actually a decrease in efficiency. As we have noted, "Britain, although as fully occupied with work in 1910 as any country can hope to be was not stirring industrially as America and Germany." Furthermore, Britain was no longer an exporting monopolist but had, after 1900, been forced to face less favorable terms of barter, give more of her goods in exchange for her needs.

This later British production problem has been studied by several groups. As early as 1930, a report on textile industries showed that a large percentage of machines still in use were over thirty years old. British management seemed to feel that any machine which would still operate should be retained—a sharp contrast with the American industrialist who was always ready to discard a good machine for a better. Thus, as late as 1939 automatic looms were used by only 5 per cent of the cotton industry of Britain whereas 95 per cent of American mill capacity was so equipped. Similarly in the woolen textile field the percentages were 6 and 70, respectively. Conditions in some other British industries were not far different and, in many cases, factory buildings were found to be well over fifty years old and little provision was made to provide a continuous forward movement in the manufacturing processes. In coal production, a study made in 1936 indicated that the output of coal per man-shift in Britain was about 27 per cent of that in the United States. In this case the less favorable natural conditions in Britain doubtless account for an important part of this difference but, while no inclusive studies are available and these are merely samplings, they are samplings of the major industries on which the British economy has largely relied.

What has caused this static condition to develop? In part, perhaps, it has been due to the apparently assured, certain, and satisfactory position Britain had built up during the Victorian Era through the exploitation of her basic industries—to a feeling of stability and complacency. Apparently British management has also been inefficient and short-sighted. In too many cases positions as directors of companies have been held by small groups who would, in American slang terms, be regarded as stuffed-shirted incompetents. It is the general practice in progressive American industries to plow back about 15 per cent of earnings into new equipment and replacements. In the interwar years the average in Britain appears to have been about 3 per cent—hardly enough to cover plant depreciation.

While the basic British industries—textiles, coal, and steel—were, in modern terms, "naturals" for Britain, considering the limitations and character of her resources, she did not lack in the scientific competence or discoveries which were essential to a diversification of her industries. The huge coal-tar field with all its dye, drug, perfume, explosive, and other chemical products was born in Britain in the work of Hoffman in 1843 and his student Perkin in 1856. But it was allowed to gravitate to Germany which thereafter held the leadership in the chemical industries until America discovered during World War I that she was dependent on German exports for many major basic chemical needs and set about remedying this situation.

Likewise the steel industry was born in Britain. Steel had long been used for tools and weapons but our modern Steel Age was, as has been noted, built on the practices and standards of an earlier era of iron, cast and wrought. With the invention of the Bessemer converter in 1856 by Sir Henry Bessemer (1813–1898) and its adaptation to high phosphorus ores by Sidney Gilchrist Thomas (1850–1885) (who, it might be noted, was a clerk in an East London police court and a night-school student) steel became a heavy industry product replacing iron in structural and machine work. The first Bessemer railroad rail was laid in 1862 and outlasted twenty of the older wrought-iron rails. Its use in ships came the next year and its general structural use followed. The Bessemer process was in turn supplemented by the almost parallel rise of the open-hearth process, developed by Sir William Siemens (1823–1883), also a British invention. Improved by the Martin brothers in France, the Siemens-Martin process is used most widely today.

While Britain followed this steelmaking development, it could not be confined to Britain. The United States came into the picture and, by 1879, its production had reached that of Britain. Home uses, however, absorbed the American product; it offered little export competition. But steelmaking has not since been subject to notable changes and innovations. Steel simply, quickly, and unobtrusively replaced iron in British industry and trade.

Perhaps geographical limitations also play a part in the British picture. A modern age of mass production requires an ever-increasing market for the distribution of its products. There are limits to the population and, thus, to the potential market, of even a highly industrialized island. In many modern processes there is a minimum economical output and Britain may not have afforded a sufficient market for further industrial diversification and expansion.

Finally what has been called "restrictionism" has also been a factor in the British problem. There has been no antimonopoly legislation in Britain. Trade associations and cartels have been so active in many cases in price fixing and market sharing that the London *Economist* remarked in 1939 that it was "an extreme rarity to find a manufacturing industry where anything approaching genuine competition prevailed."

On the labor side the British situation has also become progressively worse. The British trade union was not an outgrowth of the Industrial Revolution. In fact, the Revolution at first interrupted and retarded union growth. All through the 18th century the earlier trade clubs had been active. They sought to protect the position of each small local group of skilled craftsmen by combining to prevent the employment of "illegal" or nonlocal workers, by limiting the number of apprentices, and also to maintain standard prices for piece-work and "legal" hours of labor. They were, occasionally, successful in achieving these ends through strikes. In short they were "impregnated with craft pride, prejudice, and exclusiveness." Even the acts of 1799–1800 prohibiting such combinations in restraint of trade had little effect on these clubs which continued to exist under the guise of "friendly societies" but to act as closed unions.

As we have noted, Adam Smith had preached the gospel of *laissez faire*—that the prime drive in man is self-interest, that it is a natural law of life that the individual strivings of self-interest result in the social advancement of man, and that, therefore, the economic forces should be left severely alone, free to work in their own beneficent way. His doctrine is generally regarded as characteristic of the capitalistic viewpoint of the 19th century, but it was undoubtedly written with the adverse effect on economic progress of the obstructionist tactics both of the associations of industrialists and of the trade clubs of his day in mind. It was "a violent reaction to the elaborate apparatus of controls which the surviving feudal and mercantile institutions were still imposing on the individual."

The new machines proved to be the most effective means of breaking up this type of activity in the trade clubs. The Industrial Revolution may be regarded as having been antiunion in its immediate effects. It eliminated the highly specialized craftsmen groupings with a resulting decline in union interests and activities. There had been a multiplicity of the earlier clubs, but they were only partial and were largely local organizations.

The first major revival, the industrial union in its modern form, did not come until the '80's even though special legislation in 1875 had removed earlier restrictions and had legalized collective bargaining. Squabbles between unions as to jurisdiction, the failure of local and highly specialized unions to group together nationally in the common interest, efforts to provide benefits for their members which were beyond their resources and only the state could support—all these various factors made the union movement rather ineffective until after 1900 when the main objective of union activities—higher wages—became clear and membership increased rapidly.

The frustrations of the 20th century, the tremendous burden Britain has had to carry in two world wars, the growing realization by the British public of Britain's backward industrial position, her decline from her once proud and commanding stature, her critical status in the world of today—all these have contributed to the uncertainties, unrest, and difficulties with which the motherland of technological industrialization is now perplexed. As Sir Norman Angell remarks:

The net effect of leftist indoctrination has been to leave the impression that for a man to produce his maximum is to do some mate out of a job: that labor-saving machinery may make a profit for the capitalist but inevitably increases unemployment; that there is no such thing as community of interests between employer and employee; that the whole economic system is wrong and that therefore the sooner it collapses the better.

It is earnestly to be hoped that Britain may again, as she has so often in the past, muddle through this difficult economic and social situation to reemerge as a strong and virile power. But it is also evident that any nation which hopes to carry forward in this engineering age must profit by the lessons which Britain's bitter experience so clearly offers.

Chapter 6. AMERICAN ENGINEERING
IN THE 19TH CENTURY

Westward the course of empire takes its way;
The four first acts already past,
A fifth shall close the drama with the day:
Time's noblest offspring is the last.
> Bishop George Berkeley, *On the Prospect of
> Planting Arts and Learning in America* (*c.* 1740).

THE FRONTIER PHASE—TRANSPORTATION
AND THE RAILROADS

It was inevitable that Britain, in order to protect an economy based on the import of raw materials and the export of manufactured products, would do her best to discourage industrial development in the American colonies. This attitude continued after the Revolution and was especially marked by her efforts to prevent the importation of her textile developments into the United States. It is unreasonable, however, to put the entire blame on Britain for the lack of adequate communications and the primitive state of industry in which the colonies found themselves when they became free and independent. British colonial policy throughout the Victorian Era, it is true, was not one which would aid in the spread of industrialization among the backward peoples of her far-flung empire. Nevertheless, in 1776, Britain herself still lacked modern means of transport and was still in the throes of her industrial development.

Furthermore, it is also interesting to recall that, following a few early local works, the engineering problems to which the American people first turned their attention were not those of providing better means of transportation which would aid in physically uniting the thirteen more or less isolated states. On the contrary our first great engineering works—the Erie Canal, the ill-fated Chesapeake and Ohio venture, the Baltimore and Ohio Railroad, the Pennsylvania canals and railroad—were designed to bring to a few strategically placed states or, more accurately, to the growing coastal cities of

New York, Philadelphia, and Baltimore, the advantages of trade with the opening West, the Ohio Territory. Not only were the states jealous of their newly won freedom and self-centered in their interests, but the better lands of the old coastal colonies had been taken up before the Revolution and population increases forced younger sons to press westward in an ever-growing surge which was to end only when the Pacific had been reached. American interests thus turned Westward and the slogan "Go West, young man" which Greely later made famous received far more attention than any efforts to strengthen the union.

This "frontier phase" of American development lasted until almost the close of the 19th century. Its major problems can be summed up in one word, transportation. Furthermore, after early experiments with roads and canals the railway became king, and it was railroad engineering that dominated the American engineering picture throughout this expansion era of American history. In a decade or two after 1830, Britain had practically met all her railroad needs. By 1840, however, while America had more miles of railroad than Britain had, our greatest period of railroad building and expansion was yet to come. It was not reached until the decade 1880–1890 when 65,000 miles of new rails were laid.

This is not to say that America made little progress in other directions than railroad building during the 19th century. Preoccupation with railroad work was a natural one; it overshadowed American engineering, for our growing industrial development was almost entirely centered in one small area, the New England states, and the increasing engineering problems of our rapidly growing cities received rather scant and late attention. American industry, in spite of its remarkable growth and present outstanding position, was still in its infancy throughout the 19th century. Our rise to industrial supremacy has been largely a development of the last years of the 19th, in fact primarily a 20th century accomplishment.

It is impossible in brief space to provide even an adequate outline of this remarkable era when America was coming of age. An industrial giant and a new era in human history were in the making. The best that can be done is to touch on a few high spots of a story in which there must be many omissions.

As we have indicated, American engineering begins with a few isolated but notable local undertakings. The works of the Early American Bridge Builders, as they are called, were the accomplishments of a remarkably able and gifted group of itinerant craftsmen and designers, who created new records in timber construction. One's thoughts turn back for a parallel to the craftsmen of the Middle Ages.

The turning to timber construction in a country where "getting rid of the woods" was a major problem was a natural development.[1] Masonry construction was costly; it was a permanent form of construction unsuited to an age where future needs were unknown. Skilled labor has always been scarce in the United States, and timber long remained a major American construction material.

Other peoples from Ancient Times down through the 19th century had built notable timber constructions, but these American craftsmen were not only the creators of a new timber era but the founders of our modern age of framed construction, a development to which the use of timber naturally led and from which evolved in the 1820's and 30's the modern truss form of bridge, a major American contribution in the transportation field.

Engineers of foreign training played but a minor part in the rise of American engineering. As the late Professor William H. Burr put it:

The names of Palmer, Burr, and Wernwag were connected with an era of admirable engineering works, but with bridge analysis practically unknown, and the simplest and crudest materials at their disposal, their resources were largely constituted of an intuitive engineering judgment of high quality and remarkable force in the execution of their works never excelled in American engineering. They occasionally made failures, it is true, but it is not recorded that they ever made the same error twice, and the works they constructed form a series of precedents which have made themselves felt in the entire development of American bridge building.[2]

The west pier of Palmer's "Permanent Bridge" of 1805 over the Schuylkill at Philadelphia reached rock by cofferdam at the unprecedented depth of 41 ft below high tide. Wernwag's timber arch at Fairmont, a short distance above this work, "The Colossus Bridge" of 1812, had the record clear span of 340 ft $3\frac{3}{4}$ in. Finley, the pioneer of the suspension bridge, should be added to the list, for he fathered another form of construction which has been carried to its fullest development in the United States.

[1] The various ingenious stump-pulling devices used on the Erie Canal, for example, were the most interesting of its construction contributions. Early American canals and railroads ran through virgin forests. Dickens in his *American Notes* of 1842 describes the monotony of travel in such forest lanes.

[2] *Ancient and Modern Engineering and the Isthmian Canal,* by William H. Burr, New York, John Wiley & Sons, Inc., 1902, p. 77.

The Erie Canal, 1817–1825

A pioneer work carried out by self-trained pioneer American engineers, the Erie Canal was the first great American engineering undertaking and played a vital part in making New York the "Empire State." Showing lock, lock-keeper's cabin, and canalboat. (*From Colden's Memoirs.*)

But, as we have said, American interests turned westward. Ohio joined the Union as a state in 1803 and the competition for Western trade was under way. The earliest trails to the Ohio were opened up under Federal action by means of the Cumberland Road, which ultimately extended westward to St. Louis. New York, however, possessed the most favorable westward route—the Hudson River to a point just above Albany, then up a series of locks to the main valley of the Mohawk, and some 363 miles across the state to join the Great Lakes at Lockport on the Niagara River. Begun in 1817 and completed in 1825 with much rejoicing, it was planned to

> Join bright Erie to the Main,
> And for Ages to perpetuate
> The Glory of our native State.

It was the longest canal in the world outside China, it was built through a virgin wilderness in which the removal of trees and stumps was a major problem, it was surveyed and constructed by self-educated native talent, it was financed by one state of an infant republic, and it was the first American engineering school. Its chief engineers, Benjamin Wright (1770–1842) and James Geddes (1763–1838), were the product of a pioneering age, local lawyers, judges, and land surveyors. The able group of younger men gathered about them became the directors of important later engineering enterprises.

To the south Pennsylvania, Maryland, Delaware, and Virginia—or, more accurately, Philadelphia and Baltimore—faced far greater difficulties of terrain in attempting to cross the Appalachians to the Ohio. The Chesapeake and Ohio Canal never did reach its goal. Baltimore, doubtful of this canal project, turned to the construction of the Baltimore and Ohio railroad, which finally entered Wheeling in 1853—the American Railroad University, it was called, for it was a pioneer work in setting the pattern of American railroad techniques. The first guiding engineers of this enterprise were a self-taught Quaker surveyor, Jonathan Knight (1787–1858), and Lieut. Col. Stephen H. Long (1784–1864), a Dartmouth graduate, an explorer (Long's Peak), and the author of the earliest (1829) American *Railroad Manual*.

Located between these two great works, Philadelphia undertook the difficult task of reaching Pittsburgh by surmounting the great Appalachian barrier. Rivers, canals, a summit railway (the famous Allegheny Portage Railway), and still more canal and river work, finally brought a major engineering undertaking to completion. But it was no sooner in service than it was superseded by the Pennsylvania Railroad.

In noting these early works sight should not be lost of the Delaware and Hudson Canal of 1827–1830, of which John B. Jervis (1795–1885) an Erie product, an assistant of Wright's, and an outstanding engineering personality of the 19th century, was chief engineer. This was a purely private venture built to bring to the New York market the hard, or anthracite, coal of northern Pennsylvania. Anyone who has followed the route, down the Rondout, up the Delaware and Lackawaxen and over the hills from Honesdale to Carbondale, and pictures a small group of New York businessmen projecting this work through primeval forests, will gain a new vision of the daring and courage, the willingness to face risks, which have characterized American free enterprise and resulted in the unparalleled progress of American life.

By 1840 it was becoming evident, however, that canals were too slow and uncertain.[3] The railroad became king. On the one hand, canal building, after an era of canal enthusiasm following the great success of the Erie, which was a powerful factor in making New York the Empire State and New York City our leading port, gradually declined. On the other, the Federal government turned its pioneer road venture, the Cumberland Road, over to the states it traversed. Road building was left to local authorities, with the result that, at the beginning of the modern motor era in the earlier years of the 20th century, American roads were still almost entirely unsurfaced dirt roads, just about the same in quality as they had been a century earlier.

It was in the railroad field, therefore, that most notable progress was made. Up to 1900 the young civil engineer almost invariably began his career on railroad location. In the structural field it was the railroad bridge which dominated the scene. While British engineers built a relatively small number of great works, American builders had to provide a multitude of railroad structures. The American

---

[3] As early as 1812, John Stevens (1749–1838), a graduate of Kings College (later Columbia) and a pioneer of American mechanical engineering and of transportation by land and by water, had written: "Concede that there are now no Steam Rail-ways anywhere in the world. This is not to say that they will not come—and that soon. As civilization progresses, water-carriage will prove too slow and cumbersome to satisfy the demands of humanity. And this, too, though it remain relatively cheap. What has been accomplished in comparatively few years with Steam Boats points, as I conceive, directly at the Steam Carriage. Merely by developing a method of correctly applying the same principles on land, a great saving in time and cost will be effected."

timber truss first appeared essentially as a stiffening or bracing truss for an arched rib, reflecting, undoubtedly, a lack of early and complete faith in the truss as a self-sufficient structural form. By the 1830's however, the pure truss bridge had emerged. Cast and wrought iron followed timber, and special truss forms were evolved suited to the most economical use of the new materials. Some unfortunate failures,

Early American Railroad Train

As pictured by the famous "Print Makers to the American People," Currier and Ives. The transportation problem—and this meant the railroad—dominated American engineering during the 19th century. Finally, in 1869, the continent was spanned when locomotives from the East and West met at Promontory Point, Utah. As Bret Harte put it:

> "Pilots touching head to head,
> Facing on the single track,
> Half a world behind each back."

however, showed that cast iron was not safe for such use, and in 1863 the first American all-wrought-iron truss was built.

Few modern engineers realize that practically all our modern bridge standards were first developed in wrought iron. The modern structural shapes, I beams, channels, angles, and tees, were first rolled in wrought iron. The "built-up" column, eyebars, riveted girders—all the modern steel forms were originated in iron.

The first treatise on the analysis of truss bridges, Whipple's book of

1851, provided a basis for more accurate, reliable, and economical truss design. As locomotives and train loadings increased, the earlier assumptions of uniform loading gave way to the more accurate concentrated moving load analysis of the present day. As we shall have occasion to note, the motor era has brought notable further structural advances and bridge records in the 20th century, but precedents were established in the latter 19th century which continue to the present day. In fact the first all-steel bridge was not built until 1878, and it may be said that the task of the American bridge engineer of the turn of the century (1900) was primarily that of replacing earlier wrought-iron bridges with structures designed in steel to carry heavier loads.[4]

These earlier works were almost invariably pin-connected bridges with the advantage of a maximum of work done in the shop and of extreme rapidity of erection in the field. British practice, on the other hand, favored the more rigid, fully riveted structure—in some cases, as we have noted, reflecting shipbuilding practices rather than a framed type of construction. Controversies over the relative advantages and disadvantages of these forms were keen, and British engineers were quite convinced that the remarkable American records of speed of erection were gross exaggerations. This emphasis on the speed factor in American work simply reflected the tremendous rate of American expansion. Time became of the essence in the years following the Civil War. Not only was competition keen, but the necessity of using available capital as effectively as possible emphasized the reduction of the period of construction, the time during which interest must be paid on invested but unproductive capital, to a minimum. This became one of the most important economic factors which have conditioned American engineering planning.

When we turn to engineering activities other than those connected with railroads, the American story, although offering many notable advances, is less spectacular. Philadelphia was the first city to have a reasonably adequate water supply. The Center Square pumped supply of 1801 was succeeded by the notable Fairmount Works on the Schuylkill in 1819–1822. The first Croton supply for New York— one of the greatest of early modern gravity supplies, of which Jervis was the chief engineer—was not opened until 1842. It soon proved inadequate although it was not extended until the '80's. Boston fol-

[4] The Carnegie Steel Co. of 1892 was a pioneer steel combination, and the Pennsylvania Railroad was its major early customer. Its successor, U.S. Steel, our first billion-dollar corporation, was not organized until 1901.

Roebling's Niagara Suspension Bridge of 1852–1855

One of the first great triumphs of American bridgebuilding using a type of structure in the evolution of which American engineers had pioneered. Crossing the Gorge with a span of 825 ft, this double-deck work carried a railroad on the upper deck and highway traffic on the lower deck of the substantial stiffening truss. Note the "hold-down" cables to prevent wind vibrations.

lowed New York, but the great majority of smaller American supplies originated in the activities of the pump salesmen of the late 19th century. Even as late as 1900 many of these privately owned pumped river supplies, although contaminated, thus resulting in frequent typhoid epidemics, were common. Owing to increasing urban growth and to a far more lavish use of water in America than abroad, based on the idea that "water should be as free as air," the water-supply problem in the United States became a perpetual one—a problem of continued search for additional and improved supplies.

Highway engineering was, as we have said, practically unknown but some street paving was, of course, carried out in the growing urban centers, while works for the disposal of sewage, by drainage into and the pollution of streams, were slowly developed.

Considering our modern, widespread use of steam power there appears to be a curious gap in the story of American mechanical power development during the earlier 19th century which can be bridged only when we realize that transportation rather than industrial use was the dominant problem of the day. In 1876 the first century of the United States was marked by the famous Philadelphia Centennial Exhibition. George Henry Corliss (1817–1888) exhibited his giant, steam, twin-walking-beam engine of 1,400 horsepower, which dominated Machinery Hall and, through mechanical drives, supplied all the power needs of this epoch-marking show. With 40-in. diameter cylinders and a 10-ft stroke and running at 36 revolutions per minute, this engine (except for its variable speed-controlled cutoff) was essentially a low-pressure reciprocating engine differing in no basic way from Watt engines of almost a century earlier.[5] It was a big jump from a Watt engine of perhaps 8 or 9 hp to 1,400 hp, but one must turn to the locomotive and the marine engines of the day if he seeks to uncover the step-by-step improvements which were taking place in the mechanical power field. As we shall note later, the largest reciprocating stationary, that is, land engines ever built were of only 7,500 hp, erected in 1904. On the other hand, the famous *Campania* of 1893 and the *Oceanic* of 1899 carried two engines in tandem totaling 30,000 hp—the largest reciprocating engines ever built. The steam turbine, which became the power unit of the 20th century, made these giants seem small indeed.[6]

[5] It was later installed in the Pullman shops near Chicago where it was in continuous service for over thirty years.

[6] The largest unit in the world is the 208,000-kilowatt or about 280,000-hp turbogenerator of the State Line power plant in the Chicago area.

The truth of the matter seems to be that the major industrial power needs of the United States were, even as late as 1876, still being met by the small, isolated water powers with their mill ponds, around which many of the towns of the major industrial area, New England, had been built. Britain's industrial life had been based on textiles, coal, and iron. The American Industrial Revolution was not

Corliss Giant Engine at the Philadelphia Centennial, 1876

Of 1,400 hp, 700 from each side, this engine, with 40-in. cylinders and a 10-ft stroke, furnished the power requirements for Machinery Hall. With low pressure (15 to 22 lb) and low speed (36 rpm), it differed primarily in size from the earlier Watt engines. A modern steam turbine would occupy but a small fraction of the space required for this clumsy giant and weigh but a fraction of its 600 tons. This engine was later used in the Pullman Shops outside Chicago for over thirty years.

dependent on natural resources, on either coal or iron. Textiles were important, but it was primarily Yankee ingenuity in manufacture plus Yankee peddler marketing that made New England the birthplace of American industry. As Professor Roe remarks, while the cotton industry stimulated the development of American machine tools, it was the gun industry which was responsible for the interchangeable system of manufacture. These were the keys which unlocked the American horn of plenty, mass manufacture. There were a few larger water power sites, such as Lowell on the Merrimac and later Holyoke on the Connecticut, and there were, of course, steam plants built in other manufacturing centers, but in spite of the remarkable development of American industry in the 19th century, both modern power and modern American industry were still in their infancy. This statement finds confirmation in the fact that it was estimated that power use in the United States in 1899 was about 25 million hp or about 2 manpower per capita; that is, in the 19th century American technology had doubled man's power capacity. In the next third of a century, this increased about fifty times—to a total of 1,231 million hp. The silent slaves who served us in 1935 had increased from the two of 1899 to 60 to 100.

Throughout the 19th century the earlier agricultural home economy of the North Atlantic states, especially New England, was, of course, being replaced by a rising industrial economy, but the older order simply moved West with the exodus to the richer agricultural lands of the Central, and later, the Western states. The South, as it always had been, still remained predominantly agricultural. While American industrial development of the 19th century was, therefore, interesting and remarkable, it actually centered in and affected only a small part of American life. The industrial North was moving forward, the West was being rapidly settled, but the South remained largely class-controlled and economically static. The resulting doubts and jealousies accompanying the inevitable decline in the relative power and importance of the South in the Union undoubtedly added flame to the dissensions which, in the end, led to the Civil War. Until World War I the machine tool and highly industrialized states were still those of New England and the North Central states which were so largely settled by emigration from New England.

These facts, of course, simply give added emphasis to the remarkable influence which New England has exercised in the rise of American industry. While Britain took steps to prevent knowledge of her new textile machines being brought to the states, some early imitative machines were built through a combination of Yankee ingenuity plus the aid of one or two British workers like Samuel Slater who managed to get away from Britain. As Benjamin Franklin put it, "A word to the wise is sufficient." Ingenious men needed only a start and an idea. In 1787, the first feeble efforts of American cotton manufacturing began, but by 1850 these manufactures had overcome British competition and become masters of the American market. The prices of textile goods dropped by 1850 to from one-fifth to one-tenth of what they had been in 1800, and, as in Great Britain, the American textile industry continued to grow and expand.

This evolution added greatly to the demand for cotton, and the importance to the South of Eli Whitney's (1765–1825) cotton gin is emphasized in many textbooks. Less attention is given, however, to another technique which he also introduced, namely, interchangeable manufacture. Jefferson, when he was Ambassador to France, had written home describing this plan, but it apparently never came to fruition in France. In 1794, however, Whitney took the parts for 10 muskets to Washington and, selecting them indiscriminately, assembled 10 complete muskets. All earlier gunmakers had filed and fitted each part by hand. Whitney devised filing jigs, or guiding patterns, by means of which the parts could be made so closely alike that no special fitting was required. Here was the key to the opening of a new era in industry—mass production.

Yet these interchangeable parts were shaped and formed by hand. A few years later a British engineer, Mark I. Brunel, in cooperation with Sir Samuel Bentham of the British Navy, devised some 44 separate machines each of which performed one or more operations in the making of identical parts which were then assembled to form pulley blocks.[7] The combination of these two ideas forms the basis for modern mass-production processes.

New England industry thus began largely in the area of textiles and small arms. These activities, however, encouraged the design of special machine tools or modifications of older devices to perform various operations. As in Britain, the adoption of standards for threads and the development of more accurate devices for measurement—parts had to be substantially indentical to be interchangeable—resulted in allowable "tolerances" being constantly decreased. The New England states, thus, became not only the center of American manufacturing industries but the home of American machine tool standards.

There was a special burst of small manufactures in the period 1840–1850, and Connecticut turned out all sorts of products from revolvers and clocks to, it was said, wooden nutmegs. Colt had invented the revolver in 1836, the first lot being made at Whitney's works, but he later established his own plant where handwork was

[7] This was in the days of sailing ships, and many such pulley blocks were required in connection with the rigging.

practically eliminated and automatic, or semiautomatic, machines turned out revolver parts by the thousand. The American brass industry, born in the Naugatuck Valley of Connecticut in 1802, was unable to supply brass needs during the war of 1812, and the inexpensive clock with wooden works won a place for itself. By 1838, however, one town, Bristol, was turning out 10,000 wood and an equal number of brass clocks a year.

So rapid and so effective was this New England growth that, in 1853, the motherland of industrialization, Britain, sent a commission to the United States to visit gun manufacturers, and 157 special American gunmaking machines, including Blanchard's famous gunstocking lathe of 1818, were exported for British use.

While Britain, however, stuck to her main industrial interests— textiles, coal, and iron and its products—American inventiveness, in response to a more progressive and dynamic spirit, created new industries. Cyrus Hall McCormick (1809–1884) patented his reaper in 1834, a milestone in the rise of agricultural machinery. Charles Goodyear (1800–1860) succeeded in 1835, after many trials, in vulcanizing rubber, and another new industry came into being. Elias Howe (1819–1867) received his first sewing-machine patent in 1846 while, for civil engineers, it is interesting to note that William J. Young made the first American surveyor's transit in Philadelphia in 1830.[8]

As has been previously noted, necessity has often been hailed as the mother of invention. We should not lose sight of the fact that it played a major part in this rise of American industry. Even before the Revolution, the most promising agricultural areas of New England had been taken up, and population growth was forcing the clearing of far less promising marginal lands. This encouraged the younger generation to emigrate to the West, and the rate of population increase in New England declined. The industrialization we have outlined, replacing the older agricultural home economy, was the answer to this basic New England problem, that of creating a new form of economic life. Its progress was marked by a new and rapid increase in both the population and the wealth of the New England states.

The two major technical industrial developments of the 19th

[8] This was a much simplified form of the European theodolite—again emphasizing a previously noted characteristic of American engineering and industry—adaption to use by relatively unskilled workers. Yet the older and far simpler surveyor's compass persisted as the major land-surveying instrument throughout the 19th century.

century were, however, the discovery of a new process for making steel and the birth of electrical engineering. The former, the result of the work of the British engineers, Bessemer, Thomas, and Siemens, was exploited in the United States largely through the series of partnerships and company combinations of a pioneer American financier, Andrew Carnegie, which led in 1901 to the organization of the first billion-dollar corporation, United States Steel. The Keystone Bridge Company was incorporated in 1865 at a time when wooden structures were rapidly being supplanted by iron structures on the major American railroads. Patents held by Jacob H. Linville (1825–1906), bridge engineer of the Pennsylvania Railroad and a famous truss bridgebuilder, played a part in this development.[9] One of the first customers of the new company was James Buchanan Eads (1820–1887) whose great arch bridge of 1874, part iron, part steel, and the granddaddy of American metal arches, long carried the westward-bound traveler over the Mississippi into St. Louis.[10]

The first steel railroad rails had been rolled in Chicago in 1865, but the Carnegie interests did not take up the Bessemer process until about the period of the famous panic of 1873. The Edgar Thompson Steel Co. was organized in 1874 with Alexander Lyman Holley (1832–1882) an outstanding American expert in the Bessemer field, in charge of construction. "Handsome as a Greek god, with the brain of an engineer, the heart of a woman, and the soul of a poet. . . . It was Holley who made the Bessemer process easy and swift . . . who made possible that immense production which has amazed the world."[11] In 1878 the first all-steel bridge in the United States was built over the Missouri River at Glasgow on the Chicago and Alton Railroad. Locomotive loads were constantly increasing and, as in the earlier replacement of many older wooden structures with wrought iron, bridge engineers of the late 19th century were kept busy not only in building some major new works but in replacing these older iron bridges in turn with steel structures designed for still

[9] Linville wrote about 1863, "I went to Altoona with a young wife, with everything new to me. The bridges on the line were nearly all a wreck; I knew nothing of bridges, and had at my disposal nothing but Haupt's old book, all wrong. Orders came in to build new iron bridges, and I had to hustle with many sleepless nights, and days spent over old patterns and new plans and calculations."

[10] Eads later became equally famous as designer and builder of the jetties at the mouth of the Mississippi which opened New Orleans to ocean shipping.

[11] *The Romance of Steel*, by Herbert N. Casson, New York, A. S. Barnes and Company, 1907.

heavier loads. Railroad needs, rails and bridges, provided, in sharp contrast with the 20th century, the principal market for the ever-increasing output of the American steel industry.

The development of electrical engineering, an evolution from the scientific toy stage which prevailed in 1800 to the important professional position it occupies today, required the efforts of many workers for an entire century. It is a curious story. This branch of engineering, on the one hand, was not an offshoot of the parent engineering stem or a development of an ancient practical art. Neither was it, as is so often stated, a mere application of the results of organized systematic research in natural science. The major steps in the evolution of this scientific toy professional engineering stature were, on the contrary, marked by a series of advances aided by physicists but made largely by a host of inventors who, at the best, can be classed only as scientific amateurs.

Before 1800 various experimenters played with electrical sparks and discharges. They included the Italian physician, Galvani; the American printer-statesman, Franklin; Coulomb, the French military engineer; and the pioneer electrical physicist, Volta, who made the first electric battery. The work of William Sturgeon in Britain and Joseph Henry in America is of more direct interest. Between 1825–1830, they showed that an electric current passed through a coil of insulated wire surrounding an iron core produced temporary magnetization of the core, thus producing the first practical electromagnets. Another physicist, Michael Faraday in Britain, in 1835 proved the reverse—that an electric current was induced in a wire when it was moved through the field of a magnet.

Working with the first of these discoveries, an American portrait painter, Samuel F. B. Morse (1791–1872), developed the electric telegraph on a commercial scale and sent his first message between Washington and Baltimore in 1843.[12] The idea of the submarine cable followed and, after the invention of gutta-percha had made

[12] The earlier history of long-distance communication is a romantic and fascinating one—signal fires, the Peruvian runners, the Pony Express, and the monument in Paris to Chappé, the inventor of the "aerial telegraph" (a semaphone system) of the Napoleonic period, come to mind. The story of Reuters, the British news agency, has been beautifully told in films. It should also be noted that two British workers, William F. Cooke and Charles Wheatstone, had communicated with each other by electric telegraph as early as 1837, and their first public line was built in the same year, 1843, that Morse's famous message, "What hath God wrought," was flashed over the wires.

underwater insulation possible, Brett, an Englishman, laid the first cable across the British Channel from Dover to Calais in 1850. A 120-mile line, England to Holland, followed in 1853, and the crossing of the Atlantic began to be considered. The man who was the driving force in this venture was an American merchant, Cyrus W. Field. His example of persistence in the face of repeated and costly failures is outstanding in human history. Mechanical difficulties led to the breaking of the cable in 1856, 1857, and again in 1858. Then two months after completion of the first cable in 1858 mistakes in electrical operation led to a fourth failure. Finally in 1865, after still another mishap, uninterrupted communication was finally established under the Atlantic.

The idea of communication by telegraphic signals thus came quickly—it was a direct and more or less obvious application once the electromagnet had been developed. On the other hand, the possibility of the electrical transmission of speech seemed completely visionary and unattainable. Yet, some thirty years after the telegraph this possibility had been realized and Alexander Graham Bell (1847–1922), an emigrant from Scotland and a professor of vocal physiology at Boston University, exhibited his pioneer telephone at the Philadelphia Centennial (1876).

The early history of the telephone industry is clouded with equipment difficulties and struggles between conflicting claimants and companies. While Bell's receiver was satisfactory, Edison's carbon transmitter of 1877 was a great improvement over Bell's device. The claims of Professor Elisha Gray of Chicago, backed by the Western Union Telegraph Co., posed another problem. By 1897 Bell's company had defended over 600 suits. In the end these difficulties were all resolved, and the various local companies joined in a wide exchange of services. Nevertheless the growth of the American telephone industry before 1900 was relatively slow; in 1897 it was estimated that not over half a million instruments were in use.

Although batteries could supply telegraph and telephone needs, a much more powerful source of electrical energy was essential before electric light and power could become possible. The germ idea was revealed in Faraday's basic discovery of magnetic induction of 1835, but it took close to fifty years and the efforts of probably at least 50 ingenious men to develop from this germ idea a practical, useful dynamo.

The British worker, Sturgeon, contributed the basic form of design.

But there were major problems to be resolved. How could a reasonably constant direct current be secured when the flow in the rotating coils, the "armature," was not only fluctuating but alternating?

The Italian, Pacinotti, proposed a ring armature in 1864, which the Belgian, Gramme, reinvented and perfected in 1871. The German, Werner Siemens, brother of the British steel pioneer, had devised in 1856 the shuttle armature, which Alteneck in 1873 developed into the drum armature, leading in time to a more effective form of coil construction and becoming standard.

In the meantime the improvement of the magnetic field in which the armature coils rotated was given attention. Wilde devised the "separately excited" dynamo in 1866, and another pioneer step in the evolution of the modern dynamo had been taken. Two British workers, Hopkinson and Compton, made the first advances which led to the modern form, a more compact design of the magnetic part of the machine. Nevertheless, even as late as the Pearl Street plant of 1879–1882, Edison used his "Jumbo" dynamo, two long electromagnets with the armature rotating between two circular "pole pieces" at their base. C. E. L. Brown of the Swiss Oerlikon works, however, building on the Hopkinson plan, devised a far more efficient and compact four-pole form from which the modern multipolar machine was a natural development. Finally Deprez, a French worker, suggested that the combination of the separately and self-excited and the "compound winding" types would provide a substantially self-regulating, constant-current machine.

While this evolution was going forward, attempts were being made to find some use for electrical power; to devise an electric light. The first successes were achieved by developing the arc-light phenomena, first observed by Sir Humphry Davy about 1801. Here again there were numerous difficulties to be overcome. First used in the Foreland Lighthouse in Britain in 1858, by the time of the Philadelphia Centennial (1876) fairly satisfactory arc-light–dynamo systems were available. In America Charles F. Brush perfected his dynamo–arc-light combination for street lighting, and the arc light held this field until well after the incandescent bulb had been perfected.

Arc lights, however, were operated "in series," that is, were inserted at intervals along a single electric circuit. This plan was of no use in general service for it was not possible to turn off any light in the circuit. In America, Thomas A. Edison, (1847–1931), successively newsboy, telegraph operator, and inventor, turned his attention to devising a high-resistance light which could be used "in parallel," that is, connected at intervals between two wires. Each "lamp" thus completed a circuit and could be shut off without interfering with other lamps.

Edison had already invented the quadruplex telegraph, making it possible to send four messages simultaneously over one line, a carbon telephone transmitter, and the phonograph. Working in well-equipped laboratories at Menlo Park, New Jersey, and aided by a group of able and devoted assistants, patiently trying one material after another (a method of "try it and see" now frequently referred to as the Edison method) the "Electrical Wizard" finally produced the carbon filament electric-light bulb. In 1882 Edison's famous Pearl Street Station was put in operation in New York—the first central power station and general electric lighting service in the world. A new industry had been born.[13]

The next step in the utilization of electric power was the development of an electric motor. There had been earlier inventors who played with this problem, but the modern electric motor seems to have suddenly appeared in a well-developed form when it was realized that all it involved was a reverse operation of the already well-developed dynamo; that is, mechanical power turning the armature of a dynamo produced electric current and, vice versa, electric current fed into a somewhat modified design of a dynamo should produce mechanical power. Frank Sprague, one of Edison's smartest assistants, applied the electric motor to railway operation and the "trolley car" era was launched. The first system began operation at Richmond, Virginia, in 1888.

The electric light and the electric motor thus created a new demand for power and ushered in a new power era which began to take form as the 19th century came to a close. It is interesting to recall, however, not only that the first great American hydroelectric power development, that at Niagara Falls, was not completed until 1895 but that an electric system was adopted for Niagara only after prolonged discussion of the best means of transmitting power some 22 miles to the Buffalo market. Cable and other mechanical devices as well as a pneumatic system were seriously considered before the decision was finally made to use electrical means.

[13] As so often happens, other men had been working along similar lines. In Britain, Sir Joseph W. Swain had also devised a carbon filament lamp but, happily, combined forces with Edison in exploiting this invention in Britain. Unfortunately, however, the British Electric Lighting Act of 1882 retarded development. It was revised in 1888, but general lighting in Britain was not effectively developed until after the turn of the century.

As Dr. Harry Emerson Fosdick says:

The century from 1830 on was lighted in by tallow-dips and out by electricity; rode in on horseback and out in an aeroplane; came in talking as Neanderthal man did and went out using a microphone; commenced with a quill pen and ended with a linotype; began with hands for labor and ended with the powers of the universe in harness.

It began with the struggles of 13 small coastal states for economic advantages and ended with American citizens occupying the entire area of a country tied together, from coast to coast and from the Great Lakes to the Gulf by arteries of rails which would be sufficient to circle the globe more than ten times. It ended with new means of utilizing mechanical power for the service of man and the advancement of manufactures. It ended after a century of remarkable inventions, the creation of new industries, and the spread of industrialization from New England into the North Central states. But, compared with the tremendous growth and development which were to take place after 1900, the 19th century seems to have been merely a "getting ready" period—the preparatory setting of the stage for a later era of engineering development beyond the wildest visions of even Jules Verne.

We have endeavored in this chapter to outline some of the major material advances involved in this stage setting. We must now turn back to another vitally important engineering development of the 19th century, the rise of engineering science, and we must postpone until still later chapters a discussion of the perplexing economic, social, and political problems which, beginning in the later years of the 19th century, have rapidly developed in the 20th and challenge the continued progress of Western civilization today.

Chapter 7. THE NEW ENGINEERING

Science is something more than a body of slowly increasing knowledge; it is the proof of a habit of mind; it is the habit of recognizing that there is a rational way of doing things as over and against a passionate, impulsive, instinctive, or partisan way of doing things, and that this way is discernible through inquiry.

F. J. E. Woodbridge, *The Importance of Philosophy.*

THE RISE OF ENGINEERING SCIENCE

Engineering, as we have seen, came into being as a practical art and, as such, dependent for increased knowledge on what has come to be called the experimental method, the method of "try it and see." But in the growth of every practical art the germ of a practical science gradually evolves and matures. Explanations for empirical relationships derived from practice and rules of thumb lead to more fully rationalized techniques, to the "reduction to a science" of earlier procedures which rested solely on trial, experience, and judgment.

In the evolution of engineering, the beginnings of an engineering science may be discovered long before the age-old grip of Greek thought had been cast aside and the close relationship of progress in the natural sciences and in engineering became clear. Engineering is not, as is so often popularly supposed, a development from natural science, nor has it been dependent solely on advances in the natural sciences for new knowledge and improved techniques. As Professor Whitehead puts it, it was a developed technology which was wedded to a developed science in the middle years of the 19th century.

We have had occasion in earlier chapters to note the remarkable achievements of engineering as an art, of the days when design was dictated solely by an intuitive judgment and almost uncanny skill growing from experience. Some of man's greatest achievements, notably in stone construction, were the products of this earlier era of engineering, products which, with all our modern knowledge, we could do little to improve upon. Yet this science-engineering wedding opened up a new era not only in science and engineering but in the life of man.

Some of the pioneers of engineering science have been noted in previous pages. Many workers, known and unknown, added, over the years, their bit to the development of more fully rationalized methods of engineering design, more exact and effective techniques and practices. A long period of courtship preceded the science–engineering wedding, and there was no sudden and revolutionary change in the relationship of the principals involved. Even today engineering still retains in many of its more general practices and decisions its older characteristics as an art.

Nevertheless, as in the case of the natural sciences, the atmosphere of the 18th century, was particularly favorable to the rise of engineering science. The engineering trail blazers in the new movement were primarily French—among others Navier, in the mechanics of materials, Coulomb in soil mechanics, Belidor and De Prony in the performance of machines, and Pitot, Chézy, and others in hydraulics. This French interest, reflected in the curricula of her early engineering schools, was to set the basic pattern of European engineering education which still prevails, and it influenced that of some later American schools. But, on the one hand, the Revolution and the Napoleonic Wars discouraged further notable engineering developments in France, while, on the other, these French workers appear to have advanced their theoretical studies beyond their abilities to use and apply the new knowledge in the solution of the problems of practice. One may deal on a scientific basis with isolated phenomena. In practice a confusing complex of variables, of unknown or uncertain effect, raises an array of new and perplexing problems. The technique of application is thus usually far more difficult than the labors connected with uncovering the basic scientific facts. There always exists, therefore, a gap between theory and practice, and we suffer even today from our inability to apply successfully the vast accumulations of experience and knowledge that man has built up.

It remained for British workers, possessing, perhaps, a more practical turn of mind than their French colleagues, to give a new impetus to this French movement in engineering. All through the first half of the 19th century the great British builders whose work we have so briefly noted, together with a number of less spectacular contributors —the engineer-priest Moseley, Tredgold of the famous definition of engineering, Fairbairn, and others—added their influence and their bit to this development. Watt's steam engine also played its part, for it exploded the earlier Caloric theory of the Heat Philosophers and led to the pioneer work of the French and British physicists Carnot and Jule. Thus many men made their contributions to the growth of engineering science during this half century, but it was a Scotch engineer-teacher, William John Macquorn Rankine (1820–1872), who

> . . . to advantage dress'd
> What oft was thought, but ne'er so well express'd.

In his *Applied Mechanics* of 1858, his *Manual of the Steam Engine* of 1859, and his *Civil Engineering* of 1862, Rankine brought together, organized, and systematized the scattered earlier accumulations of a science of engineering, adding to these earlier studies his own notable contributions. About the same time German workers also, with their usual painstaking care and thoroughness, produced what purported to be a "hand book" but turned out to be an encyclopedia of current engineering knowledge in some five or more volumes, the *Handbook of Engineering Science,* the first volume of which was published in 1853.[1]

Among the typical subjects of engineering science which were treated in these works were the mechanics of materials, the analysis of structures, soil mechanics, hydraulics, engineering thermodynamics, and machine design. In many cases the techniques involved were a combination of the basic principles of mechanics modified by the introduction of empirical coefficients derived from tests and experiments which allowed for the still unresolved factors which affected practical design. Many of these subjects still retain this curious combination of science and empiricism, although the trend is always toward more complete understanding and rationalization.

When we recall that earlier designs, largely based, as we have said, on intuitive judgment and experience, were thus subject to human errors and fallibilities, it is obvious that one of the first results of the new engineering science was an increase in the safety of design—a greater assurance that a particular design "would work." This is not to say that the failure of engineering works became a thing of the past. Even today, after a full century of searching and efforts to rationalize procedures, many major decisions in engineering rest on skilled judgment and the results of experience. The struggle to rationalize still goes forward at ever-increasing tempo, but the engineer cannot wait until complete data and full understanding are available. He must meet his problems as they arise and without un-

[1] *Handbuch der Ingenieur wissenschaften.* Other volumes followed and there have been several new editions giving additional data.

due delay. As someone has half jestingly remarked, he is expected always to be right in his decisions although they are almost invariably based on insufficient evidence. Yet the new technique has unquestionably led to greater safety and, because of its increased certainties, was essential to the planning of bigger works. The major factor influencing this rationalization movement has, however, been the fact that it led to greater economy of construction.

When it becomes possible, as it does through scientific design, to proportion each part of a machine or structure to perform successfully its function or to carry its load, and *no more*, it is clear that not only is the safety of a design increased, as well as the completeness with which it meets a predicted demand or need, but no material is wasted in the process. As the famous American railroad engineer Wellington put it:

It is beyond doubt that the true reason for the striking progress in bridge-building in recent years [written about 1880] has been not that men have been driven to excellence by the "responsibility for human life resting on them." . . . The impelling force has been the keen competitive struggle to bring the first cost of every bridge as low as possible, and yet do nothing which shall injure its permanent efficiency and compel it to be speedily rebuilt.

A similar economy resulted in the mechanical field. More scientific design led to more efficient engines, to engines using less fuel per unit of power produced. It is interesting to note at this point the differing results stemming from the rise of engineering science in the United States and in Europe, a difference which has markedly affected the entire course of engineering and industry here and abroad.

As we have said, the newer techniques in design resulted primarily in saving materials—less iron would build the bridge in which each part was proportioned to carry its computed load, less fuel would operate the more scientifically designed engine. The fact that highly skilled labor and more of it were required to produce more exact and refined designs did not affect the over-all economy of such designs under European conditions, for, on the Continent, and to a lesser degree in the British Isles, materials were relatively costly while skilled labor was plentiful. The emphasis on the mathematical and scientific phases of engineering education, which characterized the work of the French pioneers of engineering science and which are essential in scientific design, thus fell on fertile soil on the other side of the Atlantic. European engineering education continued to emphasize theory, and European engineering practice the utmost in the scientific refinements of design. Continental workers, notably German and French, led the world in uncovering, through research and theoretical studies, the basic understandings from which further refinements in practice evolved.

Not so in the United States. Here skilled labor has always been scarce and costly, while materials have been relatively plentiful and inexpensive. Such conditions inevitably resulted in practices which sacrificed economy of materials if such sacrifice led to a saving of labor and the reduction of the costs of construction or production. As early as 1838 a British engineer visiting our country remarked:

> The zeal with which the Americans undertake, and the rapidity with which they carry out every enterprise, which has the enlargement of their trade for its object, cannot fail to strike all who visit the United States as a characteristic of the nation. . . . English and American engineers are guided by the same principles in designing their works, but the different nature of the materials employed in their construction, and the climates and circumstances of the two countries naturally produce a considerable dissimilarity in the practice of civil engineers in England and America. At first view, one is struck with the temporary and apparently unfinished state of many of the American works and is very apt, before inquiring into the subject, to impute to want of ability what turns out, on investigation, to be a judicious and ingenious arrangement to suit the circumstances of a new country, of which the climate is severe—a country where stone is scarce and wood is plentiful and where manual labor is very expensive. It is vain to look to the American works for the finish which characterizes those of France, or the stability for which those of Britain are famed.[2]

To which it might be added that it was virtually impossible in many of these earlier works to predict future needs and requirements. More or less temporary constructions were, and in some cases still are, dictated by the rapidity of growth and change as well as by financial considerations such as the reduction of capital risks in new and unpredictable ventures.

It would, thus, not be too much of an exaggeration to say that the scientific movement in engineering, in contrast with the European situation, fell on inhospitable soil in America. In the first place, American engineers, seeking to increase speed and reduce costs, did not hesitate to use a few more pounds of materials if such use contributed to these ends. The simplification and standardization of

[2] *A Sketch of the Civil Engineering of North America,* by David Stevenson, London, 1838.

production were considered more important than "unnecessary refinements in design." In fact, all through the 19th century it was the practical, forceful, resourceful, pioneering type of construction and production expert, rather than the exact, calculating, scientific analyst who held the center of the American engineering stage. There can, furthermore, be no doubt that these same factors exercised a basic influence on the remarkable rise and development of the labor-saving methods of mass production and the rapid spread of mechanization in the United States.

In this American picture the American engineering schools long occupied a difficult position. They had come into being as a result of the growth of engineering science—many of them carried the title "scientific." They were established only when the scientific movement in engineering had reached the stage where it became clear that this new type of training could be more effectively and efficiently taught through the formal processes of the classroom and laboratory than by the older methods of apprenticeship. The self-styled "practical man" who had come up the hard way through the ranks naturally regarded the product of these new scientific schools as steeped in theory and not having "a practical hair on his head." The American engineering school thus fell heir to the task of encouraging and carrying forward engineering science for almost half a century before the full import of the new movement became clear to American engineers.

Some of the comments of these earlier days are both amusing and revealing. About 1850, when the movement was in its infancy, George Horatio Derby (1823–1861) unfortunately one of the few engineer-humorists the profession has produced, published a satirical "Report on the Mission Dolores Railway," a line which would now be well within the city limits of San Francisco. Under his pen name of John Phoenix, however, the reconnaissance for this "great" work is described as involving not only surveyors but a host of scientific personnel—astronomers, botanists, geologists, ethnologists with wagonloads of equipment, telescopes, microscopes, etc. Even as late as 1872 Trautwine, in the preface to his famous *Civil Engineer Pocket-book,* states:

The writer does not include Rankine, Mosely and Weisbach, because, although their books are the productions of master-minds, and exhibit a profundity of knowledge beyond the reach of ordinary men . . . they are but little more than striking instances of how completely the most simple facts may be buried out of sight under heaps of mathematical rubbish.

Yet, during this very era engineering schools increased and multiplied in America. There were but 2 in 1840 whereas by 1870 there were 70. In part this was due to the growing forces which made a more scientific education essential—the advent of more costly materials, iron and then steel replacing wood, with a consequent premium on design methods which would lead to their more economical use; the rise of the truss type of bridge, a structure requiring careful analysis if it was to be safe and securely built; and the increasing demand for bigger machines and structures, with an emphasis, therefore, on assured and economical design—all these, and later other influences, led to steadily increasing applications of and need for more engineering science. The rise of electrical engineering in the last years of the 19th century, a development from earlier discoveries in natural science rather than an offshoot of the engineering family, added emphasis to the new movement.

But a major factor in spreading the new gospel was the rapid increase after the Civil War in the demand for engineers. This was the great age of American expansion, of the transcontinental railroads, of the birth of the steel and oil industries, when any young engineer was eagerly snapped up by a rapidly growing economy. It made little difference whether his degree was earned in practice or formally granted by an engineering school. If he had a practical bent, some initiative, and plenty of gumption, a job was available. The product of the new engineering schools was, thus, rapidly passed into and had its influence on American engineering practice.

Another result stemming from the "reduction to a science" of many older judgment techniques was that men of far less than outstanding engineering genius could play a useful part in the wide expansion of engineering activities which was taking place. With engineering an art and its practice limited to those few who possessed extraordinary gifts of genius, an era of rapid growth such as America experienced in the last fifty or seventy-five years would have been impossible. The American engineering school has thus played a vital part and exerted an important influence on the spread of the engineering science movement in the United States.

Nevertheless progress in the United States toward a more complete and exact rationalization of design techniques in engineering lagged far behind the level of European practice. On the one hand, many American professional engineers continued to regard engineering schools as far too "theoretical" in their teaching and interests—lacking in their understanding of and in giving due attention to the actual needs of practice—the "practical" approach. In the early 1900's, for example, the older engineer would frequently remark that he had forgotten the day he graduated all the little calculus he had learned in school, had never found "any use for it" or any need to turn again to its study.[3]

Yet, when we review American engineering instruction of pre-World War I days it is quite clear that it was theoretical only by comparison with practice. The great majority of engineering texts were of a very practical, probably it would not be an exaggeration to say vocational, type, while the few more advanced works were, almost without exception, based on short-cut simplifications and interpretations of some of the newer techniques of European practice. This is not to say that there were no great engineering teachers in this period or that some of them did not contribute to and endeavor to encourage a more advanced scientific approach. The process we are dealing with is one of continued gradual evolution rather than of sudden change. It is clear that teaching cannot be too far in advance of —must, perforce, to a major degree, reflect—current practice and, at this time, the American engineering profession did not yet see the need for a marked change in the earlier, simpler procedures.

About the period of World War I, however, the situation began to change. The growth of engineering science is, of course, directly related to interest in and the status of research, to the pressures for the advancement of fundamental, basic understandings. As we shall have occasion to note later, the experiences of World War I were a vital factor in making America industrial-research conscious. But there were also other influences.

New materials and types of structures were coming into use. The American Portland Cement Industry, for example, was born with the turn of the century, and its remarkable growth led to the first well-rationalized design procedure for reinforced concrete, the famous Joint Committee Report of 1912. French workers had pioneered in this field, but the outstanding American worker in this new area was Professor Arthur N. Talbot (1857–1942) of the Engineering Experiment Station of the University of Illinois. It soon became apparent that the full economy of reinforced-concrete de-

[3] This attitude, even still too frequently encountered, reflects a failure to recognize that engineering education must, in view of constant advances and therefore constant obsolescence in the profession, prepare students not in current practice but for future needs. Our schools would, indeed, be deserving of criticism if they did not emphasize the more advanced techniques and send out graduates capable of carrying them into professional service.

sign could be realized only through "continuous" construction—the older methods of "simple" beam and structural analysis could not meet these needs. More advanced design techniques were essential. In general, also, the bigger structures of this new era had, of necessity, to be better designed; it was no longer possible to ignore stresses which were relatively unimportant in smaller works or could be provided for by rough approximation and generous overdesign.

The advent of the airplane also forced attention to new structural problems. A premium was placed on the most highly refined design because every pound of dead weight saved added a pound to carrying capacity. Its special problems also provided a powerful stimulus to the rise of a relatively new branch of engineering science, aerodynamics, which, in turn, encouraged new developments in the age-old field of hydraulics and led to the modern generalizations of fluid mechanics.

In the mechanical field the replacement of the reciprocating engine as a basic power unit by the steam turbine posed new problems in thermodynamics and machine design. In electrical engineering alternating current, involving far more complicated problems of transmission and utilization, was winning the battle over direct current. New problems and processes stimulated a similar awakening of interest in the more advanced theories and understandings in other branches of engineering science.

It would be ungenerous to pick out a few of the American consulting engineers and engineering educators who pioneered in this movement in the United States. The general situation is, perhaps, best revealed by the fact that the source of the new knowledge was Europe, especially Germany, and that a number of outstanding American engineers of the 20th century were newcomers to our shores who brought with them the teachings of the European schools.

Thus Gustav Lindenthal (1850–1935), of Austrian birth, was responsible for the great Hell Gate Arch at New York of 1917, a type of bridge earlier used in Germany but new to the United States, as well as the record-breaking continuous truss over the Ohio at Sciotoville. These works involved not only new types of structures but new problems of analysis and design. To mention only a few others: Othmar H. Ammann, of Swiss origin, who worked with Lindenthal, has long been recognized as an outstanding expert on bridge design; Ole Singstad, a Norwegian by birth, has become a world authority on subaqueous tunnels.

In the more theoretical aspects of engineering science our debt to men of European education, especially in more recent years, is even more revealing. In 1925, Dr. Karl Terzaghi, a native of Czechoslovakia, came to Massachusetts Institute of Technology and may be said to have pioneered in establishing in this country the new engineering science of soil mechanics. Among those who have made notable contributions in the field of advanced mechanics, stress analysis, and elastic theory are Professor Stephen P. Timoshenko of Russian and German training and Dr. Theodore von Kármán, a Hungarian by birth, who has devoted his efforts largely to aeronautical problems. In fluid mechanics Professor Boris Bakhmeteff of Columbia, one-time Russian Ambassador to the United States, has been a leader while Professor Richard von Meses of Harvard, an Austrian expert in aerodynamics, is a leader in this field.

Thus, while engineering science in the United States has lagged, as we have said, behind Europe, this, so to speak, imported talent plus a number of gifted and outstanding younger men of both European and American origin, constitute the backbone of the engineering science movement in the United States at the present time.

As we shall later have occasion to observe, World War II, with the resulting collapse of Europe, has ended our reliance on European sources for basic, fundamental advances in engineering science. The United States must, and speedily, meet this challenge and carry forward not only its remarkable record of practical achievement in construction and production but also provide the continuing advances in basic understanding from which new products, processes, and methods stem, and on which the improved techniques of the future will be based.

The urge for ever-greater rationalization of design, the search for new or better materials and improved processes, goes forward today at ever-increasing tempo. We need, as never before in our history, men of outstanding gifts and continually more advanced training. Our engineering schools face a challenge to better, more effective research and graduate service.

Chapter 8. MODERN ENGINEERING I:
TRANSPORTATION

I hold every man a debtor to his profession; from the which, as men of course do seek to receive countenance and profit, so ought they of duty to endeavor themselves by way of amends to be a help and ornament thereunto.

Sir Francis Bacon.

INTRODUCTORY, THE ENGINEERING PROFESSION TODAY

When we turn to the 20th century it becomes increasingly difficult to provide even a reasonably adequate outline of engineering development in brief form. Earlier in the 19th century not only was the field of engineering far more limited, but Britain and the United States alone occupied outstanding positions of engineering leadership. As that century came to a close, however, Germany was rapidly becoming an outstanding industrial power and exercising a most important influence on industrial and engineering development. France also, after a long lapse, was experiencing a rebirth of engineering, while, in the Far East, Japan was quickly adopting the methods which had made industrialization so potent a force in Western life. The outline here given is necessarily almost entirely devoted to development in the United States. Activities in other countries are noted only when they have affected the American story.

Similarly, while there were but two major branches of engineering until late in the 19th century, this number was increased when mining and metallurgy, which had for centuries been more or less independent practical arts, joined the engineering family. Electrical, chemical, and, still later, industrial engineering were also established as special fields of effort. Today, with increasing emphasis on specialization, there appears to be no end to the various engineering specialties which seek recognition.

Yet, the scope of activities of these several branches inevitably overlaps in some areas; the power field, for example, involves both mechanical and electrical engineering, while modern mining operations require a wide variety of services, from civil, electrical, and mechanical to chemical and geological specialties. It has, therefore, appeared wiser to discuss these modern developments from the standpoint of the functions or services involved rather than to follow the traditional professional groupings. It may not, however, he amiss to call attention to the history and status of some of the specialized branches of the engineering profession.

While in the earlier years of the 19th century, civil engineering, the oldest branch of the profession, was regarded as including all branches of engineering other than military, with the growth of the new technique of mechanical engineering—and, later, electrical engineering—the field of civil engineering has been narrowed down to include primarily the art and practice of construction. Today, the civil engineer, together with the architect, serves as the technical expert of what is known as the construction industry, a major activity but one carried on by a large number of relatively small, independent, and highly competitive organizations. In contrast to some of his other engineering colleagues, the civil engineer is engaged in "capital" rather than in consumers' goods activities. He is an expert in the investment analysis, planning, and construction of the usually long-life, basic works and structures required in both public and private life —bridges, dams, tunnels, canals and highways, railroads, water supply, sewerage, irrigation, and other "heavy" construction operations. The American Society of Civil Engineers, the oldest American society, as had been the Institute of Civil Engineers in Britain, was founded in 1852.

The American Institute of Mining and Metallurgical Engineers, founded in 1871, represents, as we have seen, one of the oldest of the practical arts. Its mining members are engaged in the discovery and mining of our mineral resources while the metallurgical engineers are occupied with the extraction from the ores and the preparation for use of the precious and useful metals. Two of the more recent developments in this field are a great increase in interest in the concentration, or "benefaction," of ores at or near the mine so as to reduce the increasing transportation costs of shipment to the metallurgical plant, and increasing emphasis on "physical metallurgy," the study of the structure and behavior of metals and alloys, their heat-treatment and other factors which provide desirable properties essential in meeting the special exacting requirements and conditions of modern metal use.

American mechanical engineers were first brought together in a nation-wide professional society in 1880 when the American Society of Mechanical Engineers was founded—33 years after the founding of the similar British Institute. The members of this group are, of course, primarily concerned with what a famous earlier engineer, George S. Morison, characterized as "the manufacture of power," the turning of inert matter, fuel of various kinds, into useful, rotative motion. The steam engine has been followed by the turbine, while the gasoline engine has created a new power age. Today new areas are opening with the possibilities of the gas turbine and jet engines. But the field of the mechanical engineer also includes the use of power in machines and tools of ever-increasing scope and application. Practices not only in all branches of industry but in all branches of engineering have literally been remade through the use of the modern tools provided by mechanical and electrical engineers.

It was in 1884, just a year or two after Edison's pioneer electric-light plant in Pearl Street, New York, began operation, that the American Institute of Electrical Engineers was founded. Now one of the largest of our national societies, the electrical engineers are responsible for all the problems connected with the ever-broadening uses of electricity and electrical devices in modern life. Historically, of course, electric communication came first—the telegraph and the telephone—and these were followed by the power development, the dynamo, arc and incandescent lights, and the motor. Today, the electrical utilization of power is the key to our modern industrial life. New inventions, continued improvement in methods and applications—alternating current replacing in large measure direct current, long-distance transmission, radio, and now television—are characteristic of this field. Indeed electrical devices, especially in the electronic field, have opened new areas in the precision control of production operations, in computing, and in many other applications.

The modern chemical engineer serves a group of practical arts, many of which, as in the case of mining and metallurgy, have a history almost as old as that of civilized life itself. Glass and leather making, dyes, cements, and a number of earlier industries and home occupations were the forerunners of the modern chemical industries which comprise one of our major and certainly one of our most dynamic and progressive, modern industrial activities. The chemical industry in the United States was established well before World War I—the American Institute of Chemical Engineers was founded in 1908—but, to a major degree, it was the discovery during World War I that the world was largely dependent on the German chemical industry that gave new life and purpose to this most important field. One after another new developments have resulted from continuing research and extremely able, active, and far-sighted industrial leadership.

Industrial engineering is the youngest branch of the engineering profession, although all engineering activities have long required the planning, organization, and management of labor forces and industrial and construction activities. On the one hand, industrial engineering may be regarded as involving the extension into the field of industrial operations and management of the basic principles of the engineering method of study and analysis. "It is just as important," says Alfred P. Sloan, Jr., of General Motors, "to apply research to all the functional activities of business as it is to the technological phases of an enterprise." It has also been remarked, on the other hand, that in its earlier phases the industrial and power revolution and its modern development in machine manufacture and mass production emphasized the adaption of man to the machine. The industrial engineer, it is said, in endeavoring to improve man's productive capacity still further, seeks to adapt machine operations to man's peculiar physical, mental, and psychological abilities and limitations. World War II has given a great impetus to industrial engineering, for to a major degree America's remarkable production record during the war, a vital factor in the Allied victory, was based on the know-how of organization and management which the industrial engineer has aided in developing.

There are, of course, many other specialized branches of engineering—from aeronautical to water power and from sanitary to safety engineering. What has been happening, and is still under way today, is a spread into other service areas of the honest, unbiased, soundly scientific, rationalized, quantitative methods of analysis, study, and synthesis which have been so successfully applied in the older branches of engineering. These newer fields offer attractive opportunities for young engineers who are prepared and qualified to undertake such pioneering ventures.

It has been estimated that probably half those who find occupation in the professions in the United States today have not been formally educated and are of technician rather than professional status. Thus a large number of draftsmen, surveyors, detailers, designers, checkers, and similar technical workers are required in carrying out the minor, routine duties of an engineering office. The total membership in the major professional societies is well over 100,000, but it was estimated in 1948 that there were some 350,000 engaged in engineering work in the United States. With licensing to practice, a requirement now universal in the United States, it is becoming increasingly difficult to enter the profession other than through the formal channels of education plus experience in practice. Some 120 or more engineering schools throughout the country provide "accredited" undergraduate educational programs while graduate instruction leading to the master's and doctor's degrees is securing increasing recognition. Among the groups which have exercised an important influence in the profession have been the Engineers' Council for Professional Development, founded in 1932, and the American Society for Engineering Education, established in 1895.

TRANSPORTATION

It is their care in all the ages to take the buffet and cushion the shock.
It is their care that the gear engages; it is their care that the switches lock.
It is their care that the wheels run truly; it is their care to entrain,
Tally, transport, and deliver duly the sons of Mary by land and main.
                              Rudyard Kipling, "The Sons of Martha."

Railroads. In 1887 a famous American student of railroad economics, Arthur M. Wellington (1847–1895), published a huge volume on *The Economics of Railway Location,* based on a small book which he had written some ten years earlier. Wellington remarked that, while the ill-designed bridge fell down and the bungler's bungling was thus revealed and evident to everyone, the weaknesses of a poorly planned railroad, its sins of location, bad grades, and other factors which affect its income and operating costs, are so hidden that it fails through "a gentle but unceasing ooze from every pore which attracts no attention." Wellington was not the first to study and analyze the costs of railroad operation and relate them to the problems of economic location, but he did develop and perfect such analysis, thus exercising an important influence not only on railroad economics but on the development of the entire technique of economic "investment" analysis in engineering.

One of the earliest comparisons of the relative operating advantages of two alternate locations was that made by John B. Jervis (1795–1885) in planning the extension of the Hudson River Railroad from Poughkeepsie to Albany in 1845. Albert Fink (1827–1897), who began his service on the Baltimore and Ohio (the famous Fink truss, still widely used for roofs, was a product of this period), later undertook a careful analysis of the operating expenses of the Louisville and Nashville.[1] Wellington developed these studies in analyzing such problems as the added capital expenditure which would be justified to reduce the controlling grade (by increased excavation and fills) on a proposed line, thus reducing operating costs. His definition of the engineer as a man who can do that well with one dollar which any bungler can do with two after a fashion has long constituted a guiding principle in American engineering.

Even in Wellington's day, the Era of Railroad Consolidation, however, abuses were creeping into American railroad operation which were to lead to the creation of the Interstate Commerce Commission in 1887 and, ultimately, to the very difficult—almost impossible—situation which American railroads face today.

In the earlier years American railroads had followed a natural and normal growth, and although exercising a transportation monopoly and built because they offered opportunities for profitable investment to their promoters, they were an effective and vitally important means of opening the country to settlement and providing the transportation essential to economic growth. By 1869 the American continent had been spanned with the junction of the Union and Central Pacific lines at Promontory Point in Utah. This was a work of which General William Barclay Parsons, writing some thirty years ago, remarked:

Although in the building of these lines there was not a single piece of spectacular or outstanding designing, and nothing worthy of describing in text books on engineering except the discovery of the most favorable pass crossing the Rocky Mountains, nevertheless, in their entirety they stand unsurpassed in the art of construction. Here was a railway projected before the Civil War began and completed soon after it was ended, extending westward from a sparse agricultural settlement on the Mississippi River to the mining camps on the Pacific Coast. The intervening 1,500 miles were almost a *Terra incognita*. . . . To do the planning, to gather the materials, and to carry such an enterprise to successful completion demanded an extraordinary combination of vision, executive ability, technical skill, unflagging enthusiasm, and indomitable courage, and the result was not merely the laying out of a railway but the making of an empire. What calling can point to a single act of comparable achievement?

The next phase of development, however, witnessed the battles of railroad strategy, the struggles of the "railroad kings" who, controlling the lines which had been consolidated into systems, sought to

[1] Published in 1873–1874 under the title *The Cost of Railroad Transportation.*

secure control of the remaining lines or, through new constructions, of the remaining undeveloped traffic areas. In the Far West two such giants of the day, James J. Hill and Edward H. Harriman, clashed over the control of the transcontinental routes. The famous Northern Pacific "corner" on the New York Stock Exchange in 1901 finally led to a compromise. Closer at hand, George Gould battled with the Pennsylvania interests to gain an entrance to one of the greatest centers of origin of freight traffic in the world, the Pittsburgh area. The story of these and other battles of railroad strategy involve political corruption and encounters of opposing forces which almost approached the tactics of open warfare.[2]

At the same time railroad management was brought into similar battles between the leaders of America's growing industrial empires and, through special rates or secret rebates, favored this or that particular business enterprise. The chief source of railroad income was freight traffic, and this was the era in which the general railroad attitude was said to be reflected in a "public be damned" policy. It was obvious that, sooner or later, these high-handed monopolistic abuses by the group of operatives controlling American railroad transportation, at that time the only available means of transportation for many inland areas of the country, would have to be brought, "in the public interest," under government control.

While the original purpose of the Interstate Commerce Commission, created, as noted, in 1887, was to ensure fair, just, and reasonable rates, the powers of the Commission have been extended to cover almost complete supervision of modern American railroad operation. They include the control of all rates, minimum as well as maximum, all proposals for consolidations, extensions, or abandonment of lines, the division of proceeds from the joint operation of lines or use of other facilities, the allocation of rolling stock, public safety, and the issuance of securities, or, in the event of bankruptcy, the control of reorganization. At the same time the railroads have had to face increasing costs of operation owing to the activities of the various unions of railroad employees involving both increased wages and such restrictive requirements as minimum train crews and other so-called "feather-bedding" activities.

[2] This struggle has been outlined by Spearman in his *The Strategy of Great Railroads* (see Bibliography). *An Engineer's Recollections* (New York, The Engineering News-Record, 1935) tells the fascinating story of one of the last of the great forceful, resourceful, and romantic personalities of this era, John F. Stevens, chief locating engineer for James J. Hill.

The Tunkhannock Viaduct, 1915

One of several notable constructions by means of which improvements were effected in the alignment and grades of the Delaware, Lackawanna and Western Railroad, resulting in better operating conditions.

Finally, the American railroad today no longer occupies an unchallenged transportation monopoly. New means of transportation—the highway, the pipe line, and the airplane along with water transport—have entered into active competition with rail traffic. As has been noted previously, the greatest era of American railroad building came in the decade 1880–1890. Since 1920 there has been a progressive decline in mileage as unprofitable branches and other lines have been abandoned. We are, in fact, in the process of adjusting a vast system of rail lines, built in an era of uncontrolled expansion and speculation, to the needs of a new age in which other forms of transportation are taking over special services formerly provided only by the railroads.

In view of the fact that the railroads are one of our major taxpayers, paying something in the order of a million dollars a day, whereas these newer services are largely subsidized by the government, and also recalling that railroads are still the absolutely essential backbone of the American transportation system, it is evident that the major problem we face today is that of making it financially possible for the railroads to provide this essential service. It has been said that our railroads are the least dynamic and progressive of American business enterprises. Yet there have been constant and notable advances on many lines and in all departments from line and track to locomotives and cars. Constant improvement has, indeed, been necessary in order to meet mounting costs, and the remarkable record of American roads during the two World Wars is evidence of the fact that rail transportation provides the basic arteries and veins through which the economic lifeblood of the nation flows.

Space forbids any detailed note of these improvements. As locomotive weights have increased, roadbed, ballast, ties, and rails have been continually strengthened. The standard locomotive loading has doubled from a E 40 (*i.e.*, 40,000 lb on each pair of driving wheels), the standard design load of fifty years ago, to an E 80 today.[3] Rails have similarly had to be increased in depth and weight to secure greater distribution of this increased loading and modern rails vary from 120 to 160 lb per yard as compared with 60 to 80 in 1900. In motive power there was a period when electric engines seemed destined to wide use. The electrification of the suburban services of

[3] It should be recalled that the tractive effort of a locomotive ultimately depends on the frictional resistance of the driving wheels on the rails and, thus, on the weight on the drivers. Locomotive weights have increased from the few tons of Stephenson's *Rocket* to over 1,000,000 lb. for some of the larger freight locomotives and tenders of the present day.

the New York, New Haven and Hartford and the New York Central entering New York City in 1907 was a pioneer venture with the former using a-c overhead transmission while the latter held to direct current and a third rail. Some freight lines followed, the Norfolk and Western in 1915 and the Great Northern in 1927. Today, however, some 90 per cent of the locomotives being built are Diesel-powered.

Freight-car design has also been greatly improved, and the older ratio of almost two-thirds dead load to only one-third "paying load" has been reversed in new and lighter cars. This railroad progress is best told, however, by the fact that the speed of freight-train movements has been doubled and that, during World War II, our railroads carried the greatest load in their history with far fewer cars and locomotives than were used during World War I, an era which itself marked a notable increase in the efficiency and effectiveness of rail transportation.

In passenger service also there have been important developments in recent years. These began on the lines west of Chicago, notably with the introduction of the lightweight "Zephyr" Diesel-powered trains on the Burlington in 1934 and resulted in regular runs at speeds over 80 mph. Eastern roads, facing far more difficult problems of track and curves, have been following in this bid for modern, rapid, passenger service.

During this same period, of course, great railroad lines had also been building in other countries. The rapid development of the Pacific Coast of the United States stimulated Canadian interest in linking the far-flung provinces more closely together. Lines had been built in the Eastern Provinces in the 1850's and '60's, but it was not until 1885 that the Canadian Pacific was completed. Begun in 1875, construction did not actually get well under way until 1880 and involved probably the greatest obstacles to successful railroad building ever encountered—from the Lake Nepigon area of swamps and virgin forests to the difficult crossing of the Canadian Rockies. This has been called the Canadian Railroad University and its first chief engineer, Sandford Fleming (1827–1915) of Scotch descent, has been hailed as the Father of Canadian Engineering. When turned over for completion to a private company in 1880, an American railroad man of great force and determination, William Van Horne (1843–1915), assumed control and carried the line through the Rockies to the coast.

Another great undertaking was the Trans-Siberian Railroad strik-

Modern Diesel-powered Passenger Train, 1934

The Chicago, Burlington and Quincy Railroad pioneered in the introduction of high-speed Diesel-powered passenger service. The Chicago–Denver run of 1,017 miles was made in 1936 in a little over 12 hours at an average speed of 83 miles per hour.

ing eastward from Moscow across the great plains and forests of Siberia to reach the Pacific at Vladivostok. In 1891 Nicholas II, then Czarevitch and destined to meet his end at the hands of the Bolsheviks some twenty-five years later, placed the first stone of this great work. Successive sections were completed in 1895, '96, and '98, and in 1905 the last link, by-passing Lake Baikal, was finished. The entire "story of the railroads" forms, in fact, such a fascinating and romantic record of pioneering and adventure, of danger and courage in overcoming obstacles, that it stands unsurpassed in the annals of engineering.

The future of the American railroads, however, is dark and uncertain. Ground between the millstones of strict regulation, mounting labor costs, burdensome taxation, and increasing competition, it is obvious that they face almost insuperable barriers in meeting their responsibilities for improved public service. There is no reason to expect that the plan of government ownership and operation followed abroad could possibly provide more efficient management; our roads simply face a vicious situation which no form of management can resolve.

Highways. Few engineers of the early years of the present century would have regarded as even remotely possible the highway development which has taken place in the United States in the past thirty years. A brief review of American highway history reveals the successive steps in this surprising evolution.

After its early ventures with such projects as the Cumberland Road, the Federal government had abandoned interest in road making to the states. These in turn had left the problem to local government with the result that, after a century of neglect, the roads of the United States—with few exceptions—were still dirt roads, almost impassable in the spring in northern areas when the frost was coming out of the ground, and showing little or no improvement over their condition a hundred years earlier. The situation in 1902 is strikingly reflected in a pioneer American text on *Roads and Pavements,* published that year by Professor Ira O. Baker, an outstanding American engineering educator. He states in his preface,

It is frequently claimed that the public would be benefited by placing the care of the roads in the hands of engineers, but there is no evidence that any considerable number of engineers comprehend either the principles of road making necessary for the improvement and maintenance of our country roads, or the economic limitations and political difficulties of the problem.

The "good roads movement" in the United States may be said to have begun with the advent of the bicycle in 1885, a sport which swept the country from coast to coast. It was not until the coming of the motorcar, however, that the road problem became so acute that attention was forced to actual improvement on a large scale. The movement was, as Professor Baker indicates, dependent upon two major factors: research and education in the art of road building plus the vital problem of how to finance such improvements.

As early as 1891 the state of New Jersey had provided aid for its counties by appropriating funds to be used in cooperation with local authorities. Similar "state aid" followed in 1892 in Massachusetts, in Connecticut and California in 1895, and in New York, Vermont, and Maryland in 1898. In 1893 the Federal Bureau of Public Roads had been established under the Department of Agriculture. It was destined to play an important role in the development of the Highway Era in the United States. Its activities have passed through three stages of development: educational, Federal aid, and comprehensive planning.

It must be recalled that in its earlier stages the road problem was a local one and the first efforts were thus directed toward the utilization of available local materials, such as gravel and broken stone, in providing a reasonably smooth and hard surface. The Bureau built demonstration and test sections of highways in various localities using local materials and sent demonstration cars over the country preaching the gospel of good roads.

Needless to say these gravel and similar "water-bound" roads, while satisfactory for slow-moving, horse-drawn vehicles, proved unable to withstand the action of faster moving automobiles. Various dust preventives and binders were first tried and in the end, of course, the answer was found in the far most costly concrete and the various forms of bituminous surfacing.

Likewise the problem of financing road improvements began as a local one, many farmers "working out" their road tax by laboring with their neighbors on road maintenance. It was realized, especially when the automobile came into use, that it was both unreasonable and impossible to finance better roads by increases in local taxes. In 1916 Federal aid came into the picture, such aid being dependent upon the existence of an adequate highway department in the states aided. The organization of state highway departments in all states naturally followed rapidly.

Even Federal aid, however, failed to provide the funds demanded by the Motor Era. As late as 1921, texts on highway finance and administration were still seeking such support through increases in local taxes, state and Federal aid, or the issuance of highway bonds. Finally, in 1923, the answer was found—the gasoline tax was discovered to be a most productive source of income and an equitable means of distributing mounting costs of construction and maintenance. By 1926 all but four states had adopted it. Today both state and Federal taxes are in force, and so productive has this source of revenue become that gasoline taxes are being used in some states to finance many public activities other than roads.

In the more technical aspects of highway building, there have been successive improvements, notably in alignment, in better construction techniques, and in adequate foundations. In the earlier days attention was given to smooth surfacing and the dangers of frost action, and the need for a well-drained foundation was largely ignored. Today it is realized that no form of surfacing can be properly maintained unless due attention is given to providing an adequate and stable subgrade.

To the public, however, the apparent lack of foresight in planning the alignment of new roads is probably the item most frequently noted. Unlike the railroads, passenger service rather than motor haulage constitutes the major part, usually 90 per cent, of the highway traffic load. Safety and speed for passenger cars rather than low grades for trucking are thus the determining elements in highway alignment. As successive improvements are made, dangerous curves are eliminated or made less acute through new alignments often involving heavier excavation, increased cuts, and fills. "Blind summits" are likewise reduced while intersections are improved—all to permit faster travel with greater safety. Even twenty-five years ago motor speeds of 50 mph and over, now permitted in many states and on many parkways, would have been regarded as suicidal.

From the planning angle the Bureau of Public Roads still continues to exercise a constructive and far-sighted influence. In general in American highway planning first attention has been naturally directed toward local relief, devoted to the improvement of roads of high traffic density. The Bureau, however, has emphasized the longer range comprehensive planning of nation-wide highway systems. At least three major factors in addition to financing influence highway planning: local pressure for improvement; the needs revealed by traffic surveys; and the degree to which a particular improvement fits into the comprehensive plan of highway development of the state.

The balance sought in evaluating these factors varies widely. Connecticut, for example, developed under the late John Macdonald a project plan for a grid network of main traffic highways crossing the state both in north and south and in east and west directions at intervals of approximately twenty miles. It was argued that the best procedure was to disperse traffic by favorable new routes rather than add to its concentration by building four- or even six-lane highways in sections of high traffic density. In improving old highway alignments, also, this state has not favored too great a compromise between alignment and grades but has eliminated or greatly reduced curves even when in doing so rather steep grades became unavoidable.

In the maintenance of modern highways, local forces, usually unable to command modern tools and skill, have been progressively superseded by state agencies. Yet, it would seem wise not to carry this trend to the point where local interests are entirely eliminated from the highway picture.

As a result of these widespread highway activities, our cities and country have been provided, practically within the past twenty-five years, with over 3 million miles of streets and highways, as shown in Table 1.[4]

TABLE 1

	Miles
Federal aid systems:	
Primary	231,278
Secondary	372,761
State systems:*	
Primary	39,358
Secondary	143,214
Other	16,768
County roads*	1,507,859
Township and local*	634,349
Local city streets	255,309
Total	3,200,896

* Excluding Federal aid projects.

It is interesting to recall that one of our most far-sighted and able leaders, Woodrow Wilson, stated in 1906 when he was President of Princeton: "Nothing has spread socialistic feeling in this country more than the use of the automobile. To the country man they are a picture of arrogance and wealth with all its independence and carelessness." Today there are far more automobiles then there were

[4] Compiled by American Association of State Highway Officials, March, 1949.

horses and buggies in 1906; with over 50 million licensed operators the travel horizon of the average American family has been incredibly broadened. Yet our highway problem, and especially the problem of town and city parking, continues to grow. It has been stated that we need to spend 3 billion dollars a year for eight or ten years to provide adequate highways. The adjective "adequate" seems hardly reasonable, but the fact that we have not yet solved all the problems which a Motor Age has created cannot be denied.

Airplanes. Man has envied the birds their ability to fly since the earliest ages, as witness the ancient Greek legend of Daedalus, who lost his son, Icarus, on a flight from Crete to Samos in the days when fancy, at least, had wings. Centuries later Leonardo da Vinci, made drawings which make us wonder how much he really knew of the problem of flight. Two centuries later the Montgolfier brothers in France actually made their famous and successful ascensions in "lighter-than-air" craft, the hot-air balloon. The 19th century ended, however, with mechanical flight, the heavier-than-air machine, still in about the state described in the well-known poem, "Darius Green and His Flying Machine."

There were two major problems which had to be met before such flight became possible: the one aerodynamic, the other motive power. A host of experimenters made contributions to the theory of flight, to the gradual accumulation of the understandings necessary to develop wings and, especially, to the problem of balancing or maintaining the stability of the plane in flight. Many of them paid for their experiences with their lives. Modern methods of study and experiment, large wind tunnels, and modern basic aerodynamic theory were unknown. The German, Otto Lilienthal, studied the problem for over twenty years before he began, in 1891, the glider experiments that ended with his death five years later. He attempted to balance his device by shifting his body, the principal weight on his glider. Percy Pilcher in Britain, also a glider pioneer, died in 1899 in a crash. In America, Octave Chanute, a well-known bridge engineer and a friend of the Wrights, carried out some pioneer experimental work. The Wright brothers were, however, the first to develop a mechanical means of securing the essential balance through distorting, "warping"—changing the curvature—of the tips of the wings, a method long since abandoned for the far simpler ailerons, or hinged rear wing-tip sections.

In 1896, Samuel B. Langley, working with the Smithsonian Institution, flew a large steam-driven model, but his later full-sized machine met with disaster. It was the development of a light, compact gas engine that solved the motive-power problem and, here again, the Wright brothers were the pioneers.[5] Wilbur (1867–1912) and his younger brother Orville (1871–1948) Wright, sons of Bishop Wright, were simple American machinists who, after an earlier printing venture, established a bicycle repair shop in Dayton in the days when this sport was the craze. They made enough from repairs and sales to finance their flying experiments. Their machine was a biplane and carried in front two small wings which served to maintain a fore-and-aft balance, a device which, of course, has since been transferred to a tail position. It was the fancied resemblance of this "ship" to a flying duck which led the French to call the Wright planes *canards*.

In October, 1900, the first Wright glider was tested at the isolated spot on the North Carolina coast, Kittyhawk, where the Weather Bureau had advised them that a moderate, steady wind would always be found. A winter of new experimental work followed the 2 minutes' air experience of 1900. The 1901 glider lacked lift and showed that earlier data on wing camber or curvature were not reliable. The Wrights thereupon built a small wind tunnel for experiments, and their 1902 glider made over a thousand successful flights. They then turned to the motor problem, built their own gas engine and, in December, 1903, just after Langley's failures, made the first successful power flight—852 ft requiring 59 seconds. Their second powered plane was exhibited near Dayton in 1904, and by 1908 they were making flights of 12 to 21 miles in sight of huge crowds. But their funds were exhausted, and they received little encouragement at home. After earlier demonstrations in France, however, they met, in 1909, the War Department requirements of a flight of 25 miles at 40 mph with two passengers, and the airplane became an established invention.

The earlier great flying records were made in 1909 and 1910. Blériot flew the Channel in the former year, and the Rheims Meet in France proved that man was at last able to emulate the birds. Glenn Curtiss pioneered with hydroplanes while Paulhan and others continued to break cross-country and altitude records.

[5] The claim that Langley—too modest and too honest to make any such claim himself—was the first to make a successful airplane, seems to have been based primarily on the desire to attribute this honor to a scientific man rather than to the patience, understanding, and inventive genius of two humble bicycle mechanics of Dayton, the Wright brothers.

It was World War I, however, which brought flight out of the sports category and made it a serious art. German, French, English, as well as American designers vied for supremacy. After the war there was continued and rapid progress. American Navy planes crossed the Atlantic (1919) while Alcock accomplished the first non-stop flight. Lindbergh "made it alone" from New York to Paris in 1927, and new records for altitude, cross-continental, and 'round-the-world flights are still being established.

The importance of the plane in modern warfare was thus early recognized. It has been the struggle to find a proper place for it in normal, commercial life which has been critical. Britain had used it for mail service in 1911, the United States established the New York-Philadelphia-Washington route in 1918 and, in 1919, regular passenger service between New York and Atlantic City was inaugurated. Today, of course, the world is spanned by commercial air lines; Europe is but 10 hours away, Los Angeles to New York has been accomplished in a little over 4 hours, and records for circumnavigating the globe are being constantly lowered.

The trend in flying has been continuously toward greater speeds and size. The biplane has long since given way to the monoplane while the modern gas engine has stepped up speeds to over 600 mph. It is a long jump from the Wright's 4-cylinder 30-hp engine of 1903 which weighed 7 lb per horsepower, or even Manley's ingenious 5-cylinder radial engine of 1901 of 52.4 hp, to the modern engine of some 3,000 hp. Similarly in growth in carrying capacity. The ill-fated German DO-X established a record when it took up a crew of 10 and 159 passengers in 1929, but this proved to be a mere stunt. The modern large passenger plane seems to have compromised on an average of 50 or less.

Beginning in 1920, Juan de Cierva undertook the study of autogyro, and the helicopter has now won a place for itself in special services. The spectacular work of Count Ferdinand von Zeppelin (1838–1917) who began his study of rigid but lighter-than-air craft in 1898, however, seems to have been forgotten as has that of the pioneer nonrigid airship experimenter, Santos-Dumont of the same period. Yet Zeppelins played a part in World War I and the *Graf*, piloted by Hugo Eckener made the 'round-the-world trip in 1929. The great cost of such "airships," their vulnerability, and the fact that one tragic accident after another has ended their days, plus the rapid improvement of planes, have, apparently, discouraged their further development.

The airplane has, thus, on the one hand, come to supply a standard, everyday channel of transportation, while, on the other, secret, jet-propelled military planes may even now be hurtling men through space faster than the speed of sound (780 mph). Airfields are as common as railway terminals used to be; new devices are being constantly developed to increase safe travel and permit night and blind flying, such as radio beacon, radar, and other aids, while new areas of conquest are being attacked. "Strato-cruisers" bid fair to become everyday affairs while gas-turbine and jet engines are pushing speeds up, as we have noted, into the supersonic zone. Yet, vital as the airplane is as a military weapon and important as it is that we maintain a high productive capacity, a relatively small production can, apparently, meet all the needs of peacetime commercial aviation. The age when planes will be as common as automobiles are today is still in the future.

Water Transport. Developments in ships and shipping, in river, lake, canal, and sea transportation have received scant attention in this volume. Yet there is no more fascinating story than that of the evolution of the sailing ship, the rise of steam navigation, and the part played in modern life by ships and shipping.

It seems strange that ship design should be the last branch of engineering to retain the old designation of architecture, yet it is still known as naval architecture, although courses in this specialty are commonly combined with those dealing with the mechanical problems of ships, marine engineering. This whole area seems to be one which, although clearly an important engineering branch, has followed, at least in the United States, its own, almost independent, and isolated course of development. There are ample reasons for this limitation of interest. In America it is our Navy, with its remarkable and colorful record of national service, which offers an inspiring but the almost solitary example of progressive and effective development. On the other hand, after the glorious and romantic age of the Yankee Clipper, which, in the last days of sailing ships, held the records of the sea, and of American whaling ships and voyages, our merchant marine has fallen to a distinctly secondary position in world commerce. Britain, as we have said, not only ruled the waves but built the steamships of the world while foreign sailors have manned the world's ships. America's struggles to maintain even a reasonable merchant marine—still an essential to national defense—has been maintained only through government subsidy. When war has threatened us, our ability to produce ships, as witness the Liberty ships of World War II, has no parallel but the other opportunities of employment which American labor enjoys seem to have discouraged successful participation in the calling of the sea.

Canals. One must distinguish clearly between inland canals and ship canals. In their day, canals and river canalizations were important means of inland transportation—they preceded both modern highways and the railroads. But, with the advent of the latter, they suffered almost complete and total eclipse. While water transport is the least costly per ton-mile, it is also the least satisfactory form of transportation. It is slow. Modern life demands speed. It is seldom complete in itself. The railroad can deliver from shipper to customer. Water transport usually requires transfer to other services for delivery with costly terminal, handling, and other charges. In northern areas canals and rivers are seasonal in operation—they are frozen during the winter months. Yet canal enthusiasts still preach the gospel of this low-cost transportation.

In New York State the Erie Canal, undoubtedly a major factor in the earlier rise to fame of the Empire States, was rebuilt as a barge canal in 1905–1918 at a cost of 175 million dollars. It seems beyond dispute that it would have cost the people of the state less to pay the railways which parallel this canal to haul the traffic it carries during the 7 or 8 months it is usually open.

In 1929 a most ambitious, excellent, and well-designed canalization of the Ohio River from Cairo to Pittsburgh was, after close to a half century of labor, completed. One can secure some idea of the problems involved from the fact that at Cincinnati maximum high water is no less than 72 ft above low river level while at Pittsburgh the flow varies from 1,600 to over 440,000 cu ft per sec.

From the business standpoint, however, the use of these and similar works has been very disappointing. As a hard-headed president, Calvin Coolidge, put it:

Our whole century-old policy of developing navigable streams at tremendous cost is either a piece of inconceivable and colossal folly, or else we as a people have been inexcusably remiss in taking advantage of our opportunities.

Yet this work of canalization has gone forward both by the Corps of Engineers on the Upper Mississippi, and on the Tennessee under the Tennessee Valley Authority.

These are, of course, free waterways built at public expense and, unlike the railroads, paying no taxes. But it was felt that the Federal government could encourage through example the use of these opportunities of which private companies seemed slow to take advantage. Accordingly, in 1924, the Inland Waterway Corporation, with the stock all held by the government, began to operate a barge line on the Mississippi—the former scene of a romantic era of "steam boating" of which Mark Twain wrote so interestingly in *Life on the Mississippi*. Opinion differs as to the success and value of this venture which, in itself, reflects the doubtful value of such works in modern life.

Comparison of these ventures with railroad operations is difficult. Ardent canal enthusiasts argue plausibly that it is not a problem of waterways vs. railways but of each being used to the best advantage in a well-coordinated system of rail, highway, and water transportation.

Yet the American experience parallels that of Britain where it has been remarked: "The last important canal work was completed in 1834, attention thereafter being directed to railway extensions." France, as we have said, is especially blessed topographically with opportunities for inland waterways—opportunities she led the Western World in developing. While these French canals and rivers are still in use, they have been a constantly decreasing factor in French transportation. Germany, on the other hand, was active in canal building notably before World War I, but here it is difficult to separate economic from military considerations; it is also true that the decline in use has been even more marked than in France. In 1925, for example, the total waterway tonnage in Germany was 15 per cent less than in 1913, and there had been a 25 per cent decrease in the miles of waterways operated. Yet, the hydraulic expert will find in these various foreign and American works most interesting and novel constructions—not only locks but movable dams and other designs—not encountered elsewhere in hydraulic practice.

When one turns from inland to ship canals, the situation is quite reversed. In general ship canals have amply justified their existence. In the United States the famous Soo canal, bringing Lake Superior into the extensive Great Lakes system, built in 1855 and enlarged in 1870, continues to maintain one of the heaviest tonnage records of any canal in the world. Abroad the success of the Suez Canal, opened in 1869, acted to stimulate other works which would shorten shipping routes. In Greece, the Corinth Canal was begun in 1882; in Britain the famous route from Manchester to the Irish Sea—the scene of Brindley's early canal triumph and of the equally historic Liverpool and Manchester Railway—was further reinforced with the Manchester Ship Canal, built in 1887–1894. Begun the same year, the Kiel—or as it was later known, the Kaiser Wilhelm Canal—finished in 1895, joining the Baltic with the North Sea, was designed largely as a naval rather than a shipping venture. In Holland, the Amsterdam Canal was begun in 1865 and has been successively enlarged in 1877, again in 1889, and later reinforced with the world's largest lock at Yumiden. The 20th century, however, has witnessed "the greatest of geographical surgical operations" in the completion of the Panama Canal.

It seems inevitable that the United States fell heir to this four-centuries-old project. During the California Gold Rush of 1849, Panama became an important route to the new West. The Panama Railroad was built during the '50's with such appalling loss of life that every sleeper laid represented, it was said, a human life. In 1876 the French company, under the leadership of Ferdinand de Lesseps (1805–1894), fresh from his triumph at Suez, began plans for Panama. Work began in 1881 on a sea-level route. By 1889, however, the company was bankrupt, and lack of funds, inefficiency, the greed of adventurers, and the death toll of yellow fever brought this venture to an end.

In the meantime the United States had turned to the Nicaragua route, but in 1902 the Panama rights were secured and, under President Theodore Roosevelt's dynamic leadership, the project went rapidly forward.

There was much discussion of a sea-level vs. a lock canal. Experts differed, but all agreed that a lock project was not only feasible but could be most quickly completed. The President again, as he had in the negotiations with the French and with the Republic of Columbia, quickly took action—a lock canal was built.

In addition to the President, at least three other leaders deserve the major credit for the completion of the work. The labors of Dr. William C. Gorgas (1854–1920), one of the pioneer United States Army Medical officers who stamped out "yellow jack" on the Isthmus and made the Isthmus one of the healthiest spots in the Western Hemisphere, were essential to success at Panama. John F. Stevens (1853–1943), a forceful and determined Western railroad builder, was selected by Roosevelt "to make the dirt fly." Finally, having organized the excavating operation and with success assured, Stevens resigned, leaving the lock construction, in which he was not experienced, to an expert Army hydraulic engineer. It was under the leader-

Panama Canal Construction, 1912
The approaches to Gatun Lock from the lithograph by Joseph Pennell. Inspired, as he put it, by the Wonder of Work, this drawing, made on the spot in
1912, illustrates the impressive scale and magnitude of this "greatest of geographical surgical operations." (*Courtesy of Metropolitan Museum of Art, New
York.*)

ship of Colonel, later General, George W. Goethals (1858–1928) that the canal was completed, and the first ship passed through August 3, 1914. Earth and rock slides in the great Culebra Cut, however, temporarily closed the canal prism, and it was not until the following year that uninterrupted traffic was restored.

Rising 85 ft from the Atlantic in a series of three double locks at Gatun, shipping passes through Gatun Lake and the Culebra Cut, down to Miraflores Lake by a single-lift double lock at Pedro Miguel, and, finally, to the Pacific level through the two double locks at Miraflores—50-miles total from deep water to deep water.

Tolls are charged on all shipping through the canal, and there has been much discussion of its operating finances. With due allowance for the costly military expenditures for the protection of the canal, the record is not too unsatisfactory. This great work, however, cannot be judged solely on a business investment basis. Its strategic value to the Western Hemisphere and the fact that the whole world looked to the United States to "make good" at Panama are factors which cannot be ignored.

Docks and Harbors. Here again we face one of the most romantic and colorful stories in man's battle against the adverse forces of Nature—one which has, perforce, received little attention in these pages. The Greeks, we have noted, were the first harbor builders and developed a fortified breakwater type of plan which persisted for centuries. The first modern work, the Digue or Breakwater of La Rochelle, was not built as a harbor work but to close, in 1628, this last Protestant stronghold from relief from the sea when it was under siege by the King and Cardinal Richelieu, as so interestingly described by Dumas in *The Three Musketeers*.

Vauban, of fortress fame, pioneered in the last years of the same century in the plan of confining flow by jetty construction to a narrow channel, thus causing the water to scour out a deeper waterway, in his famous work at Dunkerque, undoubtedly his favorite and greatest engineering undertaking. In the following century, De Cessart began the famous Digue of Cherbourg in 1781, but it required such constant reinforcement against the Channel storms that it was not completed until 1858.

By this time the British engineers were carrying forward harbor work. Smeaton and Rennie built "harbors of refuge" for the fishing fleets on the bleak coast of Scotland and northern England as well as harbor and dock works for the Channel ports. The famous West India Docks at London (1800–1802) were built by William Jessop

(1745–1814), protégé of Smeaton and a pioneer railway builder in the presteam days, who also built the Bristol Docks (1803–1808). Additions have continued to be made to the great London dock system—the East India and Milwell docks in 1868, Victoria and Albert in 1880, Tilbury in 1882—and the story has become one of continuous additions and improvements.[6] French and other European harbors have also been notably improved; in fact harbor improvement goes steadily forward attracting little attention because it is a continuous process.

In the United States—with one notable exception—harbor, as well as river, work has been a special responsibility of the Corps of Engineers of the United States Army. The one exception was the building of the jetties at the South Pass of the Mississippi River delta, maintaining a 28-ft channel through the pass and over the bar and assuring access from the Gulf to New Orleans some 18 miles up the river. James B. Eads, of St. Louis Bridge fame, undertook to carry out this task in spite of the fact that his plans were condemned by the Army Engineers and he was to be paid only if the work was successful. With his customary skill and audacity, he went ahead with his work, beginning in 1875, completed it with full success in 1879, but not until twenty-five years later was final payment approved.

In large part the harbor works of the Corps of Engineers have been devoted to the never-ending problems of maintaining channel depths in the approaches to the larger ports of the country. The Ambrose Channel at New York and similar other dredging operations require constant attention. The Corps is also responsible, under the Secretary of War, for the approval of any constructions on, under, or over the "navigable waters" of the United States, a term which includes not only those now so used but many other rivers and streams which may possibly at some remote date be rendered navigable.

[6] It should be noted that, in British and foreign usage, the term "dock" is applied only to closed basins in which the water level is maintained by suitable gates, irrespective of tidal fluctuations. Our American "docks" are, properly speaking, piers.

Chapter 9. MODERN ENGINEERING II: MATERIALS

> There is not a single mineral substance of which the quantity used in the past century is less than the total of all the centuries that preceded. For many of them the principal uses are to supply needs that have arisen within the century, and these uses enable men to do many things that previously were quite beyond their power. So man, by his mastery of minerals, has increased his own stature.
>
> Thomas T. Read, *Our Mineral Civilization.*

Next to power in its various modern forms, probably no factor has more vitally affected human life than man's ever-growing command of materials. Many materials still widely used have, of course, been known for centuries. The past hundred years, however, have been marked not only by vast increases in the available quantities of older materials, such as steel, copper, and petroleum, but also by the rise of a host of new products—the steel alloys, such as chromium and nickel, aluminum, and such modern chemical products as Portland cement, fertilizers, plastics, artificial fibers, and synthetic rubber.

No other nation on earth has had at its command so wide a variety and abundance of these new products as the United States. With, it has been estimated, only one-twentieth to perhaps one-fifteenth of the world's population the United States produces and uses two-thirds of the world's annual output of petroleum, one-half of the steel, probably one-third of the coal and copper, and a quarter of the lead and zinc. Many of the needs which these uses reflect—the gas engine and motorcar, the widespread use of electric light and power, for example—are creations of recent years in which the United States has also led the world.

While the main task of the 19th century was that of increasing the quantity of essential mineral and chemical products produced and of reducing costs, the 20th century has been marked by improving quality and creating new products. We have passed, for example, into an era of alloy steels, of electrolytic copper, of special metals for

122

special needs, and of the creation of new chemicals never known to man or even found in Nature.

The task of discovering and making available to engineering and industry the raw mineral materials of the earth falls on the shoulders of the mining engineer. Few of these materials are useful in their raw state, that is, without processing. The metallurgical engineer has the responsibility of extracting the metals from their ores and of processing them by special treatment, combining them in useful alloys, and making available the special qualities required by the exacting conditions of modern use.

The chemical engineer, a more recent addition to the engineering family, has, within the present century, become an outstandingly important and dynamic figure in modern life. He uses to a major degree mineral products but also utilizes a wide variety of other raw materials, transforming them into new products to meet both old and new needs. The world's dependence on chemical products has become so complete that we could not live without the support of a vast chemical industry. Many of the older home industries, such as soap- and candlemaking, home dyes, textiles, breadmaking, and preserving, involve chemical understandings and have become mass-production undertakings.

The beginnings of these two major branches of materials engineering—the mining–metallurgical and the chemical—extend, as we have noted, far back in human history. Their modern development has, however, been quite different in character. Mining and metallurgy have, as in the case of the other long-established engineering branches, been undergoing a transition during the past century from the traditional methods and empirical techniques of age-old practical arts into the more fully rationalized and scientific practices of the present day. This evolution has been necessarily a gradual one. Highly specialized and deeply implanted manual and craftsman skills acquired through long centuries of practical experience are not easily abandoned and replaced overnight by new methods based on more fully scientific techniques. Similarly, resistance has also been natural to the replacement of older methods by the new tools of an age of power and mechanization. All the older branches of engineering have faced this problem. Almost invariably the pressures of economic change have exercised a fundamentally important influence on such transition. Older mining, for example, relying on hand skills and lacking modern power equipment, although accomplishing wonders in making the world's mineral wealth available to man, was limited in the depth and extent of its operations and in its productive capacity. As it became necessary to delve deeper into Mother Earth for her mineral treasures and as man's growing needs demanded greater output, science became more important in prospecting, engineering planning more necessary in development, mechanization replaced hand methods, adequate capital became essential, and the modern highly organized mining industry was evolved. America has led in this modernization of an ancient practical art. As we shall have occasion to note, the experiences at the famous Comstock Lode in Nevada between 1859–1886 marked a new era in mining history—the development of modern mining machinery, the first silver metallurgy in the United States, and man's first experience with really deep mining. To a major degree Comstock was an American Mining University, and it was because of these and similar later experiences that American mining engineers became widely known all over the world and were called in as experts on such new developments as those in the South African Rand.

Similarly, the art of metallurgy has long been in process of transformation from the empirical techniques of earlier centuries into the more fully rationalized procedures of the present day. We are apt, these days, to belittle the power of empiricism in comparison with the admittedly far greater powers of more exact, scientific understanding. No human achievement offers a more outstanding example of man's ability to learn through experience than that exemplified by the metallurgical art. Many practices and procedures of ancient origin still remain not only powerful and reliable but, in some cases, even yet not fully rationalized and understood. Here again, however, the inexorable pressure of economic change—demands for more economic and efficient production in greater volume—continually force a search for ever more complete knowledge and understanding.

The modern American chemical industry, on the other hand, has resulted to a major degree from a renaissance, a new birth, rather than from transition. While its antecedents are ancient, its present outstanding and important position in the United States dates largely, as we have noted, from the World War I period. Germany became, in the late 19th and early 20th centuries, the world leader of the modern chemical industry. Since that war, the United States has achieved a leading position in the chemical field. Here new products have constituted the outstanding characteristic of industrial progress. Back in the latter years of the 19th century the attempt was made to control prices through securing the monopoly of a product. Today we have entered an era in which not only are new chemical products produced to meet new needs but older output is being constantly replaced by new products which better meet quality requirements at lower costs. The once annoying and useless by-product of the gas industry, coal tar, has become the parent of a host of drugs, dyes, perfumes, and other products. The labors of the silkworm have been replaced by synthetic fibers. Native rubber, once tightly controlled on a national scale, has been challenged by the artificial product. The plastics have given rise to a new industry. The age of composites is upon us with various new combination materials replacing many older products—and the end is not yet.

MINING AND METALLURGY

The mineral industries in the United States have had to face rapid increases in demand in the face of ever-mounting difficulties. The coming of the Power Age put new burdens on coal mining. The rise of the petroleum industry, in which new methods of geological and geophysical exploration as well as continued improvement in refining and production have been continually developed, has encouraged and stimulated a more scientific and exact approach to many of the problems of "hard rock" mining and metallurgy. Similarly the rise of a true Age of Metals—the production of iron and steel on a scale that permitted their use as construction materials, the achievement by copper of a new position as a result of the evolution of electrical engineering, the advent of the airplane with an increasing demand for aluminum and its alloys—all these influences of the past hundred years or less have brought about a new relationship of these ancient arts to our modern needs and economy. Yet there probably is no field of engineering in which a larger number of confusingly related variables vitally affect the status, position, and trends of its products and activities than is the case in the mineral industries. The health and prosperity of one product after another—coal and steel, gold and silver, copper, lead, zinc, and a host of minor metals—are dependent upon world conditions, economic, labor, and other varying factors and influences. Mineral production, in turn, has long affected both the internal and external economy of nations.

Coal. In his interesting little book, *Our Mineral Civilization*, the late Professor T. T. Read tells the story of coal under the heading "Modern Magic."

The production of coal is the principal mining industry of the United States, which is the same as saying it is the principal mining industry of the world, since our country with its one-twentieth part of the world's population produces nearly half of all the world's coal, or somewhat under two million tons daily . . . Simply to do the job of bringing this enormous amount of material to the surface has employed (in good years) over 500,000 persons, while its surface transportation and distribution to consumers engages the activities of many more. . . . Perhaps the most remarkable thing about coal is the low cost at which it is produced . . . ten pounds for one cent has been the usual price at the mine . . . even the small buyer has paid only a half-cent per pound . . . And since two pounds, properly utilized, will do the work of a man for a day it is the equivalent of being able to hire an able-bodied man for one cent per day. If that is not magic when our present wage scales are considered, what is?[1]

The mining of soft coal in the United States started in the Richmond basin soon after 1700. The hard coals of northeastern Pennsylvania were opened up shortly after 1800 and led to the building, as we have noted, of one of our first great private transportation ventures, the Delaware and Hudson Canal of 1827–1830. Bituminous or soft coal is the major product, anthracite or hard coal, normally 90 per cent pure carbon, constituting usually but one-tenth of the total production.

The history of coal is one of continued evolution in use. A major step forward was made with the adoption of the coal-iron process in Britain in the early 18th century. This created a new market for coal in the form of coke, and the ironmakers in making furnace coke simply drove off and wasted the volatile matter in the coal. Others, however, became interested in obtaining the gas from this volatile matter to burn for illuminating purposes. William Murdock (1754–1839), associate of Boulton and Watt, pioneered in gas lighting in 1792. But it was not until some fifty years ago that the making of coke in "by-product" ovens, which produce a coke satisfactory to the ironmakers and, at the same time, save the volatile contents, was developed. In fact, as late as 1913, less than a third of American coke was made in these by-product ovens but, by 1919, this had grown to nearly two-thirds (a change influenced by World War I conditions) and by 1928 over 90 per cent was so produced. A great waste of our fuel resources was, thus, at long last, arrested. (A similar waste of natural gas in connection with petroleum operations will also be noted.)

Of the by-products obtained from bituminous coal (far higher in

[1] *Our Mineral Civilization*, pp. 7ff.

volatile matter than the hard, high-carbon anthracite) gas is the principal item. Ammonia, light oils, and their derivatives are also recovered, but it was an annoying by-product, coal tar, that resulted, as we shall later note, in the birth of a new and vitally important chemical industry, the coal-tar industry with all its products, including a remarkable number of dyes, drugs, and perfumes.

As Professor Read observes, one asks, therefore: Why burn coal? Why not recover the by-products and burn coke? The answer is, in part, that not all the bituminous coal produced is capable of being made into good coke and that, as yet, the over-all economy of this technique has not been demonstrated. As the price of coal increases, however, and, especially, as transportation costs rise, the problems of converting coal into more easily transportable products at or near the mines will become of even greater importance.

The story of coal mining offers some interesting examples of the persistence of traditional practices and methods. Until quite recent years coal mining was a pick-and-shovel job, the miner often furnishing his own tools. It has also been a variable industry, with times when purchases were fast and furious and other times when mines had to shut down. The miners also, have been irregular in their working, taking days off and not returning to work until their funds were exhausted, while frequent strikes have threatened coal famines. As a result the coal workers of the country have been employed on the average only about half the days of the year. The truth of the matter seems to be that our capacity to produce coal is perhaps double our needs and there are more coal miners than can be usefully employed. The rise of other sources of fuel, especially oil and natural gas, plus a remarkable increase of efficiency in the use of coal[2] has been an important factor in bringing about this declining market. The Diesel locomotive is rapidly replacing coal-burning engines in an industry which, at one time, absorbed close to a third of the bituminous output. Oil heating is increasing in general and in house use, owing to lower cost, easier operation, and to the uncertainties of the coal situation.

These factors tend, of course, to encourage efforts to reduce the cost of coal, and there have been notable improvements in mining methods and handling in more recent years. The per cent of coal

[2] Between 1920–1945, for example, the pounds of coal used by the railroads per thousand gross ton-miles hauled decreased from about 175 to about 115; pounds per kilowatt-hour in central power stations from 3 to 1.15; the pounds of coking coal per net ton of pig iron in blast furnaces from 3,000 to 2,500.

mined by machine, for example, has increased from about one third in 1905 to about 90 per cent in 1945. Improvements in loading have been slower. Loading underground was done almost entirely by hand until 1925, but almost 60 per cent of this task is now accomplished mechanically. The famous old mine mule is also becoming a thing of the past. Electric mine haulage has been continually improved, although, when it is recalled that the number of miles of track underground in the one state of Pennsylvania is greater than that on the surface, it is clear that radical changes must come slowly. The average tons produced per man per day has, as a result of all these improvements, risen from about 3.5 at the opening of the century to close to 6 today.

A major development, however, has been in the increase in "stripping," the mining of coal in open workings by the removal of the overburden. It has been found less costly to mine this way in open cut, even where it is necessary to remove 7 yd or more of overburden to reach a single yard of coal.

In this method the basic tools are the huge power shovel, gasoline, Diesel, or electric, the largest shovels in the world, handling over 15 tons in a single mouthful, and also dragline excavators, being used in this work. Beginning about 1914 not only has strip-pit mining increased steadily, until today over 20 per cent of bituminous and 25 per cent of anthracite are mined in this way, but the lower grade lignites of the Western states—notably Montana, the Dakotas, and Texas—have been made commercially useful through the development of this technique. Some 75 per cent of their output is mined in open pits.

Mechanical cleaning methods have also, during the present century, largely replaced the older hand methods; the breaker boys who hand-picked the coal have given way to the wet process, the "float and sink" technique of the modern washing plant. In 1927, the first year that full data were available for the bituminous industry, only 5.3 per cent of the product was mechanically cleaned. By 1944 this had increased to 25.6 per cent.

Coal production in the United States doubled every 10 years with the growth of power demands between 1870 and 1900—and almost doubled between 1900 and 1910. It then fluctuated with little trend to go up or down until 1940. The war created a new peak of over 600 million tons in 1944 while there has since been a decline. Recent declines have been due primarily to strikes. It is estimated that there were 485 strikes in soft coal mines in 1946 and that almost 20 million man-days were thereby lost. Apparently the coal industry faces a dilemma. Areas suited to stripping operations are limited. Further marked increases in output per underground worker would apparently result, in view of the limited coal market, in a continued decrease in employment. Better pay for the coal miner can be secured only through increased prices for coal, and this will react unfavorably in the competitive market which coal faces today. The coal industry is, thus, in the process of adjustment to changed conditions and, as usual, this results in difficult and painful changes which cannot be completed overnight.

Petroleum. As in the case of modern metal mining in the United States, the petroleum industry was a new venture; it had, in fact, no established precedents whatever, technical or legal, in any land, to serve as a guide. It had no earlier history as mining had, and as a result an entire new technology and procedure suited to its special needs and requirements had to be evolved—a new industry was created. The major part of this new development, from discovery, through production, refining, and transportation to marketing, has been of American origin and constitutes one of the most notable accomplishments of American engineering.

Petroleum and gas springs, bituminous deposits, and crude oil have been known to man certainly since Biblical times, were in some cases developed by shallow diggings, and had been used for various purposes from waterproofing to embalming and from lighting to medicinal uses. The modern petroleum industry was born, however, less than a century ago when Drake's well came into production on August 27, 1859. Here for the first time in man's use of these products was a well drilled for the sole purpose of securing petroleum.

In the early 1850's Samuel Kier of Pittsburgh collected some oil from his salt wells, bottled and sold it as "Rock Oil," a cure for almost every conceivable malady. Credit is usually given to George H. Bissell, a young New York lawyer, for first conceiving the idea of drilling for oil. He had seen Kier's Rock Oil, brine wells had been drilled for salt, and the method of refining oil by distillation was already in use but was limited by small supplies. Bissell saw the possibilities of a new industry and interested some business friends, a lease was secured on a farm near Titusville in western Pennsylvania, and Edwin L. Drake, "Colonel Drake" as he was known, was sent in 1858 to drill for oil. He finally secured the services of a local blacksmith and brine-well driller, "Uncle Billy" Smith, and, in 1859, oil was found in the first well the company drilled. "Drake's Folly," as it was known before oil was found, was only 69½ ft deep and the oil, about 20 barrels per day, was brought to the surface by pumping. It sold for as much as $20 a barrel.

As a result of this venture, an oil rush developed to the western Pennsylvania wilderness. One of the largest boom towns was Pithole City, a few miles from Titusville. A flowing well giving 650 barrels of oil a day was soon sunk, and the population of Pithole jumped to 50,000. The price of oil, however, rapidly declined as production increased and, 10 years later, Pithole was, as in the case of similar gold-rush towns, deserted. The oil rush had moved to new areas.

There has, of course, been a continuing development of such new areas ever since these pioneer Pennsylvania ventures. New York and Ohio fields were developed, West Virginia and Illinois followed in 1886, Indiana in 1889, and Kentucky in 1899. The search in far-off California began in 1864, but the first commercially successful well apparently did not come until 1875. Kansas came in 1886, Texas in 1887, and Oklahoma in 1891.

One of the most interesting technological improvements in the oil industry has been in the exploration and the discovery of new oil fields. The origin of petroleum is still not fully established, but it is known that oil is trapped under anticlines or folds in impervious, sedimentary rock layers, or under oil "domes" of similar character. A pocket of gas is usually above the oil and a brine area below. Oil geologists, through their knowledge of geological structure aided by modern methods of geophysical prospecting, have been able to predict the probable occurrence and location of oil areas.

In drilling methods, Drake's drilling procedure, using an improvised rough timber rig, a rope hoist, a hand-made drilling bit, and a 6-hp engine, has been vastly expanded and improved. Today huge steel derricks with rotary drills, using mud for cleaning and lubrication, are in use, and wells may reach depths of close to 4 miles. Drake made about 3 ft per day in drilling. The modern record is 10,024 ft in a bit over 38 days, or over 250 ft per day.

There have been improvements also in the operation of wells. In earlier days natural gas was regarded as a nuisance by oil men and was "flared," that is, burned and wasted. The aim was to get the oil out as quickly as possible. Today gas is used for both lighting and power and is "recycled," pumped back into the well, in an effort to improve total recovery. Precautions have also been taken to control

The World's Record Oil Well

In June, 1949, in the Wind River Range, Wyoming, this huge Diesel-powered drilling rig of the Superior Oil Company reached the unprecedented depth of 20,251 ft, or almost 4 miles. While revealing important geological data, the well—like many others—unfortunately did not prove to be a producer. (*Courtesy of National Supply Company, Pittsburgh.*)

flow and prevent the losses which formerly occurred when a "gusher" became uncontrollable as, for example, in the case of the famous Spindletop gusher of 1901 in the Texas Gulf area.

A process of oil refining by distillation was patented in 1847 by James H. Young. Working first with coal and shale, the early refineries quickly turned to oil. The technique was extremely simple. Kerosene was almost the only product sought—it was replacing the older whale oil for illumination in days before electric lighting was possible. The more volatile naphtha was, therefore, driven off in the heated still and wasted. In some cases, however, this was not fully accomplished, and explosions occasionally occurred when attempts were made to light kerosene lamps. It seems almost unbelievable but kerosene remained the major oil product, until, in the period between 1910 and 1914, a new era began as a result of the growing demand for gasoline for gas engines and motorcars and the eclipse of kerosene by electric lighting.

Today, of course, gasoline is the most valuable product. It is recovered from natural gas as "casing-head gasoline," but, primarily through the so-called cracking process which has superseded the older crude distillation, there is added to the gasoline content of the crude oil the gasoline produced by cracking the content of heavier oil. The earlier thermal cracking (heat plus pressure) made it possible to break up about one-sixth of the heavier content of a barrel of oil into gasoline. By 1936 new methods involving catalytic procedures came into use. Notable among these was the Houdry process developed by Eugene J. Houdry in France. Through these modern methods, gasoline production has been increased to half or better of the crude, and the oil chemist can, to a remarkable degree, control the production of the various modern oil products from naphtha and gasoline, fuel and ship oils, to lubricating oils and waxes.

The name most widely associated in America with oil is, of course, that of John D. Rockefeller. Rockefeller entered the oil business in 1860 when he invested in a refining process invented by Samuel Andrews. It prospered. In association with his brother, William, with Stephen V. Harkness, and others he organized the Standard Oil Company in 1870. By purchase and through various deals, mergers, and combinations which, although sanctioned in their day, were later roundly condemned and legally outlawed, Standard continued to grow.[3] Among others the Pacific Coast Oil Company was absorbed and, while Standard had done much to stabilize and rationalize the industry, it became evident that through such mergers, through efficient management, and through a command of capital, it was the intention of this giant organization to dominate the American oil industry. After legal bickerings in the '90's, following the Antitrust Act of 1888, the Standard Oil Trust was finally dissolved

[3] See, for example, one of the first great books of the "muckraking" era, *The History of Standard Oil*, by Ida M. Tarbell, New York, McClure & Co., 1904, 2 vols.

in 1911 into a number of separate organizations although many of them still retain the name that Rockefeller had made famous.

Still another stirring chapter in the story of oil has had to do with transportation. In 1864, Charles P. Hatch transformed a freight box-car into a tank car, and a few years later the familiar horizontal, cylindrical steel tank car appeared. The first trunk pipe line for oil was built from the oil fields into Pittsburgh, 60 miles, in 1874. Four years later a line over the Alleghenies to the Atlantic seaboard, the Tidewater Pipe-line, began to pump oil into Williamsport, charging some 16 cents a barrel instead of the $1.25 to $1.40 cost by rail.[4]

By 1880–1881 the National Transit Company had some 1,330 miles of pipe lines in operation, and this form of land transportation had come into wide use. Greatest of the many lines which today join the fields of the West with refining and market centers is the so-called "Big Inch" (22-in.) line from Longview, Texas, to Phoenix-ville, Pennsylvania, 1,254 miles long with a daily throughput of 300,000 barrels. Today over 95 per cent of the crude-oil requirements of refineries is supplied by pipe line, and there are over 125,000 miles of such lines in use. In addition, close to 150,000 railroad tank cars and a world total of 1,700 ships transport oil and its products. Similarly, the earlier waste of natural gas has been curtailed and gas is now delivered great distances for lighting and other uses. The need for such vast facilities becomes clear when we consider the growth in the production of oil. The total American oil production from 1857 to 1899 was a little less than 1 billion barrels. By 1929 yearly production had reached this astounding volume. It then drop-ped for some 6 or 7 years but by 1943 reached $1\frac{1}{2}$ billion and is now about 2 billion.

This tremendous use and the vast amounts of gasoline and oil consumed during the war have, naturally, raised the question of whether we are not too rapidly exhausting this irreplacable natural resource. Estimates of reserves are difficult to make. There are sup-posed to be "proved" reserves of over 20 billion barrels, but this does not include new areas of promise which have not been tested. Allow-ance must also be made for improved methods of discovery, recovery,

[4] Herman Haupt (1817–1905) among whose activities were service on the Hoosac Tunnel in Massachusetts, the first great American tunnel, and some ex-traordinary military bridge constructions during the Civil War (Lincoln de-scribed one of them as built of bean poles and cornstalks) was engineer of this venture—one of the last efforts of the independent producers who were being forced out by Standard Oil.

and use. Guesses of how long the world's supplies may meet man's needs vary from well less than a century to over three.

The story of oil, here so briefly outlined, is, thus, that of the creation of a new industry of world-wide scope and of vast importance in international relations. So important have gasoline and fuel oil become that the world is being searched for new fields and nations are competing for their control. Following World War I there was a scramble to secure control of earlier, vital, basic, natural resources. The importance of many of these resources has decreased with the rise of new, synthetic products or substitutes. Oil is today, however, the outstanding resource without which any great nation cannot survive in this age of airplanes, motor transport, and other gas and oil equipment.

Iron and Steel. In spite of Britain's efforts to limit the Colonies to the production of raw materials which would be shipped to Britain for processing, it was impossible to prevent the early rise of an infant iron industry in America. Iron was essential for the blacksmith, for tools, nails, and hardware. The iron industry was, thus, well established in the United States before 1800, and Cort's puddling process for wrought iron was introduced in 1817. An abundance of wood for charcoal, however, delayed the use of coal in ironmaking until about 1840. In fact, it was not until 1855 that more pig iron was produced through the use of anthracite coal than by charcoal. The use of bituminous coal (coke) followed, but it did not pass charcoal until 1869 and catch up with anthracite until 1875.[5]

Swank explains the relatively slow growth of the iron industry in the United States as due to the competition of foreign products caused primarily by higher labor costs, longer distances in the transportation of materials, and low import duties. After the Civil War, that is, with the advent of the Age of Steel, the United States went forward more rapidly but it was not until 1890 that American pig-iron production exceeded that of Britain's record year, 1882.

The earlier American iron furnaces, which constituted the earlier iron industry and were mainly scattered over the North Atlantic states, were soon abandoned when steel came on the scene, when the great ore bodies of the Lake region came into use, and when the newly created American steel industry became centered in the Pittsburgh area.

[5] According to Swank, *History of Iron in All Ages*, p. 376 (see Bibliography) pig-iron production from charcoal even in 1890 still amounted to about one-fifteenth of the total and was double that of 1854.

We have already mentioned the pioneers of American steelmaking
—Holley, the technical expert, and Carnegie and his associates who
created United States Steel. The first Bessemer steel was made in
Michigan late in 1864, just a few months before Holley's first works
at Troy, New York, came into production. The factors which led to
the growth of Pittsburgh as a steel center were primarily its strategic
fuel location and the supply of Lake Superior ores.

Early ironworks in the Pittsburgh area, lacking adequate supplies
of ore, had been unsuccessful, but a thriving manufacture of "iron-
mongery" developed in the area as early as 1810, and it was as an
ironworking center that Pittsburgh first became noted. With the
resulting demand for iron, furnaces then began to be developed, the
first in 1859. The famous Connellsville coke added to their success,
and ore, secured from a few native mines and from Missouri, but
chiefly from the Lake Superior area, completed the transformation.

While the main copper deposits of the Lake region are on the great
Keweenaw Peninsula, which juts out into Lake Superior, the iron
ores of Superior are located in two groups, those south of the lake
in the Marquette, Iron Mountain, and Gogebic areas, and those at
the western end of the Lake near Duluth. The first discovery of iron
ore in the region was in 1844 by William A. Burt in the Marquette
district. Four years later some ore was mined and hauled to a local
forge, but this and other local efforts failed until, with the opening
in 1855 of the St. Mary's canal, joining Superior with the other lakes
and now known as the Soo, large shipments could be made by boat
to the East. Two years later a railroad was completed from the Lake
to the mines and, in response to Civil War needs, shipments grew
rapidly.

The Menominee, or Iron Mountain district, was, apparently, discovered in 1848 but forgotten for twenty years, and it was not until
railroad facilities were provided in the late '70's that production
went forward. Gogebic, a narrower ore belt south of Duluth, had
also been noted in 1848 but was not actively explored until 1881.

The greatest of all these deposits, the Mesabi range,[6] some 70 miles
northwest of Duluth at the western tip of Superior, was discovered
in 1890. The Vermilion range to the northeast of Mesabi had been
opened in 1884, and the first ore was shipped from the Cuyuna area
southwest of Duluth in 1911. Of these the Mesabi, over 100 miles

[6] So-called because the ore usually occurs in mountain ridges or ranges. These
run in a general SW-NE direction, and the deposits disappear under deep cover
to the west.

long, is the greatest, with the Cuyuna next, while the Vermilion is first in the quality of ore. Within a few years of its opening, the Mesabi passed all the other properties in production and became the main source of iron in the world.

While the earlier Marquette and similar ores were mixtures of wide variety, including magnetite and siderite, and were mined by underground methods with the usual accompanying problems of water and timbering, the Mesabi ores, the softer hematites and limonites, could be reached by steam shovels operating in open cuts. As a result of these competitive advantages, Mesabi, as we have said, soon came to dominate the situation. The flat-lying ore bodies vary from a few to over 300 ft in thickness. Exposed in some locations, they are covered with 200 ft or more of overburden in others. But, since the mines of the Mesabi range have been opened, more earth and rock have been moved than in any other human undertaking, and stripping of this overburden to reach the ore has been carried down to depths of over 150 ft.

It should be noted that it was in the copper mines of Superior at Isle Royal that, in 1864, John Mabbs built the first hoist with large diameter drum, installed the first air compressor and air rock drills, and was the first to use dynamite in this district. The growth of the Superior iron mines has resulted in the creation of another series of developments of great engineering interests which are peculiar to this area: the great shovels, operating in open pit and loading directly to ore cars, excellent railroads extending to the loading docks on the Lake, mechanical loading of the Lake steamers or ore carriers of special design, and mechanical unloading at the port of delivery. Recalling that the average iron content of the Lake ores is close to 50 per cent and that they can be handled in this fully mechanized way, at least one factor in the remarkable growth of the American steel industry—once it got under way and Mesabi ore entered the market—becomes clear.

In order to reach Pittsburgh, however, this flood of iron ore must be transferred from ore carrier to ore train and, accordingly, in 1906, the main plant of the U.S. Steel Corporation was created at Gary, about 25 miles east of Chicago just over the Indiana line at the southern end of Lake Michigan.[7] The Indiana Steel Company and

[7] Named after Elbert H. Gary (1846–1927), judge, corporation expert, a founder of the American Steel and Wire Co., of the Federal Steel Co., chairman of the board of U.S. Steel, and organizer of the American Iron and Steel Institute (1909).

the American Bridge Company plants, plus sheet, tin plate, car and foundry, cement,[8] locomotive, and other works make this steel city, with its excellent rail and water facilities, the greatest steel center in the world.

At the present time 85 per cent of the iron ore mined in the United States comes from the Superior region. The southern Birmingham mining area in Alabama contributes another 7 or 8 per cent, and there are imports from Chile, Cuba, and Sweden. Three quarters of the American output comes from open-pit mines. One of the interesting facts in the steel industry is the large percentage of scrap iron which is used. Roughly half the raw iron materials used in steel-making furnaces is scrap, the other half pig iron, consuming about two-thirds of the pig production.

The principal changes in steelmaking have been this shift to open-hearth operation and increases in the size of operations. In earlier days, as we have noted, ironworkers knew how to make the high-carbon–iron alloy we know as pig iron from the ore and how to use it in castings. They could also make wrought iron from pig by ridding it of its high carbon and other impurities. And they could restore to the wrought iron, itself too pure and, therefore, too soft for many practical purposes, the small amount of carbon needed to harden it and produce the alloy we call steel. Following the rise of the Bessemer and the Siemens processes for making steel, eliminating these intermediate steps and producing steel directly from cast iron and at low cost, quantity production became the controlling factor. The older blast furnaces which produced say 10 tons of pig per day have been increased in capacity to 1,000 tons or more.

For many years the standard method of producing steel was by the Bessemer converter, but by 1907 the Siemens open-hearth process had become the major method. It would handle pig, especially that from high-phosphorus ores not adapted to Bessemer treatment, and the process could be more easily controlled to produce steel of a higher quality. Today Bessemer production has thus declined to 5 per cent, while over 90 per cent of our steel is from open-hearth and about 4 per cent (mainly high-alloy steel) is made in electric furnaces.

[8] Between 1914–1918 a slag cement was produced, much of which was inferior, irregular, and unreliable in quality. The modern blast-furnace cement, however, is a far better product, can be used in some cases as a substitute for Portland cement, and is produced at a lower cost. It seems probable that there will be an increasing market for this by-product of the steel industry.

We shall have occasion to note the rare use of nickel, silicon, and manganese steels in large bridge structures. In the automobile, machine, and other manufacturing industries, however, there has been a constantly increasing use of alloy steels. In the past few years this demand for special alloys to meet special needs has resulted in an increase in the percentage of alloy steels to about 10 per cent of the total production. These alloy steels include, in addition to the above, chrome, vanadium, molybdenum, tungsten, and various combinations such as the "stainless" iron-nickel-chromium alloy.

In the rolling and fabrication of steel there have also been notable developments. The 12- and 15-in. I beams of 1884 had grown to 24 in., the largest rolled sections at the close of the century. In 1907 the heavy 24-in. beams, 115 lb to the foot, were produced, and in 1928 a 36-in. section came into the market. The addition of vertical end rolls to the older horizontal grooved rolls has made possible the rolling of the modern "wide-flange" I beams (largest 36 by $16\frac{1}{2}$ in., 300 lb) as well as the newer H section, widely used for columns in steel frame buildings and made up to 14 by 16 in. in size and weighing 420 lb to the foot.

The part played by steel in modern life is well illustrated by the fact that, whereas a century or so ago there was annually available about 15 to 20 lb of new iron products per capita and these were principally cast and wrought iron, every man, woman, and child in the United States today commands well over 1,000 lb of steel. Railroad and structural uses have declined in relative importance while sheet, tube, and similar products, used in automobiles, refrigerators, and a thousand and one household and other gadgets, account for much of this increase. Steel production has thus climbed to astronomical figures.

The curve of pig-iron production, for example, although showing sharp declines in periods of depression, such as 1907, 1921, and 1932, which are characteristic of the heavy industries serving capital-goods needs, has steadily mounted. From about 5 million tons in 1880 a peak of over 60 million was reached in 1944. Steel, while subject to similar sharp setbacks, has risen to even higher figures and American steel capacity has hovered around the surprising total of 90 to 95 million tons annually. It is estimated that the United States produces about half the steel output of the world.

Copper. As with gold the metal copper is one of the oldest known to man; it occurs in the native metallic state and is widely distributed over the earth. Native copper has been used by primitive people all over the globe—even the American Indians fashioned pendants and other ornaments from it. Early fused with tin to form bronze, it was not until about the opening of the Christian Era that brass, the more difficult alloy with zinc, was developed.

During the 18th century the major part of the world's copper supply came from the ancient mines of Cornwall in southwest England. A smelting center had developed in South Wales, primarily at Swansea, where the Cornish ore was sent for treatment. These Swansea operators continued to hold a practical monopoly on the world's copper output until 1850 or '60. In fact, as we shall note, some of America's early ore was shipped in the form of matte to Swansea for refinement. By 1900, however, copper from Chile, where modern copper mining had begun in 1830, plus American production predominated, and the British monopoly had been broken.

It is reported that early settlers discovered copper in New England in 1632, but copper remained scarce in the United States until in 1844, when a start was made in developing the great deposits of native copper in the Lake Superior region. Apparently the Indians of this area had secured some of this native copper from surface outcrops. One of the larger of these surface masses, over 3 tons in weight, was removed to the Smithsonian in 1843. In 1857 a single mass of 420 tons (maximum length, width, and thickness, 46, $12\frac{1}{2}$, and $8\frac{1}{2}$ ft) was found in the Minnesota mine.

In 1864 the famous Calumet lode was discovered, a great copper-bearing bed of conglomerate, and in 1871, the Calumet and Hecla companies were consolidated. These deposits, contrary to usual experience, carried down deep into Mother Earth, and the shaft of the Calumet and Hecla ultimately went down well over a mile.[9] By the '80's, however, other mines had come into production, and one of these, the Anaconda property in Montana, soon made Butte the most important copper camp in the world.

The first interests in Montana were, as usual, in placer gold deposits, but the barren steep hill, or butte, on which one of these early ventures was located, turned out to be a combination activity. Silver was first discovered in 1865—the news of the Comstock lode,

[9] It is interesting to note that it was at the Calumet and Hecla property in 1878 that the machine drill was extensively used in mining, a quarter century after the development of the rock drill in tunneling. Many of the Lake Superior miners were Cornishmen, men of an old hand-drilling tradition and notably adverse to the introduction of machine tools. Yet, as we have noted, mechanization in mining in more recent years has been well in the forefront of American industrial practice.

to be later noted, had spread northward—and a period of interest in silver followed. A peak was reached in silver production in 1887 overlapping an era of copper mining which had begun 5 years earlier. Butte had, thus, passed through the three stages—gold, silver, and copper—when the Anaconda Copper Mining Company was organized in 1895.

Butte is one of the great historic mining sites of the United States. Here the early battles of the "copper kings"—men like Marcus Daly, Senator William A. Clark, and the sharp F. Augustus Heinze— exercised an important influence on the development of mining geology, surveying, and mining law. The vein system of the hill at Butte was very intricate and was further confused by many faults, so that the older "apex" law of claims had little meaning. Heinze bought up various parts of claims and started predatory legal operations in the course of which geological and engineering experts frequently contradicted each other but, nevertheless, aided in clearing up a number of very difficult geological, legal, and engineering problems. Heinze secured, it is said, 10 million dollars and left Butte for New York where his attempts to corner United Copper shares started the mining Panic of 1907 and led to his downfall.

The building of smelters was a major problem in the rise of American copper mining. The plan followed at Butte was the ancient one of saving on fuel by utilizing the sulfur in the sulfide ores to produce what was known as copper matte. The ore, averaging 12 per cent copper in the early years, was concentrated mechanically, than smelted in roasting furnaces to a 64 per cent matte. Facilities were not available, however, for the further smelting and refinement of this matte. In fact, until 1892, when converters similar to the Bessemer device were added to the works, matte was shipped both to Baltimore and to the ancient copper center in Swansea in Britain for reduction.

Beginning before 1900 but not fully proved and put in operation until about the time of World War I, the flotation process later became basic in the concentration previous to smelting not only of copper but of lead and other ores. Successive improvements, conflicting patents, and other problems make it difficult to attribute the development of this notable mineral innovation to any single individual. In brief, the method is based on the fact that fine particles of ore adhere to bubbles of oil in an emulsion and may be floated off in the froth, while the lighter nonore particles sink to the bottom and are discarded. The importance of flotation does not seem to have been appreciated until about 1905, when it was realized that this process involved the reversal of all previous operations. Instead of granulating the ore and expecting the mineral particles, because of their greater weight, to sink, this new method relied on the floating and skimming off of finer particles. In 1914 experiments were started at Anaconda, and a large part of the earlier loss of mineral in the tailings was avoided. The Arizona copper interests, which had come to the front in the meantime, also took up the new method.

It is said that the first copper mining in Arizona was in 1854. Difficulties with the Mexicans and with the Apache Indians held up development, but by the '80's several ventures later to become famous were under way. The Copper Queen deposit was discovered in 1877 and, in 1885, was taken over by Phelps, Dodge and Company who pioneered in this area. In 1883 the United Verde Copper Company was organized to consolidate earlier interests and was later bought by Senator Clark of Butte fame. Miami copper operations began in 1906. These Arizona ventures marked a new era in copper mining. They were low-grade ores and methods had to be developed to handle them at a profit. Close to 5 million dollars were spent, for example, in securing and developing the Miami property into a dividend-paying mine. The large-scale capital ventures that such modern low-grade ore projects require and the risks in such operations are thus obvious.

Miami later became the scene of one of the most important developments in underground mining methods which had taken place in centuries. As the richer ore at Miami was taken out, it became necessary to find a low-cost method if the remaining low-grade ore, with only 1 per cent or less of copper and no precious metal values, was to be successfully mined. The basic method adopted was originated on a smaller scale in the Lake Superior iron mines. It involved undercutting huge vertical blocks of ore, 150 ft square to 150 by 300 ft in cross section, and permitting these huge masses of ore with their overburden to cave or settle down. Properly planned it was found that through this settling action the ore was crushed and broken into small pieces and could be taken out by drifts under the crushed mass. Production per man-shift, including all underground labor, had been 8 tons. The new method brought this up to the remarkable figure of 28 tons. Block caving was hailed in 1929 as "the best conceived and best executed achievement in large-scale underground mining to date."[10]

One of the most remarkable American copper mines, however, is that at Bingham Canyon, near Salt Lake City in Utah. For many years, until mining encouraged a spread of population over the Rockies, the Mormons (1847) at Salt Lake constituted an oasis of white settlement in the entire Rocky Mountain area. The deposit at Bingham Canyon was not discovered, however, until 1863, and earlier activities overlooked copper and were limited to a silver-lead ore and to gold. Copper operations began nearby in 1896, and in 1903 the Utah Copper Co. was organized as a consolidation of earlier interests. Here was a huge mass containing only 1 to 2 per cent copper, but, by open-cut mining in the huge pit at Bingham and using electrically operated shovels, more rock had been excavated by 1930 than was required in digging the Panama Canal and more was taken out in a single day during World War II than on the best day at Panama. Ore from Bingham is taken for smelting to the nearby great Magna mill near the lake at Garfield.

Finally it should be noted that there are so many other metals which combine with copper, it has so many "friends," while it is so important to its special qualities, to its behavior and use, that it be pure, that it has become the almost universal practice to refine the final copper ingots of the smelters by electrolytic means.

Recent changes in the copper situation reflect the wide number and difference in the effect of factors and influences which confront the metal industries. It seems impossible to generalize; each metal is affected by its own peculiar relationships of market, production, use, and demand. Thus, in 1944–1945 "grave concern was expressed by well-informed observers that, with the termination of hostilities, war stocks augmented by a flood of copper from war-stimulated mines throughout the world would engulf the domestic mining industry and result in stagnation such as followed World War I." American copper production, however, did not mount to extraordinary heights during the war because much of the normal copper market simply ceased to exist. Postwar production, as a matter of fact, turned out to be less than postwar demands. When the price ceiling of 12 cents was removed in 1946, prices rose to $19\frac{1}{2}$ cents, the highest since 1929, and, for the first time in history, aluminum, copper's competitor, was cheaper than this older metal. In part, this situation

[10] See paper by F. W. Maclennan, Manager of Miami, who received the medal of the American Institute of Mining and Metallurgical Engineers, *Trans. Am. Inst. Mining & Met. Engrs.*, 1929, p. 167.

Modern Open-cut Copper Mining, Bingham Canyon, Utah

A small section of this great open cut, a basin a mile and a half in diameter, from which 170,000 tons of ore and waste have been removed in a single day by means of huge electric shovels and hauled in 100-ton cars operating at several levels, or benches (100 miles total length). (*Courtesy Kennecott Copper Company.*)

was due to serious strikes in mines, smelters, and refineries which reduced current production. Demobilized workers also did not return to copper mining, while others apparently found other activities more attractive. In fact, American copper mines in recent years have produced little more new metal than has been recovered from old scrap. While consumption in 1946 set a new peacetime record, even production abroad was adversely affected by similar labor and other difficulties; in Chile, Northern Rhodesia, and Canada, strikes reduced output while lack of coal for smelting also affected Rhodesian mines and the Belgian Congo area. The United States produces about one-third of the world total, and the discovery in 1946 through drilling of a major new deposit—the first in a generation—near Tiger, Arizona, indicated that an adequate future supply of this metal was assured.

Aluminum. Although aluminum enters into some 8 per cent of the earth's crust and is, thus, the most abundant, useful metal (iron 5.5), this element was not isolated until 1824 and not commercially produced until over a half century later. It is distinctly a modern metal. While its German discoverer, Wöhler, produced the first globules of metallic aluminum in 1845, it was Sainte Claire Deville, a professor of the French École Normale, who developed in 1855 the reduction with sodium, and it became possible to produce bars by a process which, later improved by H. Y. Castner, reduced the cost to $4 or $5 a pound.

It was the electrolytic process, however, developed, after earlier workers had been discouraged, by Charles M. Hall of Oberlin, Ohio, in 1886, that made really low-cost aluminum possible. In a modification of this process, patented by Héroult in France and England in 1887, the ore is fused by electric arc, and it thus becomes clear that the cost of aluminum production is intimately tied up with that of electric power.

The total world's production of aluminum up to 1892 has been estimated at about $2\frac{1}{2}$ million lbs. In 1893 it jumped to $1\frac{1}{2}$ million lbs for the year, and there has since been a continued increase in production as the aircraft and automobile industries have developed and new uses for this metal, from kitchen utensils to furniture and even bridges, have been found. Aluminum is a new metal with special peculiarities and, both for this reason and because a market for it had to be created, aluminum producers also became aluminum manufacturers, turning their product into consumers' goods. Today this situation is changing, and an increasing tonnage is sold to other companies for manufacture.

By 1918 the United States was producing over 100,000 metric tons[11] of aluminum annually, over half the world output. After World War I the consumption and use of aluminum in the United States fluctuated from 40,000 to over 100,000 tons and dipped to a low of about 35,000 in the depression of 1932. Thereafter there was a steady climb to a wartime peak of 900,000 tons in 1943. By 1946 world output had dropped 40 per cent below this peak, but new uses were constantly being found for this metal. New alloys as well as new processes and methods of production—improved rolling of sections, increased use of high-accuracy forgings, and the development of improved extrusion methods—appeared to promise a future market well up in the hundred thousands of tons. The price of aluminum has declined steadily since 1925, and in 1946, for the first time in history, with the rise in the price of copper, aluminum became the cheaper metal.

Lead and Zinc. Lead may be regarded as having been a major metal in Ancient Times, when all metals were so costly that their use was avoided whenever possible. The Romans, for example, used lead quite extensively for water pipes. In the United States lead has been mined for many years, and small lead mines in the Northeastern states were operated before the Revolution. It was the extraordinary deposits of galena, or lead glance, a sulfide, in the upper Mississippi Valley which were of prime importance in the rise of American lead mining and smelting. The two major areas were near Dubuque, where the states of Illinois, Iowa, and Minnesota join, and in the district south of St. Louis in southeastern Missouri.

Early French explorers had encouraged the Indians in the Dubuque area to mine surface deposits of lead. Some recovery of the metal could be made by simply heating galena and, during the entire period of Indian mining from the late 17th century up to about 1820, smelting was accomplished by means of simple so-called log furnaces. After the purchase of Louisiana in 1807, a lead rush developed, between 1822 and 1825, and white workers ultimately displaced the Indians. In 1834 the improved Scotch hearth furnace was introduced and the industry continued until about 1845 when all the easily available surface deposits of this area had been exploited. In 1864 the St. Joseph Lead Co. was organized, and in 1867 the mining of the deeper southern deposits began.

This remarkable southeastern Missouri district still ranks first in

[11] In American practice, short tons of 2,000 lb are used in stating output. British usage favors the long ton of 2,200 lb to which the metric ton of 2204.62 lb is substantially equivalent.

the production of lead, and its mines produced 40 per cent of the total output in 1946. The tri-State or Joplin region, embracing southwestern Missouri, southeastern Kansas, and northeastern Oklahoma, ranks second with some 6 or 7 per cent, but scattered secondary operations in the Western states constitute the major production areas. In other words the major output of lead in the United States no longer comes from lead mines but, as in the case of gold, from mines in which the recovery of this metal is of secondary importance. The most important of these Western producers is Idaho, the Coeur d'Alene region is the major center, and the bulk of recovery has been from lead-zinc ores and old tailings. Nine mines produced half the United States total in 1946.

The consumption of lead for various purposes reveals the importance of this ancient metal in modern life. Almost a third of the output has gone into lead pigments such as white and red lead and litharge. Some 13 per cent, the next highest use, is employed in covering and protecting underground cables, a development of the present century largely brought about through the transfer to underground conduits of the old forests of telegraph, telephone, and power wires on poles which cluttered the streets of American cities in the early years of the century. Eleven per cent goes for storage batteries and 9 per cent for the tetraethyl lead in gasoline used for motor fuel— again, creations of the present century. Lead pipes and sheet lead, in past ages constituting the major market, account for but 10 per cent of the present total.

When we examine this total output, however, the critical shortage of lead in this country is clearly revealed. In 1920 the United States produced close to 50 per cent of the world output and in the period 1925–1929 averaged over 660,000 tons per year. During the '30's this dropped to about half these figures and slowly built up again during the prewar years to close to 500,000 tons. A further decline followed during the war and in 1946 there was a sharp drop back to the level of the '30's.

For the first time in history, secondary production exceeded that of primary lead mines, as we have noted. As a result, upon the removal of price controls in 1946, the price of lead, which had been held at about 6 cents a pound back in 1941, jumped to 12.5, the highest in the history of this metal.[12] These conditions, plus the fact that the world's production of this metal has also declined some 30 per cent in the past 20-odd years, seem to indicate that either new lead de-

[12] Substantially the same price had prevailed for a short period in 1917.

posits must be uncovered or substitute materials will sooner or later be developed to replace lead. The major possibility in this direction appears to be in the use of substitutes for paint and some plastic or combination material for cable covering.

Zinc production in the United States centers in a few scattered zinc mines in the east, notably at Franklin Furnace, New Jersey, and smaller mines in Tennessee and Virginia; a major area in the Joplin lead region and in scattered Western mines. About a quarter of the production comes from the Eastern states, another quarter from the tri-state (Joplin) region. In the Western group, supplying about half the total, Idaho leads, with, as in the case of lead, almost her entire output coming from the Coeur d'Alene region.

American production in comparison with world production has varied from a low of 22 per cent to a high of over 60 and built up during the war years to about half the world total of about $1\frac{1}{2}$ million tons. This has held quite steady at about this figure for a number of years and, while zinc uses have increased, the supply seems adequate to meet demands. This is reflected in the price for zinc which has held at about $8\frac{1}{4}$ to $8\frac{3}{4}$ cents per pound. Galvanizing claims the largest per centage, 40, of zinc production in the United States, with brass products second at about 20 per cent.

Tin. The United States produces no tin but smelts a large part of the world's concentrated ores, having led the world in this operation in the past few years. This is quite a recent war development and the Longhorn smelter in Texas, built in 1942, is probably the world's largest. The United States has also been the largest consumer of tin, taking from 40 to 60 per cent of world production. It may, therefore, be stated that, while we mine no tin, we smelt the tin we need and use. The bulk of this use, the surprising total of over 28,000 tons, or about half America's needs, goes today into the making of tin plate while solder claims another 25 per cent. Bronze and babbitt account for another 15 per cent.

The main supplies of tin ore come from Bolivia, British Malaya, the Netherlands Indies, Nigeria, and Siam, with smaller amounts from Burma and Australia. Production has declined to almost half that of the 1925–1929 average and dropped even more violently during the war years from the high of 1940–1941 of over 240,000 long tons. In other words the world in general is producing today about half the tin it could use. Tin is, thus, one of the scarcest of the common metals.

Space will not permit a review of other metals or of the many vitally important nonmetal minerals such as asbestos, cement, the clays, gypsum, phosphate rock, sand, gravel, slate, and stone. Neither will it permit more than passing note of sulfur, which is now mined by one of the most interesting methods and handled as a bulk product. Sulfur domes, in the Gulf area, are reached by drilling. Steam is pumped down to the deposit melting the sulfur, which is pumped up as a liquid, solidifies in huge masses as large as a city block, is loosened by well drills and blasting, and is loaded with power shovels.

Even this brief outline indicates, however, that the era of surface or near-surface discoveries, of relatively easily reached high-grade ores, in the United States has passed or is passing. There have been few new discoveries of major ore bodies since the earlier years of the present century. Since the war also, our mineral industries have been handicapped not only by strikes but by the fact that in many cases former mine workers, upon release from military service, have turned to other employment. The mineral profession has accomplished wonders in maintaining prices in the face of rising labor costs and increasing difficulties of recovery, but a trend toward higher prices seems inevitable. As prices increase, the pressure for new discoveries and the possibilities of mining deeper and lower grade ores will increase. Improved techniques of exploration, similar to those developed in the petroleum industry, more efficient techniques of ore concentration at the mine to reduce transportation costs, the search for more economical methods of underground mining and for solutions to the problems of deep mining—ventilation, structural, and other—these appear to be the major problems which the profession must face in future years.

We now turn to the fascinating story of a quite useless metal that has, however, played a major role in human hopes and aspirations, gold, and to its sister and industrially more important metal, silver.

Gold and Silver. It has been remarked that gold is a metal which, throughout human history, has had a peculiar fascination and power in stirring the imagination of mankind. In all probability it was the first metal known to man. It is chemically inert and, therefore, is not only usually found in nature in the metallic state, "native" gold, but also retains its sheen and color—is easily seen and recognized. For over fifty years of recent history, until the abandonment of the gold standard in 1933, the production of this ancient metal, which has little practical, useful value, exercised a dominating influence in the monetary affairs and relationships of the Western World.

We have noted in earlier chapters the ancient workings in the Spanish peninsula and other areas taken over by the Romans, the influx of Central and South American gold into Spain following the discoveries of Columbus, which stimulated the initiation of a modern era of mining in Saxony and led to the publication of Agricola's great book, *De re metallica,* in 1556. In the Western Hemisphere the Spaniards robbed the Aztecs and Incas of the slowly accumulated hordes of gold they had won by patiently separating the precious metal from the sands of alluvial rivers, but the Spanish conquerors were disappointed in not finding large and rich "diggings." In fact, this experience reflects two of the characteristics of earlier gold discoveries: they have almost invariably been in "placer" or river deposits, have been limited in extent and, therefore, soon worked out.

Gold has also been closely associated with silver, and in many cases it has been silver rather than gold that has been the predominating source of income. Thus in Peru the treasure hunts of earlier days came to an end about 1540, but 5 years later the discovery of the Potosi silver deposits created a silver rush as did the rich Mexican discoveries of 1546–1558. It was in Brazil, however, where there had been practically no earlier mining, that, during the 17th and early 18th centuries, a really modern gold rush occurred. From that time to the present day there has been a succession of rushes as European man in particular has searched the remote and waste areas of the earth for this widely distributed metal.

The Russian conquest of Siberia in the late 16th century was not immediately followed by a development which disclosed gold workings. Siberian gold became of importance when, about 1750 and even later, in 1839 and '40, rich placers were discovered as a result of exploration in the Yenisei basin.

Primarily, therefore, it was the Brazilian operations which, it has been estimated, raised the annual production of gold to about $17\frac{1}{2}$ million dollars between 1740 and 1760. As these deposits were exhausted, production declined and, by 1810–1820, was less than half this amount. The Siberian placers then entered as a factor in an increase to an annual average of some $37\frac{1}{2}$ million in 1841–1850. Finally, in 1849, gold was discovered in California while Australia followed in 1851 and production jumped to $182\frac{1}{2}$ million dollars by 1852. But, by 1862, the output had again dropped and remained relatively stationary at about 105 millions until 1888. In the '90's two events—the discovery of the Rand mines of South Africa and the development of the cyanide process—increased production to over 315 millions by 1899.

It is interesting to follow the pattern disclosed in the successive new workings of the Western United States, of gold rush succeeding gold rush as new areas have been discovered. It is notable that they have almost invariably been the result of the discovery of especially rich placer deposits in areas where gold had previously been found. To work such diggings all that was required was a pick and shovel, a wooden "cradle" in which the deposit was agitated and "washed," and the heavier gold settles to the bottom of the trough. Further concentration by "panning" in a circular conical pan with a recovery of the finest dust through amalgamation with mercury followed.

But these richer deposits were soon worked out leaving only the less productive alluvial areas which could not be profitably worked by hand. "Hydraulicking," the use of a jet from a nozzle as a means of excavating and washing down the gold-bearing deposits, early came into use. Later hydraulic dredges were employed. One of these monsters takes in material at its head, processes it, extracts its small gold content, and discharges the tailings as it moves forward, carrying with it the lake or pond on which it floats and operates.

Such later operations required planning and capital beyond the capacity of the early placer workers. Furthermore, in following up placer deposits, the veins of ore from which the alluvial deposits had been eroded frequently came to light. Here again machinery and thus capital were essential to further operations. As the original manual workers moved out, the rush thus left behind the beginnings of a far less spectacular industry. Stock companies, machinery, and engineering succeeded to the task abandoned by the hand workers.

Yet some of these rush discoveries have been unbelievably rich. The great nugget, a solid lump of native gold, found at Ballarat in Australia in 1853, weighed over 132 lb. The famous Comstock Lode high in the mountains of western Nevada was discovered in 1859, after earlier placer operations in the Lower California valleys had been worked out. The Ophir Company which acquired the claims of Comstock and his partners (the real discoverers) made an early shipment of 38 tons of ore to San Francisco where it yielded $112,000 in gold and silver.[13] Even after 1900, when the days of gold rushes seemed to be over, "Lazy Jim" Butler, a "burro" prospector in south-

[13] This was the famous Washoe rush that resulted in the boom days of Virginia City where Mark Twain's early years as a newspaperman were passed. "Gold and silver were stacked up on the monte tables; dice rattled and cards were shuffled all day and all night. The ragged, greasy, dirt-covered multitude filled the saloons with loud talk and laughter, except when a pistol shot rang out sharply and the crowd swayed into the street." *The Story of the Mine as Illustrated by the Great Comstock Lode of Nevada* by C. H. Shinn, New York, Appleton-Century Crofts, Inc., 1896, p. 64.

ern Nevada, found rich ore near Tonopah. Goldfield followed in 1902, Rhyolite in 1904, and Rawhide in 1906. It is said that 48 tons of ore from this district brought $575,000. In fact, the miners are reported as having "high-graded" (*i.e.*, stolen lumps of especially rich, high-grade ore) to the extent of $1,000 per day. Twenty-mule teams dragged supplies into the Nevada Hills, cities grew overnight, but, 10 years later, the mines had "run out" and only ghost towns remained.

Klondike gold belongs to this same era. Gold had been mined in Alaska for years, but the first great discovery was in 1896 and the rush began the following year. Again, however, the rush was soon over and Alaska settled down to a more steady production as modern machinery and methods supplanted the lone prospector with his shovel and pan.

These early Western rush experiences were notably lacking in any semblance of rules and order. Local groups, "vigilantes" and others, set their own standards as to size of claims, etc. From these later developed our present-day American mining laws.[14] Among the many rushes of the Rocky Mountain area the Comstock of 1859 appears to have most clearly exemplified this change from rush to industry, from hands to machinery, from luck to engineering planning, from individual holdings to stock-company operations.[15]

Although interest in the Comstock area began with a placer gold rush in 1859, the real story is that of the silver rush which followed and which was again given new life by the discovery of the "Big Bonanza" in 1873. Prior to the experience at the Comstock in the '60's, Americans had no contact with the problems of silver mining and the reduction of silver ores. American practice of silver smelting was thus born at Comstock. Similarly these operations constituted a milestone in the mechanization of mining operations. For the first time, Americans encountered the problems of deep mining—of high temperatures, running up to 130° to 150°F, of water and ventilation in shafts which went down 3,500 ft below the outcrop.[16] Furthermore,

[14] See *History of Public Land Policies* by B. H. Hibbard, New York, The Macmillan Company, 1924.

[15] Some of the other notable American rushes: Fraser River (1858) and Caribou (1862) in British Columbia; Clear Creek and Pike's Peak (1859) which really created the city of Denver; Leadville (1876), a silver rush; Cripple Creek (1892); Boise, Idaho (1860); followed by the later Bunker Hill operations, Bannack (1862) and other Montana areas; and Deadwood in the Black Hills of South Dakota (1875) with the later famous Homestake Mine.

[16] Deep mining ceased in 1886. Some twenty-five years later, Rickard visited

speculation in Comstock stock, in the Consolidated Virginia and other ventures, had led to the establishment of the San Francisco Stock Exchange in 1862 where fluctuations in these shares and other stocks made later Wall Street operations seem rather subdued and tame. It is also interesting to note that, although the Comstock output was about equally divided between gold and silver, the exaggerated stories of this flood of silver caused the price to drop and undoubtedly led to the demonetization of that metal abroad.[17]

These various gold rushes, plus gold production as part of other ventures, maintained but did not increase the gold output after the Civil War until, in the '90's, it seemed, at least in the United States, that the production of gold had come to a standstill. Inasmuch as the gold standard limited the money in circulation, it was argued that the return to a bimetallic standard with silver in the ratio of 16 to 1 was desirable. Bryan's bid for the Presidency in 1896 and his famous Cross of Gold speech emphasized this difficulty and, according to Mark Sullivan, it was the great increase in gold production stemming from South African discoveries plus the introduction of the cyanide process that took the wind out of Bryan's sails.

There had been earlier discoveries of gold in South Africa but, as Morrell puts it: "No gold rush was destined to occur until practically all the phenomena of an alluvial gold rush had been produced by the discovery of diamonds." The first diamond was found in 1867 and Australian miners began washing for diamonds on the Vaal River in 1869. Rich discoveries followed in 1871 and the Kimberley rush was under way. After numerous political and other difficulties, diamond mining became a large-scale industry and, by 1888, the major interests had been brought together in the De Beers Consolidated Mines, Ltd., controlled by Cecil Rhodes, Barney Barnato, and Alfred Beit. It developed working and marketing standards and

---

Virginia City and remarked: "One was taken into enormous shaft-houses dilapidated by the heavy hand of time, and one was shown huge engines of antiquated design, only to feel the ponderous silence of abandonment. It was interesting, however, to note how modern winding engines had been evolved from the clumsy and complicated patterns of a former day. The Comstock was a great school of mechanical design." See *History of American Mining*, p. 112. The famous Sutro tunnel, or adit, about 4 miles long, was excavated in 1869–1877 at a cost of over 2 million dollars for drainage but too late to have any practical value. Butte, as we have noted, became an equally important school in other areas of mining—geology, surveying, and mining law.

[17] Germany adopted the gold standard in 1871 and ceased the minting of silver. The United States followed in 1873. In 1874 the Scandinavian countries took similar action, Holland in 1875, and France and Spain in 1876.

the system of compounds to which native laborers and their families are confined during their periods of work.

Those who failed in the diamond diggings were forced out into other ventures and, in this way, new scattered gold areas were discovered during the '70's, largely by Australian diggers. No single worker discovered the great Rand area, but in 1885 the brothers Struben disclosed their belief that there was gold of wide extent and depth in the huge "banket," or conglomerate formation, of the Rand. Here, at long last, was a great deposit of still uncertain geological history, which would not be worked out in a few years. The gold rush to the Rand, moreover, was dominated by men who had already made their fortunes and could afford the large investments and could secure the consulting services of American mining experts, such as John Hays Hammond (1855–1936), which were needed to develop the best means of using native labor in handling the low-grade ores and deep workings of the area. The Anglo-Boer War of 1899–1902 resulted in a temporary setback, but the Witwatersrand in the Johannesburg area constitutes today the greatest mining center in the world. To be sure the gold rushes of our West spread American civilization all over the Rocky Mountain area, similar rushes in Australia had a profound effect in spreading her earlier pastoral society, while South Africa still faces the problem of reconciling on a reasonably democratic basis the differences between white men, British and Boer, the native blacks, and the imported Indians and Chinese. The Rand has perpetuated a caste system and has not aided in solving one of the world's major problems of democratic ideals, methods, and principles.

To return to the cyanide process, this process had been experimented with on a small scale for years before the work of J. S. MacArthur and R. W. and W. Forrest, three Scotch engineers, between 1887 and 1891, resulted in its widespread adoption. Cyanide is a gold solvent, and by its use very small quantities of gold which could not be profitably separated by older mechanical and amalgamation methods became recoverable. In fact, the first demonstration of the process was in the treatment of the "tailings" of the Robinson mine in South Africa where, on an investment of £3,000, a profit of £2,000 per month was made in the recovery of the gold discarded in earlier operations.

At the present time, therefore, gold production seems to have settled down to a widespread industry in which low-grade ores are handled by various methods, in fact, where substantial quantities of gold are produced not by gold properties but through the recovery of the small "by-product" gold values so widely prevalent in base ores such as copper. Thus, during the war the leading gold producer in the United States was the great copper mine at Bingham Canyon with its gold recovery of a few cents per ton. By 1946, however, base ores accounted for only 23, placers 38, and dry ores 39 per cent of American production. But it was a declining production. The peak of American gold output occurred in 1915 and was valued at over 100 million dollars. Silver reached a top of over 70 million ounces in 1923. By 1929 these had dropped to 44 million dollars and 61 million ounces, respectively. World War II adversely affected the mining of all but essential metals. Gold production fell to the lowest figure since 1885 and silver, except for 1932, was at the lowest since 1872.

Postwar recovery has been slow. High prices of equipment, high wages, and the difficulties of attracting efficient labor prolonged strikes in base-metal mines (as above noted, a major source of by-product gold production and of gold output during war years), plus deterioration in plant and workings necessitating larger capital outlays, government price regulations restricting free markets—all these contributed to this situation.

Nevertheless deep drilling disclosed new deposits in 1946 in the Rand, predictions of an extended life of this remarkable area were made, and gold production outside the United States increased slightly. South Africa and Russia appear to be most favorably placed to lead in future developments.

Finally, mention must be made of the truly spectacular mining developments of our northern neighbor, Canada. Most of them have been of 20th century origin. They have involved battles of great hardship and daring in vast areas of hills and forests, of lakes and swamps almost impossible of access, filled with flies in summer and bleak with cold in winter. Gold again has been the first lure with some remarkable strikes, but Canada, using in some cases airplanes to fly in prospectors, supplies, and even equipment, has also discovered vast deposits of nickel, zinc, and lead, while her asbestos mines have long been world famous. It is to Canada in particular that North America looks for the new properties which will extend many of our limited mineral horizons.

These have been the major steps by which an ancient practical art has evolved into a modern engineering science. The mineral profession faces today problems on the successful solution of which much of our future material welfare depends. In general it may be said that our known and commercially available metal resources are declining. In the future man must seek more deeply hidden ores and develop them at greater cost if he is to provide the metal needs of modern life.

THE CHEMICAL INDUSTRIES

As we shall have occasion to note later, the American chemical industry, now one of, if not the, most dynamic and progressive American industries, was to a major degree a World War I baby. Many chemical operations are, of course, of very ancient origin, but the modern chemical industry may be said to have started with the development of the Leblanc process in France about the time of the American Revolution; leadership then passed to Britain where the initial coal-tar discoveries were made, and thence it was allowed to slip into the hands of the Germans who, by the time of World War I, were the world leaders of the industry and produced many of the essential chemicals, drugs, and dyes which had become so important in recent years. It was our discovery during World War I of the unpleasant fact that we had relied on Germany for these essential needs of modern life that gave a new start to this industry in the United States.

The Leblanc Process. The Leblanc process goes back to 1775 when France was more or less blockaded from the rest of the world and French industry, dependent on imported supplies, was hard put to secure the soda needed in making soap and glass, for cleaning, cooking, and many other purposes. The French Academy of Sciences offered a prize of 12,000 livres for the best method of converting common salt into soda—a prize which was never awarded but a problem which had been successfully solved by 1787. Nicolas Leblanc (1742–1806), with the assistance of the Duke of Orleans, to whom he acted as physician, erected a small factory at St. Denis near Paris and produced 5 to 600 lbs of soda a day. The story of the rise and decline of this famous process reveals very clearly some of the major factors which affect the work of the chemical engineer.

The Leblanc process was carried out in three stages: First, common salt was treated with sulfuric acid, yielding salt cake (sodium sulfate) and hydrochloric acid. The cake was then melted with coke and limestone yielding "black ash," a mixture of sodium carbonate (*i.e.*, soda) and calcium sulfide. Finally the soda was dissolved out with water and concentrated through evaporation. As the late Professor Leo H. Baekeland, inventor of Velox photographic paper and of the pioneer plastic, Bakelite, remarked:

This famous process was the forerunner of the chemical industry; for almost a century it dominated the enormous group of industries of heavy chemicals, so expressively called by the French: "La Grande Industrie Chimique," and now (1914) we are witnesses of the lingering death agonies of this chemical colossus. Through the Leblanc process, large fortunes have been made and lost; but, even after its death, it will leave a treasure of information to science and chemical engineering, the value of which can hardly be over estimated.

What were the reasons for the death of this process, which "in its heroic struggle for existence had drawn upon every conceivable resource of ingenuity furnished by the most learned chemists and the most skillful engineers"? "There is no better example," says Professor Baekeland, "of the far-reaching effect of seemingly secondary conditions upon the success of a chemical process." It was superseded by the Solvay, or ammonia-salt process; but let us hear the story as Professor Baekeland tells it.

Strange to say, its competitor, the Solvay process, entered the arena after a succession of failures. When Ernest Solvay (1838–1922), who became the "Carnegie of Belgium," as a young man, took up this process, he was himself totally ignorant of the fact that no less than about a dozen able chemists had invented and reinvented the very reaction on which he had pinned his faith; that, furthermore, some had tried it on a commercial scale and had in every instance encountered failure. At that time, all this must undoubtedly have been to young Solvay a revelation sufficient to dishearten almost anybody. But he had one predominant thought to which he clung as a last hope of success and which would probably have escaped most chemists. He reasoned that in his process, he started from two watery solutions, which when brought together precipitated a dry product, bicarbonate of soda. On the other hand, in the Leblanc process, the raw materials must be melted together, with the use of expensive fuel, after which the mass is dissolved in water, losing all these valuable heat units, while more heat has again to be applied to evaporate to dryness. . . . Another tremendous handicap of the Leblanc process is the fact that hydrochloric acid is one of its by-products. Profitable use for this acid, as such, can be found only to a limited extent . . . furthermore, in its commercial form it is an aqueous solution containing only one-third real acid so that the transportation of one ton of acid involves the extra cost of freight for about two tons of water.

For many years an outlet was found for some of this acid by converting it into a dry product, namely, chloride of lime or bleaching powder. This market was limited, however, and the establishment of the electrolytic alkali processes in 1900 at Niagara Falls made the manufacture of caustic soda and chlorine primarily a matter of cheap electric power. In the heavy chemical industries, the cost of basic materials—they must be plentiful and inexpensive—and of the fuel or power used in the process rather than labor costs—as in construction or manufacturing—is controlling. Needless to say, the value or lack of value of by-products is also a determining cost factor. These were the defects of the Leblanc process that led to the downfall of this "chemical colossus," and it was the struggle to remedy them that made this process such a stimulating influence in the development of modern chemical engineering.

Sulfuric Acid. In his *Introduction to Industrial Chemistry,* Dr. Levy writes:

Sulphuric acid is beyond doubt technically the most important substance produced by the chemical industry. Its manufacture was undertaken on a large scale originally as a stage in the preparation of washing soda, hydrated sodium carbonate, by the famous Leblanc process. Partly, perhaps, owing to this early manufacture, but more especially by virtue of its valuable properties and ease and cheapness of production, it became the accepted acid to be employed wherever possible as chemical industry expanded.

The uses of sulfuric acid are too numerous even to enumerate, but two major markets are in the manufacture of explosives and fertilizers. The history of the manufacture of sulfuric acid reveals changes in the basic materials employed, a steady evolution in the long-established "chamber process" and a more recent trend toward "contact processes."

In early days the raw material used was sulfur, or brimstone, the bulk of which came from volcanic deposits in Sicily. A monopoly was created in 1835, prices were raised, and this encouraged the further development of a process, based on the use of copper pyrites, which had been tried experimentally in France a few years earlier, in 1830. While pyrites is still widely used abroad and while sulfur is recovered in American copper smelting, there has been a trend toward the use of mined sulfur in the United States because of the remarkable recovery methods, already noted, by which the deep deposits of the Gulf area have been brought to the surface.

The modern manufacture of sulfuric acid may be said to have begun with the work of Ward at Richmond, England, where, in 1740, he began manufacture, using glass vessels of large size—60 gals. The famous Dr. Roebuck, who had aided Watt in the early days of the steam engine, introduced lead chambers in lieu of Ward's glass vessels and, by the late 18th century, these chambers had exceeded 1,400 cu ft in capacity.

In the earlier days the operation was intermittent. Sulfur and saltpeter were ignited and the chamber closed. When the sulfur had burned to form SO_2, it was then converted to the trioxide, SO_3, and this was united with water (H_2O) to produce the acid, H_2SO_4. The first change occurred early in the 19th century when steam came into use in French plants and the process was made continuous. In 1827 the Gay-Lussac tower was developed to recover the nitrous gases, and in 1860 the Glover tower further perfected the process.

Sulfuric acid is required in industry in various degrees of concentration. In dye making, in particular, a "fuming acid" is used. This need led to the rise about 1875 of the contact method of manufacture. This was a German development by the Badische Anilin und Soda Fabrik, and was finally revealed in 1901. The so-called Grillo converter is used in burning and converting the sulfur charge, and this method, producing fuming acid and being less expensive than the chamber process, is now widely used.

Coal-tar Products. The fact that this development was German in origin brings to mind one of the most interesting chapters in the history of chemical engineering—the story of a new and remarkable field of chemical development, which, beginning in Britain, was neglected or ignored but, taken over by Germany, became the foundation of her later chemical greatness.

One of the most useless and annoying stepchildren of the coal-gas industry was the coal tar, which, in addition to the gas, was volatilized in the process of gas manufacture. Getting rid of this troublesome and, apparently, useless by-product became a major problem. In 1845 a German chemist and pupil of Liebig, August Wilhelm von Hofmann (1818–1892), whose work in agricultural chemistry had attracted attention, was called to the newly founded Royal College of Chemistry in London. In 1843 Hofmann found the basic compound aniline in coal tar and, in 1845, the discovery of benzene in this tar made it possible to prepare aniline and similar bases in larger quantities. Finally in 1856, one of Hofmann's students, William Perkin (1838–1907) prepared a coal-tar dye which he called mauve. Against Hofmann's advice he withdrew from college and began its manufacture on a commercial scale. The aniline dye industry was, thus, born in Britain. Other dye discoveries followed. Fuchsin appeared in 1859 and another pupil of Hofmann made (1858–1866) the studies which led to the important series of combinations known as the Azo dyes.

Hofmann, however, returned to Germany in 1864. The importance of these discoveries was not clearly realized in Britain, research languished, and the most important discovery to date—that alizarin, the coloring principle of the madder plant, was a derivative of anthracene and could thus be prepared from coal tar—was made by German workers in 1867. This ended the cultivation of the madder plant—a major French activity—and other dye discoveries followed, notably that of indigo from naphthaline in 1894. The magic of coal tar, however, does not stop with dyes but goes on into numerous important products including drugs, perfumes, explosives, and almost countless other valuable compounds derived from what was, at one time, a useless and annoying by-product.

Nitrogen and the Fertilizers. Chemistry occupies such an important place in our lives that we frequently find exaggerated statements which claim all branches of human activity as fundamentally chemical. Thus, it is said that agriculture is simply a very important branch of chemical industry. When we remember that it is a photochemical reaction which causes the carbon dioxide of the air to be assimilated by the chlorophyll of plants and that continuous farming without replacing the chemicals taken from the soil in plant growth leads to soil impoverishment and abandoned farms, we can see that there are basic chemical problems involved which at least give some color to this claim.

In Europe it has been necessary for many years to restore to the long-worked soil the necessary nitrogen and other fertilizers. American farming has moved westward to new areas as older Eastern lands became less productive through continued cropping. An end, however, has already come to this continued robbing of the soil, and the Central states are now heavy purchasers of fertilizers.

Chemically, the difficulty is primarily due to our taking nitrogen from the soil much faster than it is supplied through natural agencies. Enriching the land with manure or other fertilizers is insufficient—more nitrogen is required.

For a time the island guano deposits of Peru, the richest of which, in places 120 ft deep, were on the Chincha Islands, sufficed. In a few years, however, these were exhausted and the older deposits of the mainlands of Peru and Chile, discovered in 1809, were developed. These deposits, in the form of impure sodium nitrate and other salts, came into use during the last quarter of the 19th century.

Considerable disagreement arose, however, as to how long the Chile supply would last. During the World War I, Germany was, moreover, forced to turn to other sources for this chemical which is essential not only in agriculture but in the manufacture of modern explosives, for example, nitroglycerin and nitrocellulose (gun cotton). It is also required in treating carbolic acid to form picric acid, the base for the various national "secret formula" explosives, such as the British lyddite, French melinite, and Japanese ohimose. Again it is necessary in preparing the famous trinitrotoluene (TNT), the last and most effective of the three main groups of explosives. Isolated from the rest of the world, Germany had to secure her nitrogen supply for both fertilizers and explosives from home sources. The fixation of atmospheric nitrogen had been successfully accomplished before the war, and this was the source from which Germany met her war needs. Thus World War I, which had such a marked influence on technological progress, may be said also to have brought the nitrogen problem to a head.

It was Sir William Crookes who in 1898 turned attention to the possibilities of nitrogen starvation, with the exhaustion of the Chile beds, and the need of developing other supplies. The experiment on which the fixation of atmospheric nitrogen is based, however, dates back to the work of Priestley and Cavendish in 1785. The first application was by Bradley and Lovejoy at Niagara Falls in 1902, and the first successful commercial plants were those of the Birkeland-Eyde process installed in Norway.

Several processes have been used. Most of these are dependent upon cheap electric power, for the basic method consists in forcing, by the use of the electric arc, the inert nitrogen of the air to combine with oxygen. In the Birkeland–Eyde furnace a series of arcs are spread out by electric magnets into a flaming disk 7 ft in diameter. In the Pauling furnace two curved tubes cooled with water form the arc. So far the best production has been a few ounces of nitric acid per kilowatt-hour of current consumed. Norway, with cheap electric power, leads the world in this development. Germany just before the war, however, gave up her interests in plants of this type and turned to the Haber process, which requires about one-eighth the electric power and was preferable because Germany has little water power. In this process nitrogen is combined with hydrogen, using uranium as a catalyst, to form ammonia. Ammonia is useful as such or may be converted into nitric acid.

This was apparently a carefully thought out move on the part of

Germany to prepare for World War I. She had been the largest buyer of Chile saltpeter and had large stores on hand when war began. Nevertheless, the Haber process for ammonia and the Ostwald process for converting ammonia to nitric acid solved the German fertilizer and explosive problem, and the world is now turning to the fixation of atmospheric nitrogen as a means of meeting her agricultural difficulties.

A Modern Chemical Plant

Among the largest of modern chemical plants those developed in response to the tremendous growth of the petroleum industry are especially notable. In major part "outdoor" plants (a modern trend also followed in certain water power as well as other chemical and industrial designs), this oil-refining unit, built in the Texas area, is typical of modern construction. (*Courtesy of The Lummus Company, New York, Designers and Builders.*)

The nitrates, however, are but one element of plant food. In old days wood ashes furnished the required potash and dung some nitrate and phosphate. Germany had, and still has in her famous Stassfurt mines, a natural monopoly of potash similar to the Chile nitrate supply. There are some potash sources in the United States, but as yet the cost of preparation is too high to compete with the German product.

On the other hand the phosphate beds of Florida, bone deposits of prehistoric animals, have been one of the principal sources of the world's phosphate supply. The Florida deposits were discovered in 1888, and other deposits in the South and West assure a long-life supply. Treated with sulfuric acid, the product, the more soluble "superphosphate," is widely used at home and abroad. Germany, however, lacking this source, turned to the use of the ground lining from Bessemer converters, used in removing the phosphorus from high-phosphorus iron in the steel process. Several other products are also available.

Food Products. There is no field in which more notable chemical advances have been made than in foods, and at the same time no field which has aroused more discussion and protest. Since the earliest days, some men have shown a stronger love for money than for ethics and have adulterated foods or sold substitutes. Legislation thus became essential to public health. In the United States, indeed, legislation and taxation both have been employed, not only to protect the public but almost to prohibit the use of many useful modern chemical food products. On the other hand, such use has been encouraged abroad. The American manufacturer has also had to combat the prejudice against "artificial foods," of a public aroused against such products by memories of earlier outrages and by constant propaganda fathered by other food interests.

"Pure white sugar is the first and greatest contribution of chemistry to the world's dietary." Ever since the early days when crude "sukkar" was carried to Europe from India, the process for extracting, refining, and cleaning the juice of the sugar cane, although largely a chemical matter, has been looked upon by the public as a normal manufacturing activity. On the contrary, the great modern competitor of cane sugar, the beet-sugar industry, is distinctly a chemical problem.

It was in 1747 that a Berlin chemist, Marggraf, discovered that it was possible to extract sugar from beets. Napoleon, offering a prize of a million francs, encouraged the development of a process which was to make the northern countries independent of imports from the tropics, the home of the sugar cane. In Europe the beet-sugar industry, with Germany in the lead, grew to such proportions that by 1913 it equaled the total cane production of the world at 9 million tons. By 1917, because France and England were no longer able to secure German beet sugar, the New World production of cane was greatly increased, and Cuba and other cane areas have suffered from waves of overproduction of this important food.

The sugar field thus became a battleground between the cane and the beet interests. Beet growers have profited greatly by chemical advice in improving the sugar content of their crop, and, while the United States, the greatest sugar-consuming nation in the world, is still supplied largely with cane sugar, the sugar-beet industry is by no means neglected.

Perhaps the most interesting chemical food developments, however, are those in two typically American crops: corn and cotton.

Corn, like potatoes a New World plant, has never been widely accepted abroad. In the United States, nevertheless, it is a most important crop, and notable advances have been made in breaking it up into various useful products. The germ of the corn kernel furnishes primarily corn oil. The body supplies a wide variety of very useful products varying from cornstarch through a long list of such important materials as dextrose, glucose, corn sirup, and the dextrins, to the glutens. Glucose is now widely used in making candy, Karo corn sirup is well known as also is Mazola, a corn oil substitute for olive oil. Fermentation and other processes have increased the field of usefulness of corn products.

The seeds of cotton, the largest part by weight of the cotton crop and formerly a waste product, have also been made to yield many useful products by the chemical engineer. The hulls have been used for feed, fertilizer, and other purposes. The meats yield about 20 per cent of cottonseed oil, the most valuable of the seed products. Various grades of oil are refined and treated to secure a long list of vegetable oils and fats used in making all sorts of products from cooking oils, lards, oleomargarine, and soap to roofing tar, linoleum, and oilcloth. Even the short fibers adhering to the hull, the linters, have been recovered and are used for padding and other purposes where a short fiber is satisfactory.

One of the basic operations involved in these corn and cotton operations, as well as in the preparation of other similar products, is the hydrogenation of the oils to transform them into fats. A French chemist, Sabatier, was the first to show how hydrogen could be added to the "soft fats" or oils to transform them into the "hard fats," but, as usual, Germany was the pioneer in applying this discovery on a commercial scale. Cocoanut oil made from copra, the dried meat of the cocoanut, and peanut oil have also been made to yield most valuable vegetable fats. It was a French chemist, Mége-Mouries, who won the prize offered by the French government in 1869 for a butter substitute for army use, with the discovery of the basic operation in securing from beef fat the famous product oleomargarine. Margarine has long been legislated against by dairy interests in the United States, but abroad it is widely used and is now made primarily from vegetable fats.

Rubber, Celluloid, and the Plastics. The discovery of some of the practical uses of the gum of the caoutchouc tree was a South American contribution to progress in the utilization of nature's resources. Priestley, the famous British-American chemist, was the first to name it India rubber from the fact that it would erase pencil marks. In 1825 Mackintosh used the sticky material to cement two layers of cloth together and thus gave his name to a type of garment still used.

The story of the efforts of the Yankee inventor, Charles Goodyear, and his final solution of the problem of vulcanizing rubber has been frequently told. Pneumatic tires for vehicles were invented by Robert William Thompson of London in 1846. The auto tire industry in particular and the American demand for rubber made the United States the greatest rubber consumer in the world. The United States, however, has grown no rubber although American companies have established rubber plantations in tropical countries. Thus the hitherto limited supply and the increasing demand for this valuable gum turned attention, even before the World War, to the problem of providing a satisfactory substitute.

Synthetic rubber became an important product during World War II. Its development opened up a new and most promising chapter in the history of materials. In the past, chemists and chemical engineers had found new uses for old chemicals or had made new chemicals to meet new needs. With the rise of the synthetic rubber industry, they began to turn to the task of changing the molecular structure of chemical atoms to produce new products unknown to Nature and not created through normal established chemical reactions.

There has also been most noteworthy progress in the preparation of synthetic plastic materials which compete to a large extent with hard rubber and have other important uses. John Wesley Hyatt, an American inventor, beginning in 1863 with collodion, a solution of gun cotton in ether and alcohol, worked out, on hints from British chemists, the important product celluloid and set up a factory in Newark in 1872. This was only one of a great number of similar products marketed under various trade names, among which Xylonite and Pyralin are probably the best known.

Again in 1872, Professor Adolf von Baeyer discovered that a synthetic resin could be made by combining the ill-smelling formaldehyde gas with carbolic acid, or phenol. Professor L. H. Baekeland of Columbia, after inventing Velox photographic paper, turned his attention to the condensation products of phenol and in 1909 produced the now well-known Bakelite. This has many advantages which the earlier materials did not possess and has, like celluloid, been followed by a host of similar and useful products made from phenol or other coal-tar bases and from vegetable materials.

Rubber, of course, is only one of the natural gums—shellac, rosin, asphalt, and many other such materials also occupy important places in industrial life. The preparation of these gums, particularly their combination with inert materials to form valuable and less costly products, of course furnishes important problems for the chemical engineer. Yet it seems probable that, before many years have passed, the natural gums, as in the case of the natural dyes, will have been completely replaced by chemical industry with cheaper synthetic products possessing similar or even more valuable properties. And, on top of all this, there has been the rapid growth of the synthetic fibers. Owing to war conditions, the supply of silk from the Orient was cut off, and this gave impetus to the use of rayon and nylon as substitutes, with the result that one of the oldest of Nature's products and industries, probably doomed in due course to decline and decay, has been almost eliminated overnight. First Nature's dyes, then her gums, and now her fibers have been becoming obsolete. The chemical engineer is, thus, constantly working not only himself but others out of important industries by developing new and better methods of meeting vital needs.

Paper. The materials for writing and records have played an important part in the history of Western civilization. Papyrus was the principal material available from ancient Egyptian times until the 2d century A.D. Parchment or vellum, prepared from animal skins, then entered into competition with papyrus and became more important as the supply of the papyrus plant was reduced. Our modern paper originated in China at a very early date and was introduced in Western civilization through Arab sources about the 10th century. Its manufacture in Europe was first established by the Moors in Spain about 1150 and papermaking spread to Italy in the late 13th century. A hundred years later, paper was used for all literary purposes and in the next century it finally superseded vellum. While paper of various grades was made, it was produced entirely by hand processes up to the beginning of the 19th century and entirely from rags until about 1860.

In the hand process, used only for highest grade writing and printing purposes today, clean cotton or linen rags are cut up into small pieces, shredded, and then disintegrated and bruised to form rag pulp. A fine screen with a removable edge is then filled by hand by dipping from a tank a mixture of water and 3 to 5 per cent of pulp which is kept constantly agitated. The water drains off through the screen and leaves a wet sheet of paper, which, dried by pressing between layers of felt and by hot rolls, is sized to produce a smooth hard surface or is treated in other ways as its use may require.

The first change which took place in this process was the replacement of hand methods for dipping and the mortar and pestle for bruising and hydrating, by machines. In 1798, Nicholas Louis Robert (1761–1828), then a clerk in the employ of Messrs. Didot of the Essonnes paper mills in France, made a machine for forming paper continuously from the pulp. This replaced the old hand dipping and made it possible to produce paper in continuous rolls and of increased width. The machine was introduced in Great Britain in 1803 by Henry Fourdrinier (1766–1854), after whom it is usually named, with the assistance of the engineer Bryan Donkin.

In the papermaking machine the prepared mixture of pulp and water is fed to a continuous roll of fine wire mesh by a "breast box" which distributes the pulp uniformly across the roll and at a rate depending both upon the speed at which the roll moves forward and upon the desired thickness of the paper. As the roll used may be 40 to 50 ft long, there is time for the water to drain out from the pulp as the roll moves forward. At the end of the roll, the damp web of pulp is picked up by felt-covered "couch" rolls, surplus water is squeezed out, further rolls dry the paper, and the process may be continued through further sizing, calendering, and cutting apparatus. Today "newsprint" is turned out in continuous sheets over 21 ft wide at a rate of 20 ft a second, and single mills turn out 600 to 700 tons or more per day.

As long as rags were the principal material employed, papermaking was almost entirely a mechanical process. With the advent of esparto and wood pulp, however, it began to take on the characteristics of a chemical industry. Thus the supply of rags being insufficient to meet an increasing demand, about 1860 attention was turned to using esparto, a Mediterranean shore grass, but the present era in paper manufacture may be said to have begun in 1880 when wood was first used in its manufacture. Today the bulk of paper is manufactured from wood pulp.

A purely mechanical treatment of esparto or wood gave a "mechanical" pulp, suited only to low-grade products. For better work it was necessary to remove the "increstants" from the fibers. This requires chemical treatment. Three processes have been used for this purpose in making wood pulp: the so-called soda, the sulfate, and the sulfite processes. These all involve "cooking" bruised wood chips for periods of 8 to 48 hours.

The present demand for paper is enormous and continues to grow. It is used in huge quantities not only for newspapers, books, and other printing but new uses have been found for it such as in electric cable and other insulation. Along similar lines, a host of wallboards, substitutes for plastering in building construction, have also appeared on the market. Thus, while in earlier days iron furnaces absorbed huge quantities of wood, today single large paper mills use the lumber cut from a square mile of land in a few days. Whole areas have been deforested, and alarm is frequently expressed over the situation. It is said, however, that the demand for wood for pulp, although huge, amounts to less than 5 per cent of the total wood cut in North America and Europe.

The history of a few industries and activities here briefly outlined, it is hoped, offers some examples of the character of the interests and the nature of the economic forces and factors which inspire and control the work of the chemical engineer. An entire library would be required to cover in detail the many and varied activities of this relatively new and yet so vitally important profession. The American chemical industry has, as we have said, been largely a 20th century growth and owes much to the pressures of World War I. It was this war also, as we shall have occasion to note in discussing the place and importance of research, that did much to stimulate industrial research in the United States. In no area of industry has the importance of continued research been more fully understood or the gospel of research led to more effective action, than in the field of chemical engineering. As we shall note, one of our major American chemical companies reports that over half of its present-day sales comes from products unknown or not commercially produced only a dozen or so years ago. It is quite evident that the sage who wrote *Ecclesiastes,* preaching the unprogressive doctrine that there is nothing new under the sun and that what has been shall be, lacked even a dim vision of the possibilities of the combination of "Creative Chemistry"[18] and sound engineering.

[18] The title of a fascinating book by Dr. E. E. Slosson (see Bibliography).

Chapter 10. MODERN ENGINEERING III:
POWER

> Fire, animal strength, and written language have in turn advanced men and nations; something like a new capacity was developed with the discovery of explosives and again in the invention of printing; but the capacity of man has always been limited to his own individual strength and that of the men and animals he could control. His capacity is no longer so limited; man has now learned to manufacture power, and with the manufacture of power a new epoch began.
>
> George S. Morison, *The New Epoch*.

MECHANICAL AND ELECTRICAL ENGINEERING

Mechanically the 19th century in the United States was the century of the reciprocating steam engine, of the locomotive and steam navigation, of the birth of American industry, of the electric-light and power industry, and of the automobile and gas engine. Many of the basic tools and devices of the 20th century had, thus, been established or invented in the 19th, but their development and improvement to meet the needs of a new and astounding era of tremendously expanded use and application were yet to come.

This remarkable 20th century growth is strikingly illustrated by a comparison of the power equipment available per capita in the United States, say, in 1899 and in 1935. In the former year it has been estimated that there was installed in the United States power equipment totaling about 25 million horsepower in capacity, or about 2 manpower for each man, woman, and child in the country. In other words, earlier centuries had brought to the service of man the equivalent to two silent slaves to aid him in meeting his material needs and wants. About a third of a century later this had increased to 1,231 million, a fiftyfold increase, which, in spite of a growth of about 75 per cent in population, was an increase per capita to about 10 hp or to 60 to 100 manpower, well over a thirtyfold growth.

A study of the distribution of this power equipment is also revealing. Following Edison's first Pearl Street electric lighting station of
1882, the use of electricity for both lighting and power continued to
expand. The greatest concentrations of power in the modern world
are in the modern central stations which serve both domestic and
many industrial needs. Yet central stations account for only some 5
per cent of modern power capacity. There are over 50 million automobiles and motor trucks in the United States, and these constitute
an estimated 55 per cent of the total, with agricultural and tractive
equipment adding another 25 and locomotive power about 10 per
cent. In other words, the 8,000 automobiles of 1900—largely imported and custom-built—have grown to the point where they are
far more common than the horse and buggy of earlier days. As a result, something in the order of two-thirds of modern man's silent
slaves are concerned with his transportation and that of his goods.

When we turn to annual power production rather than capacity,
however, these figures show up in quite a different light. Our transportation slaves—motorcars, trucks, locomotives, tractors—are operated but a few hours a day. They produce relatively few horsepower-
hours. On the other hand, central stations never close down. Thus,
in terms of the horsepower or kilowatt-hours of power actually produced in a year, the central station becomes the dominating element.
There are, of course, many private power plants serving individual
industries, but it is estimated that well over half the power *produced*
today is supplied by central service stations. This tremendous 20th
century growth in power service is strikingly illustrated in a graph
originally issued by the *Electrical World* in 1928.

This power picture may be studied from another angle: Where
do we get all this power, this capacity to do work?

There are two major power sources: fuels and water. The heat
energy stored in various fuels—coal, gas, gasoline—may be transformed into useful power by steam or internal-combustion engines.
The "potential" energy of water, its "energy of position," which it
gives up when it falls from a higher to a lower level, may be developed through the use of various types of water wheels. The accompanying graph, in which our uses of these various sources of energy
are compared, shows that bituminous coal is our main source of
power while petroleum has been rapidly increasing in use, as has also
natural gas. Water constitutes, so to speak, but a drop in the bucket.

It will be noted that this graph, however, does not seem to show

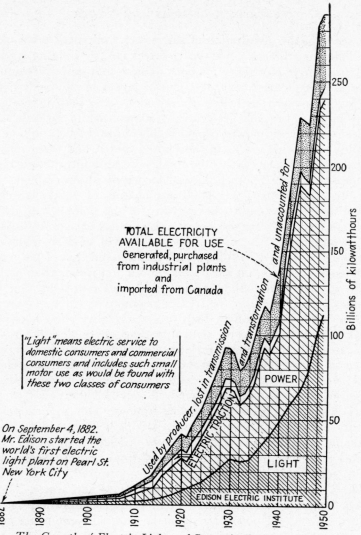

The Growth of Electric Light and Power in the United States

This chart shows the use of electric light and power since Edison's first central station was installed in 1882. Limited to public utilities, both privately and publicly owned, it omits electric power generated by mines, factories, and electric railways for their own use. Furthermore, the tremendous power capacity of the United States in nonelectric equipment, internal-combustion engines, steam locomotives, etc., is also omitted. Nevertheless, the astoundingly rapid growth in power use in the United States is strikingly portrayed. The item "loss" represents the difference between actual production and the amount delivered and billed, *i.e.,* use by the producer, plus transmission, transformation, and other losses. (*Courtesy of Edison Electric Institute.*)

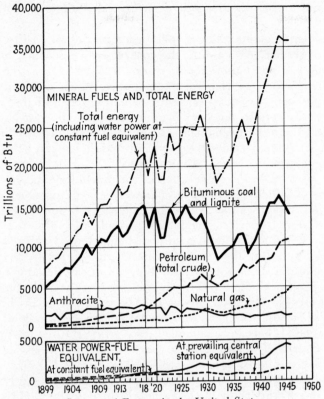

Sources of Energy in the United States

This diagram shows the sources from which our power needs have been drawn. To secure comparable data, the equivalent of various fuels has been expressed in British thermal units. Water power is represented by the equivalent fuel required to do the same work. Two equivalents are used: The constant fuel equivalent (4.02 lb of coal for each kilowatt-hour, the average of all steam-electric plants for 1913) indicates best the rate at which our water power resources have been developed. The "prevailing equivalent" (varying from 7.0 lb in 1899 to 1.3 lb in 1946) allows for the increasing efficiency of steam-electric plants. (*From "Minerals Year Book," 1948.*)

so rapid a rate of increase in source of energy with the years as the production graph. The answer is simple. Though increased efficiency in the machinery and methods used, the mechanical engineer has greatly reduced the losses of earlier days which occur when we "manufacture," as Morison called it, power from fuel or water. A pound of coal today, for example, is made to produce better than seven times the power that American central stations of 1900 could secure.[1]

In our better plants today it takes less than 1 lb of coal to provide 1 kwhr of service. As a result, the cost of service declined in earlier years and has not materially increased in spite of the tremendous recent rise in the cost of labor and supplies. When we recall that 1 kw is equivalent to $1\frac{1}{3}$ hp or about 9 manpower, and that we pay from 1 or 2 cents to not over 5 or 6 cents per kilowatt-hour, it is clear that modern mechanical engineering skill provides us with slaves at less than 1 cent per equivalent man-hour—an achievement that can only be described as miraculous.

When we turn to a consideration of the machinery and equipment by means of which this miracle of power is made possible, we note that the old reciprocating Watt-type engine has been replaced by an entirely different device, the steam turbine, and also that power plant service is almost universally distributed and utilized in the electrical form. But the most notable change seems to be in size: modern equipment is not only far bigger but, as the above figures indicate, is clearly better and more efficient than that of earlier years.

This raises the question: What part has size played in the power story? The size of power stations has, of course, grown as increasing use has created a greater demand. Edison's first station, for example, had a capacity of about 750 kw. Great modern stations have been planned for estimated capacities of 1,000,000 kw. The size of units has, however, been the most striking of these increases, and this has been an important factor in the rapid advance of the steam turbine. In the first place a machine of, say, double capacity does not cost twice as much or occupy twice the space. The first cost of a plant is thus decreased when large units are used. Turbines can be made of far larger capacity and occupy far less space than reciprocating engines, they operate with less vibration, are more easily controlled, and require less costly foundations. These factors, however, affect costs rather than efficiency. The major gains made in efficiency have been in reducing the heat losses involved in tranforming heat energy to power, through improvements in fuel combustion, in boilers, in condensers, in the use of superheaters, economizers, and other de-

[1] Statistics of earlier steam-electric plants are either not available or not trustworthy. It has been estimated that Edison's Pearl Street station may have used 30 to 40 lb of coal per kilowatt-hour produced. By 1900 the average central station requirement had dropped to about 7.2 lb. By 1919 it was 3.2, in 1927 it had been cut to 1.84, and in 1946 to 1.02.

vices. Such improvements have been made economically possible only by larger scale production.

Thus, the modern power user usually has various competing sources of supply and equipment with which to meet his needs. It is the task of the mechanical engineer not only to design and to seek continually to improve, perfect, and adapt such equipment to new requirements and uses but also to advise the user as to the most favorable source and type of development which will meet the special conditions of the desired service at the least cost. The question may be raised: Is improvement generally the origin of increased use, or does improvement result from attempts to meet recognized needs? The answer seems to be that both approaches have played their part, but that the fundamental influence has been keen competition in an atmosphere of ever-increasing demand.

We shall first review briefly some of the developments in central station equipment before turning to other forms of power machines and the applications and use of power.

Prime Movers. Sir Charles Parsons, the pioneer turbine inventor, once remarked:

As far as we can gather from the history of the steam turbine, it may be said broadly that all the chief features at present in use in turbines have been suggested or described in the rough by experimenters long ago in the hundred and more patents prior to 1880.

Yet as late as 1896 the steam turbine was still an experimental curiosity with expert opinion differing as to whether its difficulties could be overcome and it might be made of practical use and value. Ten years later, by 1906, the steam turbine had been successfully installed on land and sea and was destined to become the giant of the power world.

The largest reciprocating engines ever built for land use were placed in service in 1904 in the power station built to provide service for New York's Manhattan Elevated Railway when the old steam locomotives were replaced by electric trains.[2] Similar engines were installed about the same time in the 59th Street powerhouse built to supply New York's first subway. They were of 7,500 hp. As compared with modern turbine units of 150,000 hp and over, these two

---

[2] We emphasize "land use" for there have been "floating powerhouses," steamships, in which larger reciprocating engines have been used. For example, the *Campania* of 1893 and the *Oceanic* of 1899 carried a total of 30,000 hp in two units or twin engines operating on a single shaft.

power stations—notable and outstanding works in their day—seem puny indeed.

At least four famous names are connected with the development of the steam turbine. While the modern prime mover stems from the work of Parsons, Curtis, and Rateau the name of Karl G. P. De-

The New York Subway Powerhouse of 1904

Showing the engine room with the 7,500-hp compound piston engines, the largest reciprocating engines ever built for land use, which, in pairs with the generator between, furnished power for New York's first subway. While they are of giant size—stroke 60 in., cylinders 42 and 86 in., and shaft 34 in., in diameter—they still reflect the basic characteristics of earlier engines, with a speed of 75 rpm and operating at 175 lb pressure. (*Courtesy of Board of Transportation, New York City.*)

Laval (1845–1913) of Stockholm, outstanding and ingenious Swedish inventor and engineer, should not be forgotten.

The chief problem turbine inventors faced was that of speed. The velocity of flow of steam from a jet is extremely high and, when a high-pressure jet impinges on the blades of the turbine wheel, the speed of rotation may not only be beyond the strength of normal materials but must also be greatly reduced, a difficult problem, before it can be usefully applied.[3] DeLaval met and conquered this problem in his single-wheel turbine. Later inventors used a "compound" turbine, a sequence of wheels, reducing the steam pressure in stages, in a series of steps, thus in large measure minimizing the speed or rotation problem.

DeLaval designed single-wheel turbines which could be safely rotated at speeds as high as 30,000 rpm with rim velocities of 800 to 1,200 fps. Even with the greatest mechanical skill, however, perfect balance could not be attained, and the least "wobble" was fatal at these speeds. He adopted the daring and ingenious expedient of using a long slender, flexible shaft so that it would flex and the rapidly rotating wheel could establish and rotate about its "dynamic axis." His turbines were small—wheels from 4 to 30 in. in diameter and with capacities of 15 to perhaps 700 hp. They are seldom seen today, but the special reduction gearing which he devised—his helical gears running in an oil spray—were taken over by Parsons and others.[4]

Charles G. Curtis, a Columbia graduate (1881), developed what has been called the impulse-compound turbine, under the sponsorship of the General Electric Co. In principle he used a series of wheels and jets, thus making the drop from steam pressure to the condenser vacuum through a series of nozzles instead of in one step as Laval had done. Auguste Rateau (1863–1930) a French mining engineer, patented in 1896 his multistage impulse turbine. Sir Charles A. Parsons (1854–1931), a Cambridge graduate, on the other hand, used a series of stationary guide vanes and in effect made the entire rim or blade portion of his guides and wheels a series of diverging nozzles, relying on the reaction effect of the steam rather than on impulse. Today, of course, all these earlier patents have expired and the modern turbine designer is free to use ideas drawn from various sources.

Sir Charles's earlier work led to the building in 1894 of the small but famous turbine steamship, *Turbinia,* of 44½ tons with a 2,300-hp turbine. By 1907 this pioneer marine demonstration of the turbine had led to the construction of the *Lusitania* of 68,000 hp, destined to be sunk by a German submarine in 1915. There has been a continued development in the use of turbines in ships during the inter-

[3] For example, a steam pressure of 100 pounds per square inch (psi) will give a nozzle velocity of about 4,200 feet per second (fps). For best efficiency, the rim speed of the turbine should approximate half this figure.

[4] DeLaval's well-known cream separator was invented in 1879, and his turbine followed in 1883. His earlier career had been devoted to industry, sulfur, copper, and glass. See illustrated paper in *Power,* November 6, 1928, p. 762.

vening years, which, because of limitations of space, cannot be followed in these notes.

On land one of the earliest American power-plant turbines was that operated in the shops of the General Electric Co. at Schenectady in 1900. It was the installation, however, of a 5,000-kw unit in the Fiske Street Station of the Commonwealth Edison Co. of Chicago in 1903 that really launched the steam turbine on its central power-plant career.[5] It is interesting to note that this turbine was not only more efficient but occupied only one-tenth the space, weighed one-eighth as much, and cost but one-third that of the reciprocating engine it replaced.

The fact that a 35,000-kw unit was placed in service in the plant of the Boston Elevated Railway in 1916, 12 years later, indicates the steady growth in capacity which took place in the following years. In 1918, however, the Interborough Rapid Transit Co. in New York made a big jump forward with the installation of turbines of 60,000 kw or about 80,000 hp. These remained a record for 8 years until, in 1926, the Buffalo General Electric Co. put a 65,000-kw unit in operation at its River Station. Further increases followed rapidly and, in 1928, the century mark was passed with the 110,000-kw turbine of the Brooklyn Edison Co. This was, however, a short-lived record. The famous Hell Gate Plant of the United Electric Light and Power Co. at New York took over a few months later with a unit of 165,000-kw capacity. All records were broken, however, when, in 1929, the so-called cross compound of 208,000 kw or over 280,000 hp, equivalent to an army of some 1,700,000 men, was installed at the State Line Station near Chicago of the State Line Generating Co.[6]

[5] In the United States, 1 hp = 0.745 kw or 1 kw = about $1\frac{1}{3}$ hp. It has become customary to rate modern equipment in kilowatts as this electrical unit is the same the world over whereas the value of the horsepower varies in different countries.

[6] All modern turbines are compound in the sense that a series of bladed wheels rather than a single wheel are employed. But a confusing number of combinations of turbine units or elements is used. For example, a "single-case" turbine element may be designed with a single series of blades for one-way flow or with two series for double flow, i.e., in both directions from a central inlet through blades on each side. These elements may be "compounded," as, for example, a single flow element for the first high-pressure drop and a double unit for the final low-pressure drop to the condenser, but both connected to the same shaft. Finally, in the cross-compound type, two or more units in separate casings may be used to drive at the same or at different speeds two separate electric generators which are electrically tied together.

Generators. In the great majority of cases power is, as we have noted, converted into the electrical form for lighting, motor, or other electrical use and application. Furthermore, while in Edison's famous Pearl Street Station of 1882 the dynamos were driven by pulleys and belts from the steam engines, modern practice has, in the interest of reliability, safety, efficiency, and lower maintenance costs, turned to the direct connection of the prime mover and the electric generator,

A Modern Turbine Room

This view shows two 50,000-kw (or 65,000-hp) 21-stage turbogenerator sets, operating at 3,600 rpm installed by the General Electric Co. for the Dayton Power and Light Co. in 1949. Each of these units is equivalent to almost nine of the New York Subway reciprocating engines of 1904. (*Courtesy of General Electric Co.*)

both on the same or on coupled shafts and both, therefore, necessarily rotating at the same speed. This requirement has, of course, been a governing factor in the design of both the prime mover and the generator. A compromise in most favorable speeds has been essential.

On the one hand, turbine speeds are inherently high and, in the search for greater economy in the use of fuel, steam pressures have increased, encouraging even higher speeds. On the other, the frequency of the a-c service, now general, has been established and standardized. But frequency depends upon the number of poles in the generator and on its speed. Generators designed for either very high or very low speeds pose difficult problems of design and are more costly. In part this problem has been met by an interesting change from the older d-c generator design.

In the a-c generators, or alternators, the older function of the field and the armature has, in the interest of simpler and better construction, been reversed. The former armature thus becomes the stationary member, or stator, and it is the field member which rotates. It is remarkable to what a wide range of speed electrical designers have been able to adapt this type of design. In water power plants the range may be from as low as 60 to 600 rpm or even higher. In "turboalternators" it may run from 720 to 3,600 rpm.

One of the major problems of the electrical application and particularly of water power, however, is that of transmission. Economical long-distance transmission demands high pressure, that is, voltage. Higher voltages result in reduced transmission losses, and there have, thus, been constant efforts in this direction. As a result, one of the notable advances in alternator design has been in higher operating voltages which would eliminate or reduce step-up transformer requirements. Modern alternators, for example, generate current at voltages of 22,000 to 33,000—higher than those used for transmission lines a quarter century ago. Such machines pose major problems of insulation and also of ventilation because of the heating of the windings. Closed casings are used with forced ventilation corresponding to the water-cooling system of a gas engine. Alternators have, thus, been constantly improved, weigh much less per kilowatt output today than in former years, and, while all electrical equipment is highly efficient, are even more efficient than earlier designs.

Boilers and Fuels. To those who visualize a boiler in terms of the old, small, hand-fired device which supplied the steam hoists of earlier days, or even of those mobile power plants, the locomotives, the modern central station boiler using pulverized coal does not seem even remotely to resemble these earlier designs. Much of the heat value of the fuel in those earlier hand-fired boilers went out the stack. The boiler of a locomotive is a most remarkable device for producing the required steam rapidly and in the required volume. It has been notably increased in efficiency, but economy is necessarily sacrificed to space and weight requirements. On the other hand, in the modern central station, with large output under reasonably stable load, every effort has been made to get the most out of the fuel.

The most notable change is in the size of the combustion chamber. In old boilers the water tubes were usually placed not over 6 or 8 ft above the grate. In the modern design the combustion chamber may be 30 ft or more—three stories—in height, giving a huge "house of hell," as someone has aptly described it, in which every effort is made to secure complete combustion. The boiler tubes are located at the top of these huge chambers while wall tubes aid in keeping the walls cool and act as preheaters, thus recovering in part the heat losses through the walls.

In size and capacity, these modern steam units have, of course, had to keep in step with increases in the steam consumption of prime movers. When the New York powerhouses, noted above as the most up-to-date plants of their day, were being built in 1902, a notable step was made in taking the boilers out of the dark, hot, lower dungeons where they had usually been placed. Space was provided above ground for 72 boiler units, each having 6,008 sq ft of heating surface and operating at 225 lb pressure. Today less than a third this number would provide the same service. In fact the steam production of a modern unit is almost unbelievable. The boilers placed in the Buffalo General Electric Co. station in 1926, for example, had a capacity of 670,000 lb of water evaporated into steam per hour. Single units in the East River Station of the New York Edison Co. have handled 1,250,000 lb at peak operation. This is equivalent to over 2,500 gal of feed water per minute—sufficient for the ample supply of a city of 25,000 population! It is to be noted however, that the modern steam plant operates on practically a closed water circuit —water passes over and over again from boilers and superheaters, through turbines and condensers, and back to feed-water heaters, economizers, and boilers. The amount of "make-up" feed water is relatively small.

At the same time, steam pressure has been increasing. Watt began with 5 lb or thereabouts, but high-pressure boilers early occupied attention, especially among locomotive and marine engine builders during the 19th century.[7] In central plants in 1900, 200 lb was gen-

[7] During early days of "steamboating" on our Western rivers, notably the Mississippi, boiler explosions were not infrequent in spite of the fact that in 1838 President Van Buren had appointed three commissioners to suggest means of making steam boilers safe. These earlier boilers were of the "fire-tube" type, a form in which large volumes are occupied by water and steam, and usually involving flat surfaces which must be securely "stayed" to resist the internal pressure. There was, thus, not only a structural limit to safe pressure with this type of design (probably about 350 psi) but a failure resulted in the "ex-

erally regarded as good practice, and further increases were relatively slow—it was far easier to replace old prime movers than it was to modernize the boiler equipment. Even in 1920 about 300 lb still remained standard practice in new plants. But as turbines came into more general use, pressure was increased and reached 650 lb in 1925. The next year the Edison Company of Boston installed the first 1,200-lb unit. In 1929 the Deepwater Station of the American Gas and Electric Company at Wilmington, Delaware, went to 1,350 and the Holland Station in New Jersey to 1,400 lb. These were the first completely really high-pressure American plants.

The trend toward higher temperature steam should also be noted. It is necessary that steam for use at high velocity in turbines be dry (to avoid erosion, or pitting of the blades) and important heat economies can also be effected through superheating the steam which comes from the boiler. While "economizers" set over the main boilers —practically compounding the boiler and recovering additional heat values before the escaping gases are discharged from the stack—had been used in such early plants as the Subway Plant of 1904, superheaters are a more recent development. Added tubes, placed between the water tubes in the boiler, carry only steam which is thus superheated. This practice has, in turn, encouraged higher temperature boiler operation. In 1926 the Edison Station in Boston, mentioned above, produced steam at 725°F. The ability of equipment to stand high temperatures is the limiting factor. American practice has lagged behind European in this respect, but there has been a gradual increase as the physical difficulties of the problem have been overcome.

The handling of fuel has, of course, been completely mechanized. No longer does the horse-drawn cart deliver coal to sweating "stokers." The Subway Plant of 1904 is again worthy of note, for it marked the change from hand firing to automatic stokers. Thirty-six of the boilers originally installed were fired by hand, but 12 had automatic stokers.

In all these earlier plants, coal was used in lump size. It was not

---

plosion" of large volumes of steam and water. On the other hand, the "water-tube" boiler, now universal for large units, employed the more favorable cylindrical forms not only in its tubes but in the steam and water drums. This type, structurally advantageous and safe for much higher pressures, may be said to have "arrived" with the Babcock and Wilcox exhibit at the Philadelphia Centennial of 1876. This, and other developments and knowledge gained through the reciprocating-engine experiences of the 19th century, undoubtedly exercised an important influence on, made possible the later rapid advances in steam turbine practice.

until 1920 that the Lakeside Station at Milwaukee became the first large plant to use pulverized coal. Ground to a fineness such that over 70 per cent will pass a 200-mesh sieve, and blown in under pressure, pulverized coal burns like a gas, and, as these incandescent particles rise in the combustion chamber, combustion is completed. No smoke is observed and the fine, solid product of combustion, "fly ash," is in part recovered, and much of it finds use in industry.

Also beginning in 1920 another refinement in the combustion process was introduced. Forced draft is, of course, invariably employed to secure uniform combustion and give more rapid control when a boiler must be speeded up to supply another turbounit in meeting a sudden load demand. The heating of the air used in firing with pulverized coal effected an important economy.

In the central and western areas of the United States where natural gas is available, there has been increasing use of this fuel. In 1929 the Pacific Gas and Electric Company installed two 50,000-kw turbines which were supplied from boilers fired by natural gas.[8] It was piped 240 miles into San Francisco for this purpose. Oil has been used in some power plants, has become common in ships, and is, of course, rapidly increasing in use for heating plants in buildings and homes.

Condensers. It will be recalled that Watt's first invention was the separate condenser, a detached chamber in which the steam used in Newcomen's atmospheric mine pump was condensed back to water. With the advent of the direct-acting piston engine, the expanded steam was usually exhausted directly to the air, as it still is in locomotives and smaller steam engines. The use of steam power in navigation, however, required that the exhaust be condensed so that the feed water could be used over and over again and the necessity of carrying large quantities of fresh water avoided.[9] Condensers not only reduce feed-water use but also increase the pressure range, as the exhaust is not at atmosphere but at a partial vacuum.

To provide such service, however, large cooling surfaces and great

[8] These turbines were of a new and unique design, since used in cases where floor space is at a premium, as, for example, when a small older unit is to be replaced by a larger modern turbine. A turbounit is not high, but it does require long floor space—the shaft of the Southern California Edison's 94,000-kw unit of 1928, for example, was 100 ft long and 16 in. in diameter. The Pacific unit was, therefore, "double-decked," that is, the low- and high-pressure elements (it was a cross-compound) were placed one over the other.

[9] A marine "powerhouse" was, thus, one of the best engineered of earlier plants and represented, as we have noted, the highest level of power plant design in the precentral station era.

volumes of cooling water are essential. A condenser may be likened to a reverse boiler. The condenser shell encloses a perfect forest of tubes, and a single modern unit may have a cooling surface of 85,000 to 90,000 sq ft—over 2 acres! The amount of cooling water required is almost beyond belief. In the Hell Gate Station in New York, for example, East River water is screened and two pumps, each taking 35,000 gal a minute, serve the condensers, the heated water being discharged back into the river.

It has been suggested that we should locate our steam plants at the mines and, thus, save the cost of transporting coal. The answer is obvious. The huge modern steam plant consumes coal but it also uses water. For small plants it is possible to circulate condenser water and cool it in cooling towers or similar devices. For the huge volume of water needed in larger plants, this plan is not feasible—such plants are always located on lake or river fronts where it is also possible, in many cases, to bring in the coal by water transport.

This heat loss in condenser water is, of course, one of the major losses which we still face in making the transformation from heat energy of fuel to power. The heat value of fuels varies widely but 1 lb of coal seldom contains over 14,000 British thermal units (Btu). It was the British physicist, James P. Joule (1818–1889) who first established the mechanical equivalent of heat. If $\frac{1}{4}$ lb (0.244) of such coal is burned in 1 hr, it should theoretically produce 1 kwhr of energy.[10] In the best of older steam plants it took, as we have noted, about 7 lb of coal; that is, only 4 per cent or less of the total energy in the fuel was transformed into useful power. The very best of modern plants have increased this, through the developments above outlined, from about 25 to over 30 per cent. While this is an extraordinary achievement, it is encouraging to the young mechanical engineer, who may wonder what is left to be accomplished in the future, to note that there is still ample room for further improvement.

Industrial Power. The isolated steam plant serving a local need or industry, and, at one time, together with equally isolated water power plants, the major power units of the country, have been in many cases replaced by the purchase of industrial and similar power needs from central stations. For the many smaller power uses of modern life, the internal-combustion engine or, in some cases, electric motors have replaced the steam engine, while the transformation of the steam-

[10] It is usual to speak of "heat rate" rather than fuel consumption, namely of the Btu's required to produce 1 kwhr. Theoretically 3414 Btu should produce 1 kwhr, but the best rates today are somewhat under 10,000.

driven agricultural and construction equipment of the first years of the century to gasoline or Diesel drive has not only been complete but has given us many new and more powerful laborsaving tools.

On the other hand, many modern industries require "process steam" as well as power and, thus, find it economical to operate their own steam plants. In general, the best of these industrial power plants, although they are usually far smaller in size, have followed in their design and development the practices of the central stations. Ingenious methods have also been devised to maintain the balance between power needs and the volume of steam required in the manufacturing or industrial process. In some cases such plants needing large volumes of process steam have found it possible to dispose of surplus power to public-utility systems, while in others steam production is limited to process needs and additional power is purchased from central station sources.

This is not to say that the old reciprocating engine has passed out of the picture. It still has its special uses and applications, but the internal-combustion engine has crowded it out of many services while the development of small turbine units of 50 to 300 hp has made the old piston engine a special rather than the standard form of power unit.

Water Power. As we have noted, it was the small water power of the New England states, rather than steam power as in Britain, that supplied the needs of early American manufacturing and industry. In a few favored spots, such as Lowell on the Merrimac and Holyoke on the Connecticut, these older powers have held their own. In general, however, these earlier sites were very small and of seasonal value only. As the local saw and grist mills gave way in the rise of American industry, the small sites were abandoned and, beginning about 1870, steam plants located in industrial centers on railroad lines began to take their place.

The first great American water power development was at Niagara in 1895, but it remained more or less alone in its class for some years. Steam was supreme. The steam plant could be located where needed and while, to be sure, more costly to operate than a water power plant, it cost far less to install and was less subject to the uncertainties, risks, and hazards of hydraulic construction and operation. Furthermore a steam plant could be easily expanded as need required, whereas it was not economical to build dams and other water facilities to less than their maximum possible ultimate capacity. Water powers, except in such unique locations as Niagara, are also subject

to wide variations in flow—their "firm" power, or steady and reliable output, is usually but a mere fraction even of the average possible production.[11]

As electrical transmission and use increased, however, more water
plants were built in the most favorable locations and, about 1905, a
new era of water power development began to take form. While the
transmission problem was well in hand by 1910, other difficulties
arose to plague this new development. Favorable sites were few in
number and, when located on streams which might in some remote
age be made navigable, costly provisions for locks were required by
Federal authorities. President Theodore Roosevelt also vetoed acts
for franchises to private companies on public lands in 1908–1909,
and it was not until 1920 that the Federal Power Act cleared the
scene and Western power development became general. In some
states, such as New York, water power became a political issue. Remarkable advances in rural electrification had been made in Ontario,
and it was held that the gift of "white coal" which would bring
power into every home should be kept out of private hands and assured to the people of New York State. In the meantime, steam
plants were constantly improving in efficiency, less money was required for their construction, and it was available at more favorable
rates. Water power lagged behind.[12]

Finally in 1911, what is now an obvious development quietly came
about in a most remarkable way. In 1914 the *Electrical World* stated
editorially: "It will be startling news to some of our readers that
there has quietly grown up in the South what is today by far the
most extensive interconnected transmission system in the world." In
other words, through the normal extension of its services the isolated
plants of the Southern Power Company were finally brought to-

[11] Few people realize that it takes very great stream flow and head to produce
a sizable water power. For example, suppose a stream yields 100 cu ft of water a
second—a small river perhaps, 25 ft wide and 2 ft deep. Assume, further, that
a head of 100 ft is available. This would provide about 1,000 hp—less than a
third of the ouput of a modern airplane engine. Furthermore, the flow of many
streams varies between dry periods and flood conditions by 1,000 per cent or
more. The safe, "firm" year-round power is but a small fraction of even the
average flow.

[12] The discouraging situation retarding such developments as late as 1916 is
strikingly set forth in a paper, "The Water Power Situation, Including Its
Financial Aspects," by Gano Dunn, *Trans. Am. Inst. Elec. Engrs.*, 1916, p. 441.
For an outline of American water power legislation see *Elec. World*, June 5,
1920, p. 1328.

gether when transmission lines joined.[13] Not through planning but through growth, did the interconnection of steam and water power plants feeding into one system become an accomplished fact. A new era of water power development was born. Many water sites, having little value as isolated plants, became economically capable of development when interconnected with steam plants.

This discovery of the advantages of interconnection led to another great burst of wishful power thinking under the slogan "super-power." A new era of power was envisaged which would put electricity in every home. But, while interconnection went forward and hitherto neglected water power sites were developed, it became evident that all the water powers of the country could not possibly meet growing power needs. Fuel was still to remain our principal source of power.

As interconnection was advanced, certain well-defined power areas began to develop. By 1921 steam and water plants in the New England states had been interconnected, and it thus became possible in dry years to meet deficiencies in water power areas by supplying power from steam plants in other centers. At the same time, the plants of the upper Hudson and Mohawk valleys in New York— the Niagara–Hudson system—were joined to New England leaving only a few scattered water power plants in the northern Adirondacks and the 100 per cent steam service of New York City still isolated.[14]

Once the cotton millowners had discovered the economy of electric power, the Southern Power Company also grew rapidly. By 1923 it had joined with six other companies in a network of interconnected plants which covered five states supplying nearly 3 billion kilowatt hours annually from steam and water plants.

In between these systems, an interesting growth took place in the plants serving Baltimore, Wilmington, and Washington. The Susquehanna River, emptying into Delaware Bay at Havre de Grace, of-

[13] It is interesting to recall that "It was only after the hardest kind of pioneer work without the slightest encouragement from mill owners, that electricity was introduced in the South as a means of driving cotton mills." In 1904 the Catawba Power Company completed a hydroelectric plant near Rock Hill, South Carolina. This, the pioneer plant of the Southern Power Company, had four 750- and four 900-kw generators *driven by rope drives* from the water turbines.

[14] New York was joined to the mid-Hudson system by a 65-mile 132,000-volt tie line begun in 1931. It is an emergency tie rather than a connection planned for normal operating service.

Water Power—The Conowingo Construction, 1927

Showing this great plant, at the head of tidewater on the Susquehanna River, under construction. The dam with pen-stock openings is well advanced while the powerhouse substructure and turbine foundations are in progress in the fore-ground. (*Courtesy of Susquehanna Power Co.*)

fered three notable water power sites. The first of these, developed by the Holtwood Plant at McCall's Ferry, was built in 1910. In 1928 the great Conowingo Dam and powerhouse at the head of tidewater was completed, primarily to permit the Philadelphia steam plants to operate on a relatively steady base load.[15] The third of these plants, the Safe Harbor development of 1931, is between the other two and is especially notable because of the large water wheels of a new "propeller" type which were installed.

The Central and Prairie states have not in general been important elements in this growth of power systems. The northern members, notably Wisconsin and Minnesota, have a number of important plants. The great Keokuk plant, on the upper Mississippi at the Des Moines Rapids 144 miles above St. Louis, was a pioneer modern work of 1910–1913. It is still notable as a low-head plant, having been planned for the unusual number of 30 units operating under a nominal head of 32 ft. The Coon Rapids plant above St. Paul–Minneapolis is also of interest, and the Ozark region to the southwest is also the site of some interesting developments. The West Coast, however, is probably the most remarkable water power area in the United States.

The Coast Range and Rocky Mountain streams flowing into the Pacific, especially in the northern coast area, are fed by melting snow during the summer months, and not only is the flow well maintained but very high heads are often available. Development was rapid after 1920. Great modern steam plants, especially at San Francisco and Los Angeles, also feed into what is practically a single interconnected system spanning the entire length of the three coast states, 1,400 miles.

While few engineers of the World War I period would have ventured to predict the advent of a new era of water power development, such a development, as a result of interconnection, thus, went rapidly forward in the '20's. In 1920 central stations produced about 44 billion kilowatt-hours of which but 16, or a little over a third,

[15] Steam plants operate most efficiently and economically at steady, full load and their units are seldom fully shut down except for maintenance or repairs. The power demand varies, however, throughout the 24 hours, the peak load—usually in the late afternoon in winter months when lighting needs are superimposed on industrial and other uses—commonly being $2\frac{1}{2}$ times the average load (*i.e.,* load factor, 40 per cent). Water power may be turned on or off at will and it is, thus, economical to use it for peak needs. During periods of high stream flow it may also, of course, be used to carry part of the base load, but storage is usually limited and care is taken to conserve stored water for peak needs.

came from water. By 1928 the total had increased to 84 billion, of which water produced 36 or 43 per cent—still, we believe, the greatest "water year" on record.

Water Wheels. The evolution of the water wheel in the United States is an interesting example of the influence of physical and economic conditions on machine design. While in European practice it has been customary to design special wheels to meet the peculiar conditions at each particular site, American practice has been toward standardization, toward the development of a standard series of wheels which could be used under different conditions.

American water-turbine practice may be said to have begun with the battle between the Howd type, built at Geneva, New York, in 1838, and the French Fourneyron wheel invented in 1827 and imported by Boyden in 1844. The latter was an outward-flow wheel, that is, the turbine "runner" was placed outside the central water feeder and, thus, not only did it have to be of large size, making it costly, but it also was a low-speed wheel. This latter fact made little difference in early days when turbines were belted to machinery and speed could thus be easily controlled to suit conditions. With the advent of electric use, however, and especially of direct connection of turbine and generator on the same shaft, speed became, as we noted in discussing turboalternators, a major consideration. The type now known as the Francis turbine, an inward- and downward- (or mixed) flow wheel which has been evolved from the Howd-Francis type won the battle. Being more compact, less costly, and more easily fed with water and having inherently higher speed, it has become standard.

It has been noted that the Niagara development of 1895 was the first great American water power development. In this plant the turbines and generators operated on the same vertical shaft, a plan which has become standard American practice. But a water turbine as regards speed of rotation is similar to a steam turbine. The higher the head under which the plant operates, the higher the velocity of flow through the turbine and the higher the speed—the revolutions per minute—of the wheel. But, as we have noted, the electric alternator must be designed for a standard frequency and a favorable speed, if it is to be economically built. The major problem turbine designers have struggled with is, therefore, that of developing wheels which will give favorable speeds for various heads. For low heads, the aim is to secure a higher than "normal" speed and thus avoid the necessity for an extremely costly low-speed alternator and, vice versa, for high-head turbines. Speed can be controlled, within limits, by changes in diameter and by modification of the blade forms, but "extreme" designs operate at good efficiency over only a limited range of load. The problem has centered in securing good efficiencies in operation at less than "full gate." Remarkable results have been attained. What are known as the "wheel characteristics" have been progressively improved. Heads of close to 1,000 ft, formerly developed only by impulse wheels, are now handled by turbines.

At the other extreme, however, namely, that of developing a relatively high-speed wheel for low-head plants, the turbine has given way to a completely new and modern form of wheel, the so-called propeller type. These look like the screw propellers used on ships and were first brought forward by the Austrian, Professor Viktor Kaplan of Brünn, in 1913. First used abroad, American designers quickly took up this new wheel, following World War I, and in 1923, a 28,000-hp unit was placed in operation by the Manitoba Power Co. By 1931 units of 42,500 hp were installed in the Safe Harbor plant on the Susquehanna River, as previously noted. In these modern designs, the pitch of the propeller blades may be adjusted to give best operating efficiency under varying load. In general, the heads under which they are used are about 25 ft.

While the turbines installed at Niagara took some 430 cu ft of water per second, modern great turbine units, such as the huge 54,000-hp wheels at Conowingo, pass 6,000 cu ft per sec. Under low heads the volume of flow must, of course, be proportionately higher if the horsepower output is high. The propeller wheel is especially favorable in this respect for it offers little obstruction to flow and may handle 10,000 cu ft per sec or more.

Some mention should also be made of the impulse wheel, a distinctly western American innovation. So called "hurdy-gurdy" wheels, with flat paddles on which a jet from a nozzle impinged, were used in California as early as 1854. In 1880 a patent was issued to Lester A. Pelton (1829–1910) for a much improved form of this device with curved buckets. These buckets were still later modified in the Doble form, and the impulse, or Pelton, wheel became a standard type for the high-head installations of the Pacific Coast area.

As in the case of steam turbines, the water wheel story is one of units of ever greater capacity. No such heights have been reached as in central steam plants; in fact one modern steam turbine unit often has a greater capacity than the entire output of the majority of water power installations. One of the earlier large Western water powers, the Feather River plant in California of 1908, used Francis turbines of 18,000 hp operating under a 525-ft head. There was another jump forward with the Yadkin River development in North Carolina in 1916, where units of 31,000 hp were installed. In 1922 the Ontario Power Commission went to 55,000 hp and, the next year, the Niagara Co. built the first of their "great triumvirate of power," a 70,000-hp turbine. Still larger turbines of 90,700 hp were later installed at the Diabolo Project for the supply of Seattle and even larger in the Dnieper development in Russia. The largest impulse wheels in 1921 were $12\frac{1}{3}$ ft in diameter and of 30,000 hp capacity operating under a head of 1,008 ft in the Caribou plant of the Great Western Power Co. By 1927 wheels of 56,000 hp under the astonishing head of 2,418 ft were installed in the Big Creek plant of the Southern California Edison Co. All these big wheels are double, that is, two wheels with the alternator between, operating, of course, on one shaft.

Unlike steam engines, water wheels are highly efficient. It has been remarked that probably no improvement in the efficiency of water wheels, other than that due to increase in size, was made between 1850 and 1905. The efficiency of the original Niagara turbines of 1895 was 75 per cent. But by 1908 efficiencies had increased to 88 per cent and the great 54,000-hp Conowingo turbines of 1928 gave a 92 per cent performance. The modern hydraulic turbine is, thus, a remarkably efficient machine.

Hydraulic Power Plants. Space will not permit a review of water power plant design. A water power development brings together in a single project the skills of civil, mechanical, and electrical engineers. When a dam is required, almost invariably it, together with the powerhouse foundations, is the most costly part of the project. Plans are always made to take special advantage of any favorable topographic or hydrological conditions at the particular situation and to conserve valuable head, especially in low-head plants, by using various forms of spillway crest gates. The intakes to the turbine units with their scroll cases, or volutes, are usually formed in the massive concrete of the powerhouse foundations which must also provide for the draft tubes into which the turbines discharge as well as furnish adequate support for the turbine-alternator units themselves. In general the turbines are set below the floor level of the powerhouse, and only the alternators at the top of the vertical shafts show above the powerhouse floor. Transformers, lightning arrestors, and similar equipment, formerly placed in an upper floor or gallery, have in modern plants been moved outdoors. In fact in some plants in more moderate climates, the powerhouse itself has been uncovered, leaving in the open the "outdoor" generators with the always present overhead crane. It is probably safe to say that, while hydroelectric plants have increased greatly in scale, there have been few fundamental changes in their general planning and design during the past thirty or forty years.

Power Transmission. It is interesting to note that, when the Niagara development of 1895 was projected, electricity was but one of several means proposed to provide for the transmission of power to the main market, Buffalo, 22 miles distant. Cable drives and pneumatic methods were seriously considered. One of the factors in this situation was the uncertainty as to the use of alternating or direct current.

Earlier lights and motors were of the d-c type and a 10,000-volt d-c line had been built from Creil to Paris, 32 miles, in 1887. Yet alternating current had distinct advantages from the transmission standpoint; generating voltage could be easily stepped up to higher pressures for transmission and as easily reduced to lower voltage for use by means of stationary transformers. On the other hand, direct current required rotating transformers and raised difficult commutator problems. Inasmuch as the required cross section of the conductors—the transmission cables—for a given power load varies inversely with the voltage, this a-c voltage advantage was of prime importance. Workers like Nikola Tesla and others, however, were pioneering with alternating current and, as the possibilities of its use became more generally understood, the practicability of the long-distance transmission of power advanced rapidly.

But the factors controlling the growth of long-distance transmission were not only those of the practical use of alternating current of high voltage or of the design of suitable transformers, switching equipment, lightning arresters, line structures, and insulators suited to its use. All these made high voltage costly, and long-distance transmission was, thus, not commercially possible unless the amount of power to be transmitted was large. As a result, the rise of long-distance transmission required not only the development of special equipment but also the growth of markets for power which would justify such constructions.

One of the most important early demonstrations of a-c transmission was from Lauffen to the Frankfurt Exposition, 100 miles at 30,000 volts, in 1891. Advances in generator, transformer, and switch design were rapidly made. The oil-insulated transformer had, by 1903, been perfected for up to 60,000 volts. At this point the insulator problem entered to hold up further advances. Even as late as 1906, the *Electrical World* noted that no insulators had been developed which were safe for over 80,000 volts. The limit was reached in this same year in the 40-mile line, with two 26-mile branches, of the Grand Rapids Power Co. operating at 72,000 volts.

In 1907 the Canadian Niagara Power Co. built a new 16-mile line to Buffalo using not only steel towers, in lieu of the older wood poles, but also a string of porcelain insulators known as the "jumper" type. This, however, put a heavy line tension on the insulator, but the design was sound and, used in the suspended form, solved the insulator problem. By 1908 transmission voltage had jumped to 110,000.

Up to this point, transmission equipment advances had barely kept ahead of demand. Beyond this point, voltages increased only as the growth in power loads made transmission at increased potential economical. By 1914 a voltage of 150,000 had been reached, but it was not until 1922 that 165,000 followed, and the next year a top of 220,000 was attained. By 1929 there were 12 lines of this top voltage, and others have since been erected.

The West has led in this growth, as distant water powers were brought into service areas, but the 110,000-volt line of the Ontario Hydro-Electric Commission of 1909 was, as we have noted, the first great line of the modern steel-tower, suspension insulator type.

While these long-distance feeder lines interconnect main plants with other plants and with the transformer stations in centers of load, distribution to consumers is, in city areas, in underground conduits. It is notable that, although our city streets became cluttered with poles and telephone and telegraph lines, Edison had as early as 1882 established the practicability of underground distribution. In the "Edison tube" the wires were sealed in an iron pipe filled with a bituminous mixture. Later an oil-filled conduit was tried, but unsuccessfully, and the modern, "drawn-in" lead-sheathed cable, placed in fiber, terra-cotta duct, or other conduits came into use. In 1913 the highest voltage transmitted underground was 13,000 volts. New methods of paper insulation, however, brought this up to 66,000 by 1924. By 1927 the old oil plan combined with the new paper insulation had made it possible to build underground lines (in New York and Chicago) carrying 132,000 volts, and still higher voltages are undoubtedly possible.

The Application and Use of Power. It should be clear from the foregoing that, together with the gas engine, the electrical transmission, distribution, and use of power have been major factors in the rise of a Power Age, in making power available for the service of man in home and factory, in the city, and in rural areas.

The 19th century witnessed the attainment of a limited but, to a major degree, perfected d-c service and equipment. Before the century had closed, Edison's Jumbo dynamo had been made into a more efficient, lighter generator of modern form. The incandescent lamp was coming into general use, and the d-c motor was well understood and was turned out in various types and sizes to meet commercial needs.

On the other hand, while alternating current had been demonstrated for generation and transmission, its more general application was still a matter of doubt and discussion. As late as August, 1900, at a meeting of American and British engineers in Paris, the relative advantages of direct current and alternating current were hotly discussed. An American participant stated:

For lighting work we started with the dc system as advocated by Mr. Edison and in our smaller cities with the ac system. Today [*i.e.,* in 1900] dc seems to have not only held its own in our larger cities but, in addition, is replacing the ac system in some cases, although the alternating system holds its place for smaller cities covering widely distributed districts and for transmission to the outlying districts of our larger cities.

The battle of alternating current vs. direct current was, thus, in full swing and we had not as yet more than scratched the surface in the use of electric power.

Two of the major problems of alternating current were frequency and the a-c motor. Frequencies used varied from 25 to 130 cycles, and there was no standard. For lighting use, no problem was involved—either direct current or alternating current would serve equally well—although it was found that 60 cycles were necessary to eliminate perceptible flicker in incandescent lamps. This frequency has, thus, become standard although 25 is used in some purely power services. The a-c motor also has not been found to be so bad as painted in spite of the difficulties of speed control and the large consumption of current in starting under load. As the new century opened, both direct current and alternating current were, thus, in use.

In 1907 the New York Central Lines and the New York, New Haven, and Hartford Railroad began the electrification of their suburban services and their common line into Grand Central Terminal in New York. The former stuck to direct current using a "third rail" for the feeder. The latter installed the Westinghouse a-c system with overhead transmission. Later American railroad electrifications —the Norfolk and Western in 1915, the Chicago, Milwaukee and St. Paul (mountain service) in 1920, and the Great Northern in 1927—have followed the a-c plan. But the d-c motor has distinct starting advantages, and in subways, with the frequent starting and stopping of trains, direct current has been standard. In view of the rise of the Diesel electric locomotive, however, it seems improbable that there will be further railroad electrifications except in specially favored power areas.

While direct current thus still has its special uses and advantages, alternating current has come into ever wider use and is standard today. Our Electrical Age is, primarily, an a-c age. Even in New York, the birthplace of d-c distribution, direct current has been almost entirely replaced by a-c service. For this service electrical engineers have developed and perfected the tremendous scope of equipment needed not only to generate and transmit but to utilize electric power.

The development of the modern electric motor illustrates very clearly the type of improvement which electrical engineers and machine designers have made in such equipment. Modern motors are made in sizes from the tiny synchronous motor, of 1 "mouse" power or less, which runs an electric clock, to the huge 8,000-hp motor used to meet the exacting requirements of a modern steel rolling mill. While in 1900 motors were custom-built and a 5-hp motor weighed 716 lbs and occupied 11.4 cu ft, today such a motor is turned out on a mass-production basis, weighs only 191 lbs, occupies but 2.5 cu ft (a little over one-fifth), and costs a third or less as much as its ancestor of 1899.

The use of electricity in the home for lighting and to run all sorts of household needs and aids, from razors to refrigerators and from sewing machines to pumps and furnaces, is wonderful enough but, in all probability its use in industry, especially in the mass production of consumers' goods, has exercised an even more important influence on our lives and living standards. Not only has new power been given to industry, but the old mazes of shafting and forests of belting, which obstructed the light and added to the hazards of older machine operations, have given way to the easily controlled and much less noisy individual motor drive.

The total horsepower of electric motors used in factories was estimated in 1899 to be a little less than 500,000. By 1909 this had increased tenfold, in another 10 years it again increased about $3\frac{1}{3}$ times, and by 1927 had reached over 30 million horsepower. The increase in percentage of electrified tools and machines is equally revealing: from 4 per cent in 1899, to 23 in 1909, to 53 in 1919, to 75 in 1927, and it has, of course, subsequently increased to cover practically all modern industrial equipment.

While, therefore, the electrical engineer thus furnishes the power device which drives the machines and machine tools of modern industry, it is the mechanical engineer, the expert in machine design and machine tool operation, who designs and builds the machines themselves. Some aspects of this story are briefly noted in Chap. 11.

We must not lose sight of the fact, however, that not all power is used to drive machines. A good part of power service, something between 15 and 20 per cent, is devoted to lighting, and this application is distinctly in the electrical engineer's domain. Indeed there is probably no story which more clearly illustrates the improvements and values which flow from electrical study and research than that of the incandescent lamp.

Edison's lamp of 1881 gave about 1.68 lumens of light per watt of energy consumed.[16] Improvements in carbonizing the filament, the use of a squirted cellulose filament, and an improved vacuum did not increase the light output but did give the carbon filament lamp of 1905 a life 139 times longer than the lamps of 1881. At this time, however, Whitney's Gem lamp with a metalized carbon filament appeared and the lumens per watt jumped to 4.25 and the life span was increased $4\frac{3}{4}$ times. Then, in 1906, Von Bolton's tantalum filament lamp showed 4.8 lumens and a life $2\frac{3}{4}$ times better than the Gem. But this was not the end of improvement stemming from "purposeful experimentation." In the same year the General Electric Co. brought out the tungsten filament lamp giving 7.85 lumens per watt and a life 27 times longer than Von Bolton's tantalum lamp. The idea of the tungsten lamp was developed by two Viennese workers, Just and Hanaman, but the making of the filament from the brittle metal tungsten was a General Electric accomplishment and required 4 years of patient trial and labor.

---

[16] The lumen has replaced the older candle power as the modern unit for measuring light sources. The watt is, of course, the unit of power. We pay our electric bills on terms of kilowatt (1,000 watts) per hour. The more lumens per watt, therefore, the more light for the same power use or cost.

The task of exhausting the air from the incandescent bulb had also been greatly expedited in 1896 by the chemical, in lieu of mechanical, process invented by an Italian genius, Malignani. His method consisted in placing some red phosphorus in the bulb and making the filament incandescent. Tests were immediately made of other "getters" but, in the end, this did not prove to be the real answer.

It was Dr. Irving Langmuir of General Electric who developed the modern gas-filled lamp in which an inert gas, argon, plus about 15 per cent of nitrogen, at practically normal atmospheric pressure, is used. As a result, there has been a further increase to 9 lumens and a still longer life.[17]

While these improvements were in progress, there were also some changes in the shape of the bulb—the long-necked (to reduce heating), "tipless," inside-frosted bulb—and standard sizes have also been adopted. Finally the "unit machine" has been devised to make lamps on a mass-production scale so that the ordinary sizes may be purchased today for 15 cents or less—less than a third their cost in World War I days. It is difficult to realize that little more than one lifetime ago, our grandparents had to rely on kerosene lamps and candles for light.

The Internal-combustion Engine. While the internal-combustion engine may be traced back to beginnings in the 17th century, even as late as 1860 it was still in the experimental state. In fact its development again emphasizes the fact that important advances seldom stem from the work of one man; they usually represent the labors of many workers over many years.

After early proposals to use the explosive action of gunpowder, it would appear that Wright's British engine of 1833 was the first really practical "explosive" engine. It used the flame ignition of an explosive mixture of gas and air in a special chamber connected to the cylinders. Another Britisher, William Barnett, was the first to propose and use the system of compressing the mixture, now universal. It was the French inventor, Jean J. E. Lenoir (1822–1900), however, who actually produced a gas engine for public use.

Lenoir's engine, made in Paris in 1860, was in form substantially a high-pressure piston steam engine. In the first part of the stroke, a charge of air and gas was drawn into the cylinder, the valve then closed, the charge was exploded by an electric spark thus propelling

[17] This for ordinary size lamps. Larger sizes, such as 1,000 watts, give as high as 18 lumens per watt.

the piston to the end of its stroke. The engine operated smoothly, a number were used, but, unfortunately, gas consumption was very high—about 100 cu ft of gas per effective horsepower-hour were required. A more economical device was essential to practical use.

The great name in gas engine history is that of Dr. Nikolaus A. Otto (1832–1891) who devoted his life to the problem and, in 1876, after earlier efforts, invented the "Otto Silent" engine using the well-known four-cycle method of operation.[18] With this engine, gas consumption was reduced to 25 to 30 per cent of that required for the Lenoir engine. Brayton in America brought out an ingenious engine in 1873, but it did not equal the Otto in performance.

It was the motorcar, however, which gave point and purpose to the development of the internal-combustion engine and it was another German, Gottlieb Daimler (1834–1900) who originated the modern small, high-speed engine using the light hydrocarbons as fuel, those now classed as petrol, or gasoline. Daimler had worked with Otto but, in 1882, withdrew and devoted his time to his high-speed engine which he first produced in 1883. In 1886 he tried his first motor bicycle, and the next year he ran a motor-propelled car. Daimler really deserves the title, Father of the Automobile, although Carl Betz of Manheim had built the first road vehicle to be propelled by gas, a tricycle, in 1885.[19] In 1889 Messrs. Panhard and Levassor made arrangements with Daimler to manufacture automobiles in France and Belgium and produced their first car in 1891.

While the United States has become the outstanding producer of motorcars, the basic ideas thus came from abroad. America has contributed manufacturing methods which brought the cost of the motorcar within the pocketbook of the millions and has also led in constant improvements in design and in the invention of improved fuel, ethyl gasoline. As Mark Sullivan puts it:

What really happened in America during the eighties and early nineties was that news and photographs trickled over from Europe of "horseless vehicles" that had been made there. Whereupon, in nearly every village and town in America, especially in the Middle West, the local mechanical

[18] Although known by his name, the Otto cycle had been proposed by an earlier French worker, de Roches, in 1862, who completely described the sequence: (1) On the outstroke the mixture is drawn into the cylinder, (2) on the following instroke, it is compressed, (3) ignition takes place at the dead point of the stroke with expansion on the next outstroke, and (4) exhaust gases are discharged on the returning instroke.

[19] There had been a number of earlier steam cars as, for example, that of the Frenchman, N. J. Cugnot of 1769.

genius devoted his whole being to this new device. . . . Of the Americans who later became manufacturers to any successful degree, Winton had been a bicycle repair man, Franklin a die-caster, Ford a mechanic in an electric powerhouse, Pierce a manufacturer of bird-cages, bicycles, and refrigerators, Haynes had been field superintendent of a natural gas company. The Studebaker came out of a wagon factory, the Peerless from a clothes-wringer factory, the Stanley from a photographic dry-plate factory.[20]

We cannot follow the history of the automobile industry in the United States. By 1929 some 5 million gasoline engines were going into automobiles annually and an additional 200,000 were being used for other tractive and similar devices. Thus the modern farmer replaced horses with tractors; the old steam plow and the harvester, as well as new equipment, were gasoline-powered. The construction engineer also used these engines for older power equipment— shovels, trucks, hoists—and a complete new line of construction equipment was developed, especially for concrete and highway construction—screens, batchers and mixers, graders, bulldozers, and ditching machines. It has been primarily the internal-combustion engine which has made possible the almost complete modern mechanization of agriculture and construction.

While the earlier gas engine thus led to the gasoline engine, it should be noted that a development which was vitally tied up with the latter also gave new life to the older device. The first extensive use of gas engines in the United States was in connection with the petroleum industry. Oil wells produced gasoline and oil, but these were also usually accompanied by natural gas. What more natural than to use this gas, often wasted in earlier days, for the power required in pumping oil? Gas engines are also used as boosters on natural gas lines and for condensing casing-head gas into gasoline. The successful use of gas engines in oil service led, between 1900 and 1910 to the use of similar engines running on producer gas. They were not too successful, but it was discovered in 1895 that blast furnace gas could be used, and gas engines have been employed in plants where gas is more or less a wasted by-product. The Lackawanna Steel Co., for example, installed a 40,000-hp plant at Buffalo in 1902–1903. It has been the heavy-oil engine, however, which, after a long struggle, has at last become an important element in the modern power picture.

The Diesel Engine. Various inventors—including the British expert,

[20] *Our Times,* by Mark Sullivan, New York, Charles Scribner's Sons, 1926.

Dugald Clerk, of "2-cycle" engine fame—had continued working on gas engines and took up the use of oil as a fuel. In 1892, Dr. Rudolph Diesel (1858–1913), a German inventor, began work on the oil engine and, in 1895, produced his first engine. In this engine only air is compressed in the cylinder. This compression is so great, however, that the heat generated is sufficient to ignite a spray of heavy oil which is injected into the cylinder at the proper time.

The Diesel engine was slow in coming into use. Clerk's book of 1909, a revised edition, noted it but briefly. L. H. Morrison says,

So frequently has the statement been made that the Diesel first came into commercial use in Germany, that seldom is the claim challenged. History, however, reveals that the first Diesel engine to be put in regular power service was a 60-hp unit built in St. Louis in 1898, after Dr. Diesel's design. The story of how the Diesel came to America is an interesting study of one man's determination to carry out a plan once started.[21]

This man was Adolphus Busch, head of the famous Anheuser-Busch Brewing Co. of St. Louis.

Hearing of Diesel's work through his friend Baron Von Krupp, the German munitions king, Busch purchased the American rights for a quarter million dollars. The story includes many early difficulties in trying to manufacture practical engines. An early type, exhibited at St. Louis in 1904 and manufactured in Providence, Rhode Island, was the only Diesel used in the United States before 1912 when the patents expired.[22] Other firms then began manufacture, and by 1928 there were 440,000 hp of Diesel engines produced.

In the meantime various low-compression engines had been tried— Hornsby-Akroyd, Weiss, Price, and others—but by 1923, these had been raised to high compression thus becoming, in effect, of the Diesel type. Throughout the 1920's, development continued. During this period several hundred internal-combustion engine rail cars were built for service on American railroads on branch and feeder lines where traffic no longer justified full steam operation. Then, in 1929 an interesting application was made in switching engines for the New York Central Lines using electric drive operated by Diesel engines.

The use of Diesel locomotives has grown rapidly since World War II. "Adoption of the Diesel-electric locomotive by the railroads con-

[21] See paper in the special 50th Anniversary issue of *Mech. Eng.* (A.S.M.E.), April, 1930.

[22] It is an interesting fact that, owing to a defect in the application, the Diesel patents had actually expired in 1906. This was kept secret, and other firms waited patiently until 1912 before engaging in Diesel manufacture.

tinues to be the outstanding phase of modern motive-power development," says a recent (1949) report. "So complete has been this acceptance that one of the long-established domestic manufacturers of steam locomotives announced the abandonment of manufacture of this type of locomotive in its United States plant." Late in 1948 of 1,626 locomotives on order by Class I railroads in the United States, 1,510, or 93 per cent, were of this new type. Canadian roads are also moving—but because of price and supply differences more slowly—toward what has become known as "dieselization."

When we recall that our railroads at one time used almost a third of our coal output and that coal has been the main freight load on many lines, the implications of this change become clear.[23] Diesel-electric locomotives are more costly than steam and a high utilization factor as well as low fuel cost is essential to their use. The gasoline engine has, of course, been developed into remarkably powerful yet light and compact forms for airplane use with over 3,000 hp in a single engine. Its normal area is, nevertheless, the smaller, lighter services of, say, 100 hp or less. The Diesel, however, as now built, is essentially a sturdy, big, low-cost-fuel heavy-duty engine which competes in units of 1,500 to 2,000 hp with steam in locomotives and with the gasoline engine, especially in heavier service where it has largely replaced the latter, as in equipment of the construction type. Batteries of Diesel engines have also been installed for stand-by or emergency use in many power plants.

Thus man's abilities to manufacture power from inert materials and to develop the potential power of water power sites have kept pace with the ever-growing power demand. His accomplishments in finding new ways and means of utilizing power in meeting the many needs and wants of modern life have been a vital factor in creating this demand. When Morison wrote in 1903 of *The New Epoch,* of the new age which power was to create, his ideas seemed visionary to many, but his forecast has been more than abundantly fulfilled.

[23] A recent paper "Progress in Railway Mechanical Engineering, 1947–48" in *Mech. Eng.* (A.S.M.E.), April, 1949, p. 299, outlines recent developments including brief notes on the Pennsylvania R.R. steam-turbine locomotive of 1944 and on progress in gas-turbine development.

Chapter 11. MODERN ENGINEERING IV:
INDUSTRY AND MANUFACTURES

The over-all gains in the years 1899–1945, corrected to take account of changes in the purchasing power of the dollar . . . indicate a four to five fold expansion of the total stream of goods and services produced in the United States. The population of the country had increased, in the meantime, by 86 per cent. The average real income per capita of population had thus been multiplied by two and one-half in less than half a century. This is a staggering gain, when set in contrast to the long periods of stagnation in human history and the slow pace of advance as men have gradually won control over the forces and resources of nature. Here was such an industrial revolution as the world had never known.

F. C. Mills, *Technological Gains and Their Uses.*

ENGINEERED MASS PRODUCTION

General. We have noted the rise of manufactures in New England —with an outpost, so to speak, in the Philadelphia area—and the spread of this industrialization westward to the North Central states, states settled largely by emigration from the Birthplace of American Industry—New England. We have noted also that, while there was a steady growth in American manufactures during the 19th century, there was an outburst after 1900 without parallel in human history. Curves of production from cement to automobiles, from soap to oil, from books to power, like curves of size from bridge spans and heights of dams to size of buildings and industrial plants, went skyrocketing upward at an ever-increasing rate. What have been the forces and factors which have led to this ever-growing and ever more widespread industrial revolution in the United States—to a revolution which, as Professor Mills notes, marks an advance unparalleled in the history of man? It would be very reassuring as to our future if the answer could be found in one or two easily understood and easily controlled influences. Actually, however, it is only too clear that many factors and many conditions have played parts which it is extremely difficult to evaluate in creating the modern American industrial way of life.

There are those, for example, who would ascribe our "staggering gains" to the remarkable natural resources of the American continent. They were undoubtedly the major reason why America was the Land of Opportunity for new settlers in the 19th century. But the rise of American industry in New England was clearly not based on the exploitation of natural resources. Connecticut, Massachusetts, and Rhode Island were notably lacking in the coal and iron which had been basic to Britain's rise as an industrial power. Our mineral and other resources, our forests and vast agricultural lands have made possible in the United States an almost completely self-sufficient economy, but other factors have played a more dominating part in creating modern America.

The absence of custom and other barriers to the free flow of goods and services and to the free exploitation of a vast market for manufactured goods and modern services has undoubtedly been a very important element in America's growth. Mass consumption must go hand in hand with mass production and, in sharp contrast with Britain's economy, ours has been built on the home market and home needs rather than on export trade.

Much of our industrial success has also been ascribed to Yankee ingenuity, and certainly no people have been more inventive and ingenious in uncovering new needs and discovering new tools, products, and services to satisfy them. Earlier New England industry was, to be sure, greatly indebted to thefts of basic processes and machines from Great Britain, notably in the textile field. But New England not only added to these contributions her own improvements but went ahead in their further development and the application of the basic principles involved in new directions, to the production of a host of new products, a development which, apparently, had never been envisioned by British manufacturers. Furthermore the student of American manufacturing practices soon realizes that the Yankee peddler carried a major share in the growth of "Yankee notions." Aggressive marketing has been another factor in the American story.

There are also those who would ascribe to the growth of capitalism in America—*Capitalism the Creator*[1]—the major role in the rise of industrial enterprise. Here the answer appears to be that these two developments went forward hand in hand. American industry started rapidly forward immediately after the Civil War. The industrial North won the war, and a new era of union and promise seemed to

[1] The title of an interesting, if biased, study by Carl Snyder, New York, The Macmillan Company, 1940.

have dawned. But this too rapid expansion soon resulted in difficulties. As Clark notes: "This period of material prosperity and progress had a gloomy dawn."[2] The Panic of 1873 not only interrupted this growth, but its effects were felt for almost a decade. There was a period of financial and investment adjustment. Overrapid expansion of productive capacity and the tying up of too much capital in fixed investments led to overproduction and declining prices and to a new chapter in American history, the effects of which were to be of far-reaching consequence.

The trust movement was largely the child of the Panic of '73. Trusts were formed to "support the market," to control output, and to maintain prices. The Standard Oil Trust of 1882 was the first of the great trusts. The initial attempt to monopolize the sugar industry followed in 1887 and other consolidations, from cotton oil and flour milling to the "Whiskey Trust," were under way in the '80's and '90's. The Sherman Antitrust Act of 1888 plus the fact that the trusts failed to secure market monopolies and did not bring about the excessive profits and high prices the public feared, brought the trust scare to an end. Competition could not be smothered and, in many cases, it was found that "proprietor's management" was more efficient and economical than management by trust agents.

While the trust problem declined in importance, the corporate form of business organization continued to replace the older ownership by individuals or partnerships. In 1911, the late President Butler remarked:

I weigh my words, when I say that in my judgment the limited liability corporation is the greatest single discovery of modern times, whether you judge it by its social, by its ethical, by its industrial or, in the long run—after we understand it and know how to use it—by its political effects. Even steam and electricity are far less important than the limited liability corporation, and they would be reduced to comparative impotence without it.[3]

The limited-liability corporation has, thus, become the standard financial structure of the American economy. There are, of course, many criticisms of "big business" yet it seems quite obvious that, as Dr. Butler remarks, many of the products and services we enjoy today can be provided only by large-scale enterprise. The amount of capital which can be brought together under the individual owner-

---

[2] *History of Manufactures.*

[3] *Why Should We Change Our Form of Government?* New York, Charles Scribner's Sons, 1912, p. 82.

ship or partnership form of organization would be quite inadequate to finance such undertakings. One need only review the ownership of modern corporate securities to realize that it is no longer just a few so-called capitalists who supply the funds for American industry. It is the American people. Dr. Moulton of The Brookings Institution in a recent study, *Controlling Factors in Economic Development,* emphasizes also the vital part which the multiplication of the currency, through the evolution of modern banking and credit, what may be called the creation of credit money, has played in making possible the "staggering gains" of American industry.

It has also been remarked that the adaptability, the fluidity and flexibility of American labor, has exercised an important and stimulating influence in America's economic life. Not only the willingness but the ability of American labor to move from one industry to another have undoubtedly done much to encourage competition and maintain a dynamic spirit in industry. It remains to be seen whether recent attempts by labor to expand old-age pensions and other provisions, desirable as such securities are, may not lead to a more static and inflexible, a less progressive, and changeful-minded attitude by labor.

In recent years, the propaganda agents of the natural sciences have also placed great emphasis on the part which the creation, through research and scientific discoveries, of new products and services has played in stimulating American industral growth. Certain it is that many products and services we now regard as essential were never dreamed of by our grandparents. From the auotomobile to the airplane, from the telephone to the radio and television, new devices have been thought of, created, and made an essential part of our lives. But mass-production methods have not been applied solely to new processes and services, or to the type of activity Mr. Ford had in mind when he remarked that mass production begins with "the conception of a public need of which the public may not as yet be conscious."[4] Ideas seem to have played a greater part than scientific discovery. Mass production has become the standard method of providing practically all the needs of modern life from food and clothing to heat and light, and from travel to amusements. We must not lose sight of the fact that the major role of science to date has been the improvement of existing products and services rather than the creation of new activities.

Back of all this there is, of course, another very basic factor, namely,

[4] See "Mass Production," *Encyclopaedia Britannica,* 1926 edition.

low-cost power. The machine by itself gives man the advantage of a new and better tool, but it is the fact that we can hire the power slaves of steam, electricity, and gasoline to operate the machine that has created a new way of life and a new world. The discovery or invention of a new product or service is but the first step. The next is the planning of a series of machine sequences and operations which will produce the product with a minimum use of hands. But all this would have limited purpose and effect if we could not count on low-cost power to operate these machines. The key to our modern economy is inexpensive power, power so cheap that we can buy it for the equivalent of less than a penny a man-hour.

When we turn to the technical aspects of manufacturing, the important influence of the, so to speak, extraneous factors becomes even clearer. The basic methods and principles of mass manufacture are not new, they have been known since the turn of the 18th–19th centuries, for over one hundred fifty years. The specialization of labor goes back, in fact, to Ancient Times. Whitney's interchangeable manufacture was proposed in 1792, and Brunel was active in developing process machinery in the first years of the 19th century. Even as early as 1851, the time of the London Exhibition, the application of these methods in "the American system" was recognized abroad. The more recent technical development which has been of major influence has been the rise of what was called scientific management in the last years of the 19th century.

Scientific Management. While new machinery and new tools had been developed during the earlier years of the century, little had been done in studying how labor might most effectively and efficiently use these tools. In other words the engineering, the scientific methods of fact finding, study, and analysis, had been applied with extraordinary results to the material aspects of manufacturing, but they had not been thought of as applicable to the productivity of labor and the development of more effective and efficient sequences in the entire gamut of production from the handling of materials through all the manufacturing operations, and from the encouragement of better performance by labor to the improvement of managerial practices and techniques. Individual notions, biases, and ideas, human judgments and experiences rather than real understanding and quantitative measurement, determined how machines were used and how production was directed.

The story of "scientific management" in the United States begins with the early work of Frederick Winslow Taylor (1856–1915) at the Midvale Steel Co. in Philadelphia in the last years of the 19th century. Taylor saw that some workers produced more than others, yet little attention was given to this fact in hiring labor and, further-more, each worker was allowed to exercise his own judgment in maintaining and operating the tools he used. No factual data were available on the output of individual workers. No attempt was made to study production operations and to discover and use those methods and sequences of operation which led to increased output. Further-more, while this was basic information, Taylor sought also to estab-lish a clear vision of the far wider implications of the movement he fathered. He saw that the principles involved should be applied not only to labor but to the entire planning and management of an in-dustry. The problem of increased production was not solely a matter of improving labor techniques alone.

Scientific management as it originated at Midvale in the 1880's, although in all respects rudimentary, embraced completely the funda-mentals of scientific shop management. . . . While inspired by the pur-pose of making the facts governing production available for the settlement of disputes with workers, supplemented by the desire for larger pro-ductivity to reduce cost of the product, it was recognized almost im-mediately that to attain this with fairness to the worker, the problem in-volved all phases of management which influence the quantity and quality of the product turned out. Taylor therefore started experimental studies to obtain the knowledge required to set fair and acceptable standards for the workers, and out of these studies grew the developments that in-volved functional operation, production control, inventory control, and the various other features which have gradually established themselves in almost universal practice.[5]

During the period from 1875 to 1900 Taylor's search for better methods resulted in the development of the fundamental principles of modern shop management and applications of this new science began to be made. Bethlehem Steel introduced the Taylor method between 1898 and 1901. But it was an uphill battle, with both the older plant executives as well as labor resisting the introduction of these new-fangled practices. The problem of overcoming this resist-ance was further aggravated a bit later by the rise of a group of self-styled "efficiency experts" during the World War I period—men of little or no experience who followed blindly with a complete loss of

[5] "History of Scientific Management in America," *Mech Eng.* (A.S.M.E.), Vol. 61 (1939), p. 671.

perspective and lack of human understanding the time and motion study techniques developed by Frank B. Gilbreth (1868–1924). So strong was the resulting reaction that the use of a stop watch in timing operations was prohibited in Naval ordnance contracts during World War I.

The acceptance of engineering methods by management has, however, been complete. Sloan, Chairman of the Board of General Motors, remarks that engineering methods must be applied not only in solving the technological problems of industry but to all phases of industrial management. Labor, long regarding this movement with suspicion, feeling that it was designed primarily to exploit the worker and squeeze from him the last drop of effort, has come to realize that increased economic status for labor must, in the long run, depend upon increased productivity. This is not to say that some modern labor unions do not still resist the introduction of new and more efficient technological and managerial innovations, thus retarding the realization of the full fruits of technological progress. The situation varies in different industries. In those of stable or decreasing employment, changes which would further reduce such employment are stubbornly resisted. In new and growing enterprises, the newer techniques are fully accepted. Perhaps this is an example both of one of the factors in the inescapable lag between the discovery of knowledge and its application while, at the same time, it provides at least one means of distributing the costs of labor obsolescence.

The pressures of the depression of the '30's and of World War II, in which scientific management in America was a potent factor in the Allied victory, have done much to accelerate both the acceptance and the more widespread adoption of the principles to which Taylor devoted his life. In fact he may be regarded as the Father of Scientific Management and founder of a new branch of engineering, Industrial Engineering, which seeks to apply the methods and principles of engineering study, analysis, and design to the whole broad field of industrial enterprise from production to marketing, and from problems of personnel to those of quality control and cost accounting.

The Moving Assembly Line. Others than Taylor had, however, been thinking of the problem of increased production and Henry Ford (1863–1947) introduced another new idea in 1913 and, as a result, is widely regarded abroad as the Father of Mass Production. The moving assembly line had some earlier fragmentary forerunners, such as in earlier gunmaking, in the manufacture of the McCormick reaper, and in the meat-packing industry. It was Ford, however, who made it work on a hitherto undeveloped scale and with astounding results.

Before the moving assembly line was introduced, the Ford magneto, for example, was a one-man job, and, in a 9-hour day, one man could assemble only 35 to 40 of these devices—an average of 20 man-minutes per magneto. When Ford introduced the moving assembly

The Moving Assembly Line, 1914

Showing the early assembly line at the Highland Park Plant of the Ford Motor Company to which the company had moved in 1909. The first endless floor conveyor and chain system had been installed in 1911. (*Courtesy of Ford News Bureau.*)

line, some 29 men performed in sequence the same assembly operations as the magneto moved down the line and part after part was added to it. In this way, 1,188 completed assemblies were made in a single day, at an average of about 13 man-minutes each and a saving in time of 60 to 70 per cent.

Ford's announcement of this new development was coupled with the voluntary but revolutionary establishment of a minimum wage of $5 and of an 8-hour day—about double the average wage then prevailing in the industry and for a shorter day. Probably no single act in American industrial history has had a greater influence in creating a favorable attitude on the part of labor toward technological change than this farsighted and constructive policy adopted by Henry Ford, that of passing on to labor a major part of the gains made possible through the manufacturing improvements he initiated. Furthermore, there was a steady decrease in the price of the Ford car from $825 in 1908 to $260 in 1926 when the 10-millionth car passed out of the Ford shops.[6]

It is, thus, impossible to attribute to any single factor the American Industrial Revolution. Back of all these various influences have been the ever-present competitive battle and the rising costs of labor which have forced a continued search for better methods of production in the never-ending struggle to lower the prices and improve the quality of older products or to develop new products which possess these and other advantages. Human labor has been replaced by the modern power-driven, often automatic machine. The older craftsmen and the manual skills which were such an important element in earlier days have been progressively replaced by engineering design, teamwork, and engineered production. The engineer is apt to think of manufacturing in terms of machines rather than products. The machine and machine tool constitute, of course, a great industry in themselves. But the most impressive fact about American industry is the wide scope of the needs and wants of man which have succumbed to machine, mass-production methods.

Manufactures. Textile manufacture, the first area to feel the impact of mechanization, continues to be a basic industry. E. H. Marble has said:

The general principles which were embodied in the machinery in the textile industry in 1880 are found in the machinery in use today. While several revolutionary mechanical devices have been introduced, we find the greatest progress has been made in building machinery more durable in construction, introducing simplicity of adjustment, and an adaptability of the entire machine to meet the requirements of the several staples used in the industry.

This modest statement does not give adequate credit to such important developments as the automatic loom, first introduced in 1895.

---

[6] It was not until 1928 that competition finally forced Ford to give up the old Model T which had become affectionately known as a "Tin Lizzie." It was superseded by a thoroughly modern car; in fact, the American practice of bringing out annual models has undoubtedly stimulated, made possible, continued improvement in the American automobile.

In this machine the replacement of empty spools or bobbins became automatic. The modern loom detects flaws and breaks and stops automatically. Instead of one weaver to a loom, one worker now controls 20 looms. Instead of 200 to 250 stops a day to change shuttles, there are now only 5 to 7 stops. In 1880 it is estimated that 750 cotton fabric establishments employed 107,000 workers and produced $1,100 worth of goods per worker. By 1925 some 1,600 plants with 470,000 employees produced almost $4,000 per worker.

One of the more recent changes has been in the remarkable rise of the American baking industry. Home baking had given way by 1899 to bakeries employing 60,200 persons. By 1937 this had risen to 240,000, and the production of machines for all the operations of baking from mixing to wrapping the product had become a major machine manufacturing enterprise.

Not so many years have passed since New England was dotted with small mill working establishments, carriage and wagon shops. Each town had its cabinetmaker. The Philadelphia Centennial of 1876 seems to have marked the beginning of a great new era in modern woodworking machinery in the United States. The carriage and buggy manufacturers were turning out 40,000 units a year by 1880. The furniture factories of Grand Rapids, "the Furniture Capital of America," were started in the 1870's. The adoption of standard sizes and grades of lumber, the standardization of such mill products as sash, doors, and trim—all reflect the modernization of an ancient, largely craftsman industry. Still more recently new forms of wall and insulating board, as well as a new lumber product, plywood, have given new life to the wood industries.

It has been said that the story of fresh-food storage passed through two major stages, the Spice Age and the Ice Age, before arriving at the Age of Refrigeration.

Even the widespread use of ice is a comparatively recent innovation. A compressed-air plant, the exhaust of which was used for refrigeration, was built in Paris in 1868 but, by 1892, had developed to only 10,000 hp. In this period this type of machine was standard, and beef and butter were shipped from Australia and New Zealand to Britain using air machines. In 1873, however, the first large practical ammonia machine was built by Dr. Linde. Between 1889 and 1890 there was a not too successful artificial ice boom in New York City, but it was not until 1919 that artificial replaced natural ice in meeting the bulk of the demand. By 1925 the small, home refrigerator began to appear and the Ice Age vanished into the past. Today, of course, the whole area not only of refrigeration but of heating and ventilation has become an engineering activity of ever-increasing scope and importance.

These are but a few of the many directions in which modern methods of manufacture have played their part in creating a new world. As a result of the rise of this new industrial technique, an increasingly larger part of American industrial leadership today falls upon the shoulders of engineer-managers who have succeeded in modern corporate enterprise the old owner-managers of the days of individual or partnership organizations. The engineer has long occupied a position intermediate between capital on the one hand and labor on the other. He is now asked to assume ever greater responsibilities for over-all management, for the modern problems of production and employment which are basic to the continued prosperity of a business enterprise and have become matters requiring special technological understandings and skills.

The techniques of this new industrial engineering are still, however, largely in the empirical stage, still in the process of evolution and of gradual rationalization along scientific lines. Notable advances have been made in the application of statistical methods not only in quality control but to a host of other industrial problems. Mathematical statistics bid fair, in fact, to become the key which will open a new era of industrial, business, and economic understandings. The techniques of time and motion study are likewise being improved while the limitations and place of such studies in production processes are becoming more clearly recognized.

The activities of the industrial engineer involve a far wider range of understandings than have been recognized as essential in the older engineering branches. A new technique of "human engineering" is in process of development, and it requires the close cooperation of medical, psychological, sociological, and other experts if its problems are to be solved. It has long been recognized that the physical health of the worker exercises an important influence on his effective and efficient performance. The modern factory provides not only sanitary surroundings but gives special attention to the protection of the worker, to lighting, and to industrial safety in general. But it is also realized that modern methods of production have also posed new problems of mental health. The remarkable studies of Mayo and others are opening up new avenues not only for the improvement of production but in the creation of new team satisfactions to replace the older individual pride of craftsmanship which has inevitably been lost with the rise of the American system of manufacturing.

On the management side there have been equally important advances from the level of "top management" down. Modern engineering and statistical methods are used in planning production and forecasting markets. Active programs of "college recruiting" are employed to secure desirable personnel for positions varying from research and development through operation and management to sales. While there are still thousands of small manufacturers, frequently manufacturing a single product, often operating on a "jobbing" basis, and usually unable to afford to maintain research or to follow a thoroughly engineered program, the larger industries are constantly applying engineering principles and methods to an ever-widening range of business and managerial problems.

One cannot resist the temptation to compare this story of engineered industry and scientific management which prevails in the United States today with the situation we faced less than a century ago. Back in 1856, before he became President of Johns Hopkins, Daniel Coit Gilman had bemoaned the fact that America was "far behind" European nations in many important branches of industry. "Our agriculture," he observed, "is less productive than that of Europe; our rich stores of mineral wealth are almost unexplored; our manufactures, with the exception of staple goods, are less perfect, durable and varied, while they are also, for the most part, more costly than those of England, France, Germany and Belgium."[7]

This picture has, of course, been completely reversed, but the contrast with present American conditions is even more forcefully portrayed in a description of Baltimore of Gilman's earlier years a century ago, when

. . . the tall masts of the great clipper ships towered above the wharves, and the straggling streets, lined with low houses, mostly of frame, seemed centered at the foot of the hills and close to the water . . . covered Conestoga wagons, spattered with mud, crowded in from the West, forming long lines down the main streets, their blue-shirted teamsters gathering for refreshment at numerous inns. . . . No honk of machine or clang of trolley disturbed the quiet—a seaboard town lapped by the waves in the hush that preceded the birth of modern industry.[8]

Today the industry which transformed the handful of New Eng-

[7] *Daniel Coit Gilman,* by Abraham Flexner, New York, Harcourt, Brace and Company, Inc., 1946, p. 9.

[8] *Johns Hopkins, A Silhouette,* by Helen H. Thom, Baltimore, Johns Hopkins Press, 1929, p. 19.

land states has spread not only to the West to which the Conestoga wagons carried supplies a century ago, but to the South, in fact all over our country. A study of this widespread geographical distribution of industrialization indicates some of the more modern forces and factors which influence our industrial economy, as well as the fact that America's higher standards of living are, in due course, being brought to all her people.

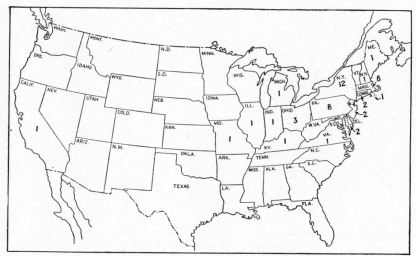

American Manufactures, 1849

Showing the concentration of manufactures in the southern New England states, the birthplace of American Industry, and in the New York, New Jersey, Pennsylvania area. Numbers on this and succeeding maps represent annual outputs of 20 million dollars of manufactured products. (*After Lauer, Engineering in American Industry.*)

Thus the concentration of industry in the North Atlantic states in 1849 is clearly shown. The South was still an agricultural, cotton area. The Central West was being opened up, but the Rocky Mountain and Coast states were still largely unknown and completely unsettled. By 1899, fifty years later, industrial growth, as we have noted, had spread to the North Central states. By 1939 the agricultural areas and even the Rocky Mountain states had been invaded. Not a single state in the Union but produced annually over 20 million dollars' worth of manufactured product. Major developments had taken place in the South: the cotton area had taken over some of the textile manufactures of New England as well as developed its own resources of coal and iron. Texas had moved sharply forward, aided, no doubt, by the petroleum boom but markedly advancing as a manufacturing area. The West Coast had grown from the earlier isolated dot in California to a widespread industrial development. These were the areas which, a few years later, were to grow even more markedly as a result of war needs and demands.

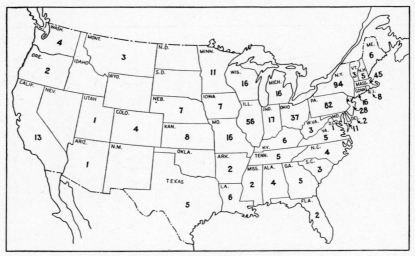

American Manufactures, 1899

Showing the situation 50 years later than the previous map, this chart illustrates the spread of industrialization to the North Central states (largely settled, it will be recalled, from the New England area) with the beginnings of growth in the South, in the Mississippi Valley, and in California. (*After Lauer.*)

One reads in this spread of industrialization some of the factors which are influential today—the availability of reasonably low-cost labor, ample supplies of low-cost power, favorable tax conditions and, as transportation costs rise, the relationship of plants to sources of supply and to markets. We shall have occasion later to look into manufactures as a source of employment for America's increasing millions. As a means of distributing opportunities for employment and equalizing the disparity of wages between agricultural and industrial labor—providing more widespread and equally distributed material welfare—these studies clearly show that the advantages of the American system are being made available to all our states and all our people.

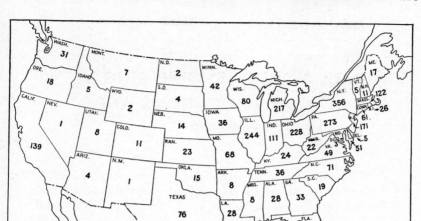

American Manufactures, 1939

During the 20th century industrialization in the United States had spread to include at least 20 millions dollars annually of manufactured products in every state of the Union. The growth in the South, in Texas, and in California is particularly notable.

Chapter 12. MODERN ENGINEERING V:
COMMUNICATIONS AND
ELECTRONICS

The extension of the spoken word by means of electrical systems of intercommunication represents a unique and revolutionary step in man's progress. . . . While Bell stated and developed the fundamental principle of the telephone with astonishing completeness, the difficulties which faced the pioneers who sought to make it commercially useful seemed almost insurmountable. . . . All improvements had to be worked out from fundamentals, but the fundamentals themselves were little understood by even the most learned. Great credit is due those who, by research, invention and development, created a new public service from the beginnings of the telephone art.

John J. Carty, Foreword to *Beginnings of Telephony*
by F. L. Rhodes.

THE TELEGRAPH AND TELEPHONE, RADIO AND ITS OFFSPRING

To one who has not followed developments in the field of communications it is surprising to discover that our present facilities are almost entirely of 20th century origin. The Atlantic had, to be sure, been finally spanned by cable in 1865; the telephone had been invented but, owing to various difficulties, its use before the turn of the century was quite restricted. It was not until 1902 that the first Pacific cable was laid; the "long-distance" telephone did not cross the American continent until 1915; Marconi's "wireless" did not span the Atlantic until 1901; radio telephony was still in its infancy in World War I days; broadcasting was not inaugurated until 1922; and commercial television is of World War II vintage, as is the remarkable technique of radar. The air, once with the sea, but one of the great and uncertain voids between which men and ships ventured at their peril, has become the silent bearer of man's messages to his distant fellow. Yet we generaly regard these wonders as so much a part of modern life that we find difficulty in understanding how they can possibly be of such recent birth.

216

Telegraphy. It was in 1900 that the Western Union Cable Co. placed a new cable of the heaviest and most modern type, between Newfoundland and Penzance in England. Radio telegraphy was still in the experimental stage and the outstanding telegraphic developments were cable constructions. By 1914 there were 14 cables joining North America and Europe. In 1902 British interests successfully joined British Columbia with Australia, far across the Pacific. The following year the Commercial Cable Co., starting from San Francisco, landing at Hawaii, Midway, and Guam, spanned to the Philippines. Later extensions reached Shanghai and Japan.

But feeble signals were received when electric current was transmitted over the thousands of miles of earlier cables. The losses were great, and extremely delicate receiving equipment was required. The earlier visual method, using a sensitive galvanometer, was finally replaced by the purely mechanical so-called siphonic, printing receiver, but the development of the permalloy cable also marked another great advance. Current passing along a conductor sets up, as Faraday first observed, a magnetic field surrounding the conductor. By wrapping the central copper cable core with a special nickel-steel alloy, permalloy, having high magnetic properties, a favorable balance between electric and magnetic fields is achieved with the result that distortion of a signal transmitted over long distance is greatly decreased.

Modern apparatus also greatly increases the speed of transmission, and the modern cable, operated mechanically, carries far more words per minute than the best of the older operators even dreamed was possible. Other developments were destined, however, to become competitors of cable transmission.

Telephony. The history of the telephone up to 1893, when the basic Bell patents expired—or even a few years later—was one of the development of equipment, of patent litigation, and of public education in the use and value of this new device. Independent companies came into the field as the telephone became a necessity rather than a luxury. By 1907, however, the limitations and inconveniences of such independent operations became evident, and telephone services were unified under the American Telephone and Telegraph Co. Growth has been continuous in the intervening years. Boston and Providence had been joined by a 45-mile circuit in 1882. New York to Boston and also to Philadelphia had followed in 1884–1885; New York and Chicago, 900 miles, were connected in 1892. These were extremely costly undertakings, possible only between centers of great telephone traffic. A new development entered this field. Rapid advances followed. By 1911, Denver was joined to New York; by 1913, Salt Lake, 2,300 miles away, had been reached and, in 1915, the American continent had been spanned from coast to coast.

As early as 1887, the now famous but, in his day, misunderstood and obscure pioneer of electrical theory, Dr. Oliver Heaviside (1850–1925), had studied telephone transmission but never attempted to apply, or even to clarify, his theories. It remained for a Serbian peasant boy, who became an outstanding teacher, research leader, and inventor, to solve and make use of Heaviside's remarkable studies. In 1900, Professor Michael I. Pupin (1858–1935) developed the loading coil method, or Pupinization as it was called, of reinforcing telephonic signals.[1] Commercial, long-distance telephony as we know it today became possible.

The search for improvement in telephone service has been continuous since the birth of the industry in 1876. First located in Boston, telephone research was brought to New York in 1907 when the American Bell Telephone Co. was dissolved and the famous "A. T. and T." was formed. In 1919, a department of development and research was formally organized and the research work of the Western Electric Co. was taken over. Finally, in 1925, the great Bell Laboratories in New York were created to seek, through research, constant improvements in the art and science of telephone communication. A stream of developments has followed.

One of the major earlier problems of telephone service centered in the improvement of the telephone exchange, in switching apparatus, and in service. The modern dial system, widely introduced for local service in the '30's and now in process of extension to long-distance operation, has beginnings going far back in telephone history. As early as 1879, patents were issued for an automatic switching system which, however, was not a commercial success. In 1889 a "step-by-step" system was evolved and "other automatic systems, containing features which have contributed in an important way to the modern dial-operated switchboards," were developed as early as 1900 and 1906. Today the United States uses almost two-thirds of the world's telephones—close to 40 million of a total estimated at 66 million. Just before the turn of the century there was probably about one telephone for every 200 people or thereabouts in the United States. Fifty years later there was one for nearly every four persons.

[1] See Professor Pupin's fascinating and interesting autobiography, *From Immigrant to Inventor,* New York, Charles Scribner's Sons, 1925.

Furthemore, telephone service has been greatly extended through the use of wireless. A telephone cable between Key West and Havana was opened in 1921, for many years the longest submarine line (105 miles) in service. Regular trans-Atlantic service by wire and radio was inaugurated, however, in 1925. In 1930 parts of South America were joined to the United States and communication with Australia was established via Great Britain. Constant extensions of this inter-continental service have been made, and today the air not only bears man's message to his fellow in distant lands but also his voice. The key to this world-wide achievement has been radio—"messages without wires."

As a matter of fact, modern telephone practice has to a major degree adopted what might be called radio broadcasting methods. "Multiplexing" has become standard practice in transmission between cities over costly trunk lines. The human voice, vibrating at a few thousand cycles per second, is used to "modulate," that is, to control, carrier waves of far higher frequency—in the order of 100,000 cycles per second—which are, of course, completely inaudible to the human ear.[2] By selecting various ranges in these high frequencies, as is done in radio broadcasting where a standard frequency is assigned to a station, one cable may carry many messages. Instead of being limited to one conversation, as many as 240 simultaneous communications can be carried on in this way. Another system, actually a special form of radio transmission, does away entirely with cables and utilizes microwave radio beams for voice transmission. This is now in process of commercial evaluation. "Scrambling" is still another modern technique which makes it impossible for messages to be understood if they are intercepted. One has to know the key to "unscramble" the jumble of waves transmitted.

In order to increase the capacity of cables to carry the wide range of frequencies used in such operations, Bell Laboratory engineers developed the so-called "coaxial" cable, a copper tube with a copper wire running through its center. In 1935 the first of these coaxial cables was installed between New York and Philadelphia. While normal telephone cables can be and are used to link up amplitude-modulated (AM) broadcast stations, such coaxial lines are also

[2] The human ear is limited to vibrations of 20 to 20,000 cycles per second or less. The present classification of frequencies is: subaudio, 0 to 20 cycles; audio, 20 to 20,000; supersonic, 20,000 to 100,000; radio, 100,000 to 1,000 million; and microwave, 1,000 million to 10^{12} or 10 million million cycles per second.

essential in order to secure the range of frequencies essential to full frequency-modulated (FM) broadcasting or to television transmission as we shall note later. Nevertheless coaxial cables are very expensive, and it seems probable that microwave radio may be increasingly used in telephone practice rather than additional costly coaxial lines.

Radio Telegraphy and Telephony. The long sequence of discoveries and ideas which have led to the radio of today carries us back to Lord Kelvin (1853) and to James Clerk Maxwell who, in 1873, showed mathematically that electric oscillations gave rise to waves which traveled from the source with the velocity of light. As in the case of the dynamo, however, the work of many men and almost a half century of advances were required to translate these fundamental concepts into modern radio broadcasting.

The name of Henrich R. Hertz (1857–1894) stands out in this development for it was this German physicist who, in 1887, first produced and studied the electromagnetic waves that Maxwell had postulated. The first stage in development rested primarily on devising a means of detecting the waves which were produced with the Hertzian oscillator. In 1892 Professor Edouard Branly of Paris invented the coherer, a small tube fitted with metal plugs and filled with metal filings. This device, normally offering high resistance to the passage of an electric current, was rendered more highly conductive under the action of such waves. By tapping the tube, the coherence of the metal particles was again broken and signals could be received.

It was in 1896 that the Italian inventor and promoter Guglielmo Marconi (1874–1937) took out the first patent on Hertzian wave telegraphy. Two years later he demonstrated the practical value of his system by communicating between the lightship on the East Goodwin shoals and the shore. The next year witnessed the transmission of messages across the English Channel and, in 1901, signals were received in St. John's, Newfoundland, which originated in Poldhu, in Cornwall, England, 1,800 miles away. The establishment of trans-Atlantic service followed the next year. Large aerials, or antennae, were required to send and receive these signals; a more sensitive receiving device, a better detector, was essential to further development.

Marconi, however, was essentially an inventor and may even be accused of having had a "one-track mind." Through his patience and persistence the value and importance of radio telegraphy were demonstrated to the world. But he seems to have been completely absorbed in perfecting his own system and ideas and to have failed to recognize the importance of the newer developments which were destined to revolutionize the art which he had been so largely instrumental in creating. When one recalls that Professor Fleming, who developed the Fleming valve, a basic device of the new radio technique, had joined Marconi research in 1899, this failure of the great Italian pioneer to lead in further developments seems even more difficult to explain.

As early as 1883 what became known as the "Edison effect" was discovered in studies of the incandescent electric bulb. In 1904 Professor, later Sir, John Ambrose Fleming (1849–1945), a British physicist and electrical engineer, became the first to make use of this effect in his radio detector, or Fleming valve. In addition to the light filament, a small plate was placed in an incandescent bulb. It was found that electric current (or, in modern scientific terms, "electrons") could pass only from the filament to the plate, that is, in only one direction. The rapid alternations of the incoming electromagnetic wave, although having variations in amplitude such that their crest corresponded to the useful message, were themselves inaudible because of their high frequency. The Fleming valve made it possible to "rectify" these variations in amplitude, to reproduce the crest of these waves, and thus recover the audible signal. In 1907 the American inventor, Dr. Lee De Forest, introduced a third element, the "grid," between the plate and filament in the Fleming tube, and the "audion" or thermionic tube, essential in both modern telephony and telegraphy, was born.[3] In 1912 a young Columbia engineering student, Edwin H. Armstrong, discovered the regenerative detector circuit by means of which feeble impulses received by radio could be "fed back," built up, and increased many times, making an exceedingly sensitive radio receiver using only a single tube.

When we recall that in earlier centuries a ship at sea was completely out of touch with either land stations or other ships, a major value of this gift of messages without wires becomes clear. In 1909 the *S.S. Republic,* for example, was rammed by the *Florida* off Nantucket. Radio brought quick relief. Similarly, had it not been for

[3] Various forms of radio or electronic tubes have been devised and are described by reference to the number of elements in the tube; a pentode tube, for example, contains five parts or elements. A highly specialized, technical language has developed in this field, far more involved than in any other branch of engineering. See "Electron Tubes 1930 to 1950," *Electronics,* April, 1950, p. 67.

radio the *Titanic* disaster of 1912, when this great new ship on its maiden voyage struck an iceberg and sank in the North Atlantic, would have remained another of the unsolved mysteries of the sea.

This, however, was all in the area of telegraphic signals. Before radio telephony became possible, it was necessary to develop a new method of transmitting signals. The older spark gap or arc oscillator could not produce continuous oscillations such as could be used to transmit speech. Mechanical methods were devised but, in 1913, Dr. Alexander Meissner of Berlin found that the Fleming tube itself could be made to produce such continuous, controllable oscillations. The foundations for successful radio telephony were thus available before World War I. The thermionic tube, as a matter of fact, had been an important factor in relaying the human voice and making possible the cross-continent telephone service of 1915.

Radio is undoubtedly a great mystery to all but a few of the millions who listen to radio broadcasts. Yet the basic principles are not difficult to understand. Radio waves, waves of over 100,000 cycles per second (*i.e.,* frequency) are, as we have noted, inaudible to the human ear. By means of the radio tube, waves of a constant radio frequency are set up and the strength (*i.e.,* amplitude) of these waves is so varied that the top, or crest, of the radio wave forms another wave pattern, an audio wave, a wave following the vibrations of the human voice, of music, of sound. At the receiving station these radio waves are received and strengthened, then filtered by means of the Fleming or detector tube, as we have noted, so that the sound wave they carry is, after amplification, transmitted to the human ear. The radio tube in its various forms is thus the key to radio telephony. It is the modulated oscillator which is made to follow the pattern of the sound wave, it is the detector, the amplifier, and the rectifier which translates inaudible radio waves back into sound. It has been said that, when we listen to radio, we are listening to the variations in amplitude of superaudible wave vibrations.

By 1922 commercial radio broadcasting was under way, and amateurs throughout the country were building "sets"—in the beginning using "cat's whisker" crystal detectors and earphones—and bragging, "Last night I got Pittsburgh, or Denver, or some other distant station." "Loud-speakers" replaced earphones, and sets continually improved until today there is not one but on an average two and one-half radio sets in every home. Broadcasting reached such a stage of development that, in 1927, the nominal control of the U.S. Department of Commerce was strengthened through the Radio Act which divided the states into zones and established a Federal Radio Commission to assign wavelengths and generally supervise the art.

While transmission by varying the amplitude of the radio wave (*i.e.,* amplitude modulation, or AM) is satisfactory during normal

The First Frequency Modulation Station, 1937

Erected at Alpine, on the Palisades opposite Yonkers, New York, by the inventor of the older AM regenerative and superheterodyne receivers and of the new technique of frequency modulation in radio communication. Professor Armstrong used this 400-ft tower to demonstrate the superior qualities and freedom from static of FM transmission.

weather, "static" continues to be the bane of radio reception during electrical storms, and sparking motors and other interference also interrupt reception. Thunderstorms produce their own broadcast by adding their bit to the amplitude of the incoming wave, and an annoying "crash" interrupts normal reception. The idea of using frequency modulation (FM) had been considered in the early days of broadcasting but abandoned because of the difficulties involved. The same Edwin H. Armstrong who, as an undergraduate, had discovered the regenerative circuit and who later, serving with the U.S. Army Signal Corps in France during World War I, developed the even more sensitive superhetrodyne receiver, turned his attention, in the late '20's, to this problem. In 1932 he applied for patents and in the face of opposition from the established AM broadcast interests and the doubts of the Federal Radio Commission, the greater fidelity of FM and its freedom from static were later strikingly and convincingly demonstrated in 1938 by transmissions from Professor Armstrong's Alpine tower on the Palisades opposite Yonkers. A bright future for this new method seemed assured, but the long and bitter battle with the well-established AM interests was far from won when World War II intervened.[4] Armstrong devoted his entire time and energy during the war to service for our military forces. In the meantime, another development had been in process of which FM became an essential part.

Television. In 1927 there was demonstrated, in the famous Bell Laboratories in New York, a successful but purely experimental electrical transmission from Washington of pictures, that is, television, using both telephone and radio. The apparatus used, however, was "inherently complicated and expensive" and it was freely admitted that "no commercial field for television was as yet in sight."

The development of television was primarily dependent upon the improvement of the photoelectric cell and of an effective means of "scanning" a picture—breaking it up into a large number of spots of light which, electrically transmitted with sufficient rapidity, could reproduce a reasonably clear and "continuous" picture. The photoelectric cell, a special form of tube sensitive to light, translates the light intensity of the successive spots scanned into feeble electric currents. These current variations transmitted to the receiving station control the brightness of the spots on a special florescent bulb or lamp.

In its earlier form the scanning was performed mechanically by a revolving "scanning disk" which with a series of holes covered all the area of the object many times a second. A similar disk revolving in synchronism at the receiving end permitted beams to be thrown

[4] See "Armstrong of Radio," *Fortune,* February, 1948, p. 89.

on the neon tube, producing in rapid succession dots of light which formed the picture.

By the early '30's this mechanical method of scanning had been replaced by an all-electronic method which not only made the disk obsolete but greatly increased the number of spots of light and thus improved the quality of the image. Three types of electronic scanners are in use: the iconoscope, an invention of Dr. Vladimir Zworykin, who came to the United States in 1919 after the Russian Revolution, which utilizes a special plate that is essentially a mosaic of tiny photoelectric cells; the image dissector, devised by an American farm boy, Philo Farnsworth of Rigby, Idaho, which uses a scanning aperture that dissects the image into many elements; and the image orthicon, the most recent development, which is basically a highly technical improvement on the iconoscope idea developed by a group of workers of the R.C.A.

It was not until 1941, however, that the United States govenment finally authorized commercial television operation. The war held up this development, and it has only been in the past few years that television broadcasts have become common and the rush to buy sets has been under way. The transmission of "sound and scene" is thus an accomplished fact and, while at present the scene is in black and white, color television is certain to come within a relatively short time.

The Federal Radio Commission, or Communications Commission (FCC) as it is now called, has required that all sound accompanying television be transmitted by FM. This method will, thus, not only grow in use as television grows but is also widely employed for police and other similar communication systems; its use for normal sound broadcasting is also increasing.

Various forms of fascimile transmission for photographs and also for written messages have also been devised. These are essentially simplified forms of television and, while occasionally used, as in the transmission of newspaper pictures, have not as yet won an important position in commercial communication operation.

Sonar, Loran, and Radar. While the longer electromagnetic waves used in regular radio are reflected from the upper level of the atmosphere, the ionosphere, and, thus, follow the earth's curvature and span great distances, shorter radio waves are not so reflected and, like similar television broadcasts, penetrate the ionosphere and thus are not effective beyond the visible horizon. Even before the war, a method of sending out sound waves and recording accurately the time before the echo was received had been successfully used in deep-water sounding and navigation. These two methods became of vital importance during the war.

Since radio waves do not travel through water, sonar (*sound* *navi*-gation *a*nd *r*anging) was highly developed and became a most successful method of locating enemy submarines. The short radar *r*adio *d*etection *a*nd *r*anging) waves were also sent out in a similar manner, in a series of rapid pulses which, reflected by any obstacle, brought back a similar radio echo. Here, however, a further remarkable development was carried out. It was found possible to project these findings of radar echoes in rapid succession on a cathode-ray tube, similar to those used in television receivers. An actual motion picture in silhouette was thus secured, and planes could be spotted not only long before they could be seen but at night or through fog. Similarly radar directed groundward from a plane revealed certain topo-grahical features, notably differences between water and land, and made accurate bombing possible even when the target was quite invisible.

Similar to radar, loran (long range navigation) is a system of radio reflections recording from known stations which makes possible the location of a ship's position at sea. Radio beams are also, of course, widely used as aids to both water and aerial navigation.

Electronics. Over the past 35 years, since Armstrong in 1914 first plotted the characteristic curves for radio tubes, there has thus been building up an entirely new electrical technique, first with applications in the field of communications, as outlined above, but a technique which, it has become clear, has many other, including probably still unknown or unrealized, applications. The electron tube has become basic in new and remarkable forms of computing machines, in devices for inspection and quality control in manufacturing, in the measurement of strains in materials and structures, in various devices based on electrical-physical analogies, until it has become clear that this new engineering science offers possibilities of application that open up a whole new area of service and use. There is also under way another and most promising development in the use of electronic equipment in "servomechanisms." While the problems of the early decades of the 20th century were those of making available the large amounts of electrical power required by the new Power Age, the problems of today and tomorrow will, apparently, center in the accurate, precise, control of power and power devices.

Such problems may involve the precise regulation of temperature, of speed, or of other quantities, or even the accurate following of a signal by a power tool. Many of the techniques developed in communication engineering are thus being ingeniously applied in this new field of precise control. Indeed so widespread are the applications of electronics in engineering that our more progressive engineering schools require all engineering students today to study this new field of engineering science.

Chapter 13. MODERN ENGINEERING VI:
CONSTRUCTION

After me cometh a Builder. Tell him, I too have known.
When I was King and a Mason—a Master proven and skilled—
I cleared me ground for a Palace such as a King should build.
I decreed and dug down to my levels. Presently, under the silt,
I came on the wreck of a Palace such as a King had built. . . .
Swift to my use in my trenches, where my well-planned ground-works grew,
I tumbled his quoins and his ashlars, and cut and reset them anew.
Lime I milled of his marbles; burned it, slacked it, and spread;
Taking and leaving at pleasure the gifts of the humble dead.
Yet I despised not nor gloried; Yet as we wrenched them apart,
I read in the razed foundations the heart of that builder's heart.
As he had risen and pleaded, so did I understand
The form of the dream he had followed in the face of the thing he had
  planned.

Rudyard Kipling, "The Palace."

CIVIL ENGINEERING

It has probably been in the field of construction that the results of bigger engineering have been most clearly brought home to the general public. Few of us have visited a great modern central station or factory, a chemical plant or mining operation, but many of us pass almost daily some great bridge or dam or travel through a tunnel or over a modern highway. While, on the surface, it is the bigness of these works that is most impressive, we also have some glimmerings, at least, of the fact that this bigness implies more accurate planning and design, more effective and powerful construction methods—better engineering.

These advances cover the entire field of construction, from buildings and bridges to dams and tunnels. They have been brought about, primarily, by the increasing demands of a growing economy, our increasing public, industrial, and living needs, for such great works are costly and are not attempted until pressing wants justify

228

their construction. Thus the growth of our urban centers has not only posed new problems but has resulted in vast expenditures for water supplies, sewerage plants, tall buildings, and great bridges, and tunnels. Industrial requirements have resulted not only in new and larger manufacturing plants but in a greater use of power with resulting developments in steam, hydraulic, and other constructions. Another far-reaching demand has been that created by the advent of the automobile. The Highway Era has involved not only highways per se but highway bridges and tunnels. Before World War I the world's greatest works of this kind were built for railroad service. The automobile has brought about a new age both of highways and of record-breaking bridge spans and tunnel constructions.

The civil engineering student too often regards improvement in design not only as the major factor in the progress of his profession but even as an end in itself. These increases in demand which have made great modern works possible have, of course, greatly stimulated the never-ending search for more exact, more economical, and safer procedures in design. The advent of new materials and of new tools, especially power machinery, has also vitally influenced progress and created new problems and needs in design. Nevertheless, design is merely a means to intelligent construction, and one must thus look to accomplishments in construction, in the actual use of new materials and methods, if progress is to be properly evaluated and appraised.

Materials. Undoubtedly the most important 20th century change in the area of materials has been the replacement of stone and brick masonry with concrete and the rise of reinforced concrete—*beton armée,* as the French call it. This development came with the turn of the century. In 1899 Professor Baker wrote that "the increasing use of concrete" had made "a complete revision" necessary in his famous textbook, *A Treatise on Masonry Construction,* published only 10 years earlier when it was devoted almost exclusively to stone and brick constructions.

Back of this change was the rise of the Portland cement industry in the United States and the fact that concrete was a mass-machine product in sharp contrast to the skilled hand labor required and the limited production output possible when stone and brick were used. Labor rates began to increase after 1900 with a declining immigration. Masons' wages had doubled after the Civil War and were rising with the turn of the century. But while Portland cement had been discovered in Britain as early as 1824, only the far less reliable "natural" cement was available at reasonable cost in the

United States.[1] Stone and brick required a minimum amount of cement, but as cement declined in price and labor increased in cost, machine-made, mass-produced concrete almost completely superseded brick and stone.

In the decade after 1897, for example, American Portland cement production increased twentyfold and, by 1907, only 10 per cent of the cement used was natural. The cost per barrel was so reduced that Portland cement concrete became standard in "heavy" construction, and the older materials which man had used for close to fifty centuries became almost a thing of the past.[2]

In the metal field, the change from iron to steel had been under way before the close of the 19th century. Bridge engineers were busily employed replacing older wrought-iron railroad bridges with new steel structures designed to carry the mounting loads of new locomotives. A number of notable new bridges were also built, but specifications for railroad bridge design and fabrication, structural

---

[1] Strange as may seem, modern cement is thus one of the most recent of construction materials. The use of lime mortar goes back to the earliest days, but lime hardens only on exposure to air (CO_2) and, hence, cannot be used either in bulk (as in concrete) or under water. As earlier noted, the Greeks used an admixture of santorin earth and the Romans used pozzuolana, which gave lime hydraulic and bulk-hardening properties. These, plus some later use of "Dutch Tarras," or trass, found in Belgium and Germany, provided the only hydraulic cements available until the 19th century, and they were low in strength, limited in amount, and relatively costly. Louis Joseph Vicat, a French engineer, pioneered in the study of cements and in the modern use of concrete in about 1820. American natural cement, having hydraulic and bulk properties but being also of relatively low strength, was produced by burning an impure limestone and was developed at about the same time by Canvass White, Wright's assistant on the Erie Canal (1817–1825). British Portland cement, so named because of its resemblance to Portland stone, was invented by Joseph Aspdin, who secured his first patent in 1796. Here, at long last, was a product of high quality which could be made from minerals (lime and clay) available in almost every area of the world. The United States, however, imported this cement from abroad until the American Portland cement industry was born with the turn of the century (1900).

[2] In the last years of the 19th century "rubble," (i.e., rough, undressed stones) was the common "bulk masonry" of construction and cost $5 to $10 a cubic yard. "Dimension" (i.e., cut-stone) masonry, "railroad" masonry, averaged about $20 to $30. A stonecutter could "dress" about a yard of "dimension stone" in a week. Today cutstone is used only as a thin facing veneer, primarily for appearance, and may cost $200 to $300 per yard. The last great work on which stone masonry and natural cement were used, and also the first in which Portland was employed on a large scale, was the New Croton Dam, built 1895–1907 for the water supply of New York City.

shapes and standards, had been quite completely developed in the earlier Age of Wrought Iron.

With the erection in 1909 of the Queensborough cantilever at New York, however, nickel steel for tension members, "eyebars," came into use. Both nickel and silicon steel were also used in the record-breaking span (720 ft) of the Metropolis Truss over the Ohio in 1917. Silicon steel, also, was employed in such compressive-type structures as the Bayonne Arch and the towers of the George Washington suspension bridge at New York, both completed in 1931.

Yet, these are exceptions, for alloy steels, although stronger, are more costly than the usual "structural grade" carbon steel, and their use is economical only in larger structures where dead weight is reduced and the tonnage is sufficient to justify the rolling of a special product. Aluminum, although standard in airplane construction, is, as yet, still not fully proved as a structural material.

Methods and Equipment. It is in the area of construction methods that advances since 1900 have been especially notable. In bridge erection, for example, earlier works were supported during construction by veritable forests of falsework or temporary timber framing. Today truss and similar construction are cantilevered out from the piers using only a few temporary supporting bents. The erection of the Hell Gate Arch (1912–1917) was a notable example of cantilevering, and the use of temporary intermediate supports was completely eliminated. Numerous later constructions have been similarly planned and designed with ease and speed of erection as controlling factors.

Speed of construction has, in fact, always been a vital factor in American practice, as we have noted, and, as works have increased in size and capital costs have mounted, the advantages of getting a project in operation as soon as possible have become even more obvious. This was an important factor in the rise of concrete construction. There was a limit to the number of masons who could work on a stone masonry dam, such as the New Croton. With the change to concrete a few years later when Kensico was built, 1910–1916, a record of 3,572 cu yd placed in one 8-hour day was made, and an unheard-of total of 84,450 yd in one month was achieved. Mechanization was replacing men's hands, and, at the Grand Coulee Dam in Washington in 1939 over 20,684 yd of concrete were deposited in 24 hours and over 400,000 in one month. One may find comparable records in almost all types of construction from the spinning of the cables of suspension bridges to the building of foundations and subways. One of the most remarkable records of this kind has been in the building field—the construction of the Bank of the Manhattan Company's skeleton steel skyscraper in Wall Street, New York, in 1930. Work was begun simultaneously on the demolition of the old structure on this site and on the foundations for the new building. The latter had progressed sufficiently by the time the old building was down so that the steelwork could go forward. As the steel went up, the foundations were completed under it. A battery of some 19 elevators then carried up the brick for the walls and the other hundreds of items required, and in just one year the new tenants moved in.

In general, these advances all reflect the development and use of power machines. One visualizes the 30,000 human ants in the "rabbit burrows" of the shafts and tunnels by which the Romans, in the time of Claudius, attempted to drain Lake Funicus, as compared to the heavy construction work of today in which, apparently, only a handful of workers are employed.

There is, unfortunately, no adequate history either of construction methods or of construction equipment and machines. The modern rock drill goes back to the great railroad tunnels of Europe and to the contemporary pioneer American Hoosac Tunnel of 1858–1876. Couch's steam percussion drill was patented in 1849, the Burleigh drill in 1866, while the Italian Sommeiler, "unlocked the stone portals of Mount Cenis" with his compressed-air drill in 1861. The steam pile driver, the steam-driven dredge, and the first steam shovel date back to the same general period.

There have, however, been some milestones in the history of newer equipment.

The French introduced in the construction of the Suez Canal in 1859–1869 some pioneer excavating and dredging machinery. In the United States the Chicago Drainage Canal of 1892–1900, now almost a forgotten chapter in engineering history, marked a new era in American machine excavation. The building of the Kensico Dam in 1910–1916 similarly established a milestone in the engineering of a modern construction project. Here engineering planning and design were, almost for the first time, applied not alone in the preparation of drawings and specifications for a great structure but to the layout, equipment, planning, and scheduling of the construction operations themselves—a task hitherto left largely to the resources and ingenuity of the contractor.

To those who recall the building of the first New York subway in

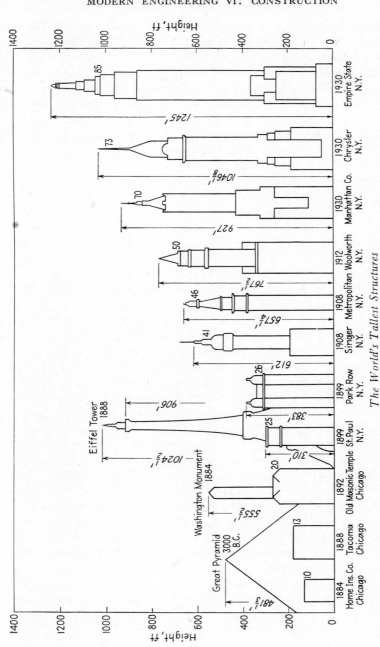

The World's Tallest Structures

Beginning with "cage" construction in 1884 (in which floors are independent of walls), the modern "curtain-wall" building, in which the steel frame carries both floors and walls, reached its greatest height in the Empire State Building of 1930.

1900–1904, this evolution in methods is particularly striking. "Parson's ditch" was an open-cut job using hand labor, horse-drawn carts, and steam hoists and drills. Street crossings were provided for by temporary wood bridges spanning the cut where, in long sections of open excavation, man and beast toiled with earth and rock. The later extension in lower New York of this first subway marked the change to a complete planking over of the streets. Under similar "decking" with little disturbance to traffic, power shovels and motor trucks have excavated the more recent maze of subways which serve the city.

Buildings and Bridges. To the uninitiated, however, it is the scale, the size, of modern constructions which is a never-ceasing cause for wonder. The Home Insurance Building in Chicago, erected in 1884, is usually recorded as America's first skyscraper. It was only 10 stories high, but it marked the change from bearing wall to "cage" construction in which the walls were independent and the floors were supported by columns.[3] Four years later, in the Tacoma Building, modern "skeleton-steel" construction was born, the "curtain walls" serving merely an enclosing function and being supported by the frame. New York finally became the center of skyscraper constructions and, in 1930, the Empire State Building in New York, reached 102 floors with a total height of 1,250 ft.

New Yorkers also could claim at one time the world's greatest dams with the Croton and the Kensico, but these have been dwarfed by the more recent works of the U.S. Bureau of Reclamation. The Boulder Canyon Dam (1931–1936) broke all records with its height of 730 ft. The Panama Canal (1904–1914) was long regarded as the greatest construction work of the ages. It was a steam-shovel job of excavation on an unheard-of scale, requiring some 270 million cubic yards of digging and the astounding total of 4.8 million cubic yards of concrete. Yet the modern electric shovels of the remarkable open-cut mine at Bingham Canyon, Utah, had moved more than this total excavation by 1930 and, during World War II, took out more rock and ore in one day than was moved on the best day at Panama. In the reverse operation, that of placing earth fill, the great earth dam built at Fort Peck, 1935–1940, still holds a record of over 120 million yards. Similarly the Grand Coulee Dam on the Columbia River has involved placing over 10 million cubic yards of concrete.

[3] This work also marked the first use of steel in building construction. The growth of "vertical transportation," the elevator, was also, of course, essential to the rise of the skyscraper era.

The Golden Gate Bridge, San Francisco, 1937

Joining San Francisco with the Marin Peninsula to the north, this world's record span of 4,200 ft, or 0.8 mile, crosses the Golden Gate, the entrance to San Francisco Bay. (*Courtesy of Institute for Steel Construction.*)

In bridgebuilding the record span was long held by the Firth of Forth Cantilever in Scotland (1889); certainly, as we have said, one of the Wonders of the Modern World. But its two spans of 1,710 ft each were surpassed in length by the 1,800-ft span of the Quebec Cantilever over the St. Lawrence completed after two earlier failures in 1917. Steel-arch spans also jumped to new records. The evolution of the steel arch from Ead's great St. Louis bridge to the building of the Bayonne Arch in New York of 1,658-ft span in 1931 and the similar but, perhaps, even more spectacular (heavier loads) arch at Sydney, Australia, about the same time, is an interesting story of step-by-step improvements in design and erection. Yet all these astonishing records have been completely eclipsed by the modern long-span highway suspension bridges. The George Washington Bridge in New York almost doubled earlier suspension records in 1931 with its single great span of 3,500 ft, but this record had hardly been established, when, in 1937, the Golden Gate Bridge at San Francisco was completed with 4,200 ft between its towers. In 1949 approval was secured for a Narrows Bridge at New York of even greater span. If we assume that anything under 1,000 ft is not a long span, then there have been two in Continental Europe, one each in Britain, India, Africa, and Australia, and three in Canada, which compare with the numerous American long-span bridges which have been primarily the result of highway growth and development—products of the Automobile Age.[4]

We should also not lose sight in this story of the continued evolution of the humble truss bridge. In 1917 Gustav Lindenthal (1850–1935) completed the Sciotoville truss for the Chesapeake and Ohio Railroad, crossing the Ohio River in two record truss spans totaling 1,550 ft, continuous over a central pier. This bridge is interesting not only for its record span but especially because it marks the first adoption of the principle of continuous design for a truly great American structure.[5]

Municipal Works. Municipal engineering also received greatly increased attention in America during the 20th century as urban growth continued to raise difficult problems. In the water-supply area, both the improvement of the quality of and the apparently

[4] See "The World's Most Notable Bridges," by D. B. Steinman, *Eng. News-Record,* December 9, 1948.

[5] Morison had first introduced in the United States the principle of continuous design in the approach spans to his famous Memphis cantilever over the Mississippi in 1892.

The Catskill Aqueduct, 1905–1917

Bird's-eye view showing the 75-mile aqueduct line from Ashokan Reservoir, passing under the Hudson (1,114 ft below river level) to the Kensico Emergency Reservoir, from thence in deep tunnel (up to 400 ft below sea level) down the backbone of Manhattan Island to Brooklyn and to Staten Island. Later extended to complete the circuit, Brooklyn to Hill View Reservoir. (*Courtesy of Department of Water Supply, New York.*)

never-ending need for additional supplies have been especially pressing. As we have noted, the larger American cities—New York, Philadelphia, Boston—tackled the problem of adequate supply early in
the 19th century. But both increasing population and increasing per
capita use have required constant extensions or the development of
new sources. New York City, after exploiting to the full the resources
of the Croton area, turned to the Catskill Mountains for additional
water. The Catskill Aqueduct, 75 miles long and costing 2 hundred
million dollars, brought a much needed additional, 600 million gal-
lons daily (mgd) in 1905–1917. In the past few years an added West
Catskill supply has been under construction. Boston's metropolitan
needs forced a westward extension of her water-collecting areas into
the watersheds of the Swift and Ware Rivers, tributaries of the
Connecticut. Even far-away Los Angeles developed, about the same
time as the Catskill supply, a spectacular Owens Valley project, but
this in turn has been reinforced by the new and daring Colorado
River supply for this great Western metropolitan center.

Koch, discoverer in 1883, of the cholera bacillus, had turned the
attention of water-supply experts to water-borne diseases and the
necessary precautions required if typhoid epidemics were to be
avoided. Pioneer filtration plants had been designed to remove
suspended matter from supplies, but the earlier years of the 20th
century still witnessed typhoid epidemics in many cities where the
supply was drawn from streams or lakes polluted by the discharge of
other towns or, in some cases, by the sewage of the sufferer itself.
Tests were finally developed and efforts made about the turn of the
century to increase the bacterial efficiency of filtration, and remarkable results were obtained in the use of this method for removing
dangerous bacteria from supplies. This movement came to an end,
however, with the discovery of the much less expensive and more
certain action secured by treating water with chlorine, now almost
universally used in public supplies.

Attention later turned in the United States to the increasing problems of stream pollution resulting from the widespread practice of
disposing of raw sewage by simply discharging it into a nearby stream,
river, or bay. In this respect American practice lagged behind that of
Europe, but sewage-treatment works on a huge scale, capable of
rendering the sewage of our largest cities inoffensive, are now under
construction.

Foundations and Tunnels. Finally, one should not forget that a
major part of all these constructions is hidden under the ground in

the form of foundations. It is probably true, for example, that, on an average, half the cost even of a bridge is buried below the surface of the ground.[6] Here again is a fascinating and interesting story of man's struggles with water, earth, and rock. We have noted that the French engineers of the 18th century seldom found it possible to go deeper than some 10 or 12 ft below water level. They worked in open excavation, damming off the water by means of cofferdams or, occasionally, open caissons or boxes. These methods are still in use, and a new record for depth in an open cofferdam of 60 to 80 ft was achieved in the construction of the west pier of the George Washington Bridge in 1930. But the rise of the pneumatic method, using interior air pressure to balance the exterior water pressure, greatly increased this depth. Here, however, there is a limit to the pressure under which men can work and live. Ead's set this record at St. Louis in 1872, and while it has been equaled, it has not been exceeded since that time. Notable advances have been made in the conduct of work "under air," however, so that cases of "the bends," the dread caisson disease, are almost unheard of. In fact, work under air pressure in foundations and tunnels has become so commonplace that such operations no longer attract either technical or newspaper attention.

On the other hand, the necessary safety precautions have made air work increasingly costly, and this has led to the avoidance of pneumatic work and the use of other methods whenever possible. Among these has been open dredging—the dredging out of material without unwatering a caisson, and when the caisson has been sunk to the required depth, the placing of concrete to fill it, again, under water, thus eliminating the entire unwatering process. Some remarkable feats have been achieved in this way.

The handling of large, heavy, and clumsy caissons used in this process and, especially, keeping them in a position while they are being sunk to their final resting place are difficult operations. Yet back in the '20's, when the Holland Vehicular Tunnel was built at New York, a remarkable caisson job was successfully carried out. The two tubes, each 30 ft in diameter, were started from land shafts, two at each end, and, in 1924, the four headings met under the river.

[6] It should be noted that foundation difficulties often dictate the character of the superstructure—the length and arrangement of spans, etc. The factors influencing the design being thus out of sight—not obvious and clear to the beholder—many bridge structures, while representing excellent and economical design for use, fail to meet the requirements of satisfactory design from the aesthetic standpoint. The reasons for their form and character are not open to sight, clear, and obvious.

But, to provide the base for the New York ventilation tower, a huge steel caisson had been made in a Staten Island shipyard. This was floated to position at the pier head line and sunk so accurately, both on line and to grade, that the shields in the tunnel headings, coming out from the land shafts, passed exactly through the 30-ft openings provided in these huge steel boxes for this purpose.

One of the most unusual bridge projects was the building of the Bay Bridges, joining San Francisco with Oakland. The main channel is crossed by two great suspensions with main spans of 2,310 ft each with a common, huge anchorage pier in the center of the channel where the spans join. Here the world's largest caisson, 92 by 197 ft, with 55 interior cells, was sunk in the swift tidal currents of the bay to a depth of over 200 ft below low tide level by interior dredging, the largest caisson operation yet attempted by man. A unique method was followed in sealing off each of the interior cells by domes and using pneumatic pressure to balance and maintain the caisson in vertical position as it was filled and sunk until it reached bottom in over 100 ft of water. Open dredging operations then began.

Other daring and ingenious foundation processes have also been devised, such as the "sand-island" method first used as an adjunct to caisson operations at the Suisun Bay Railroad Bridge in California in 1930. Probably, however, one of the most important new developments has been the extended use, particularly in building foundations, of what may be called pipe or tube piles built in place. They are actually pipe caissons, sunk by dredging or washing out or blowing out with air the interior material as the outer shell is driven through muck or silt to the level of sound material on which the pile or pier is to rest. The tube is then filled with concrete and becomes a concrete column, or small pier, supported laterally by the surrounding soil. Depths of over 100 ft have been reached in this way and groups, or clusters, of such pipe piles have been used for many foundations which, in earlier years, would have required pneumatic caissons.

Tunneling, although apparently unrelated to foundation work, involves many of the same problems, and contractors specializing in foundations are usually equipped to handle tunnel operations. Certainly no human activity can claim a more interesting history of danger, persistence, and daring than that of tunnel building. One need but recall the story of the great Alpine tunnels, the Mt. Cenis of 1857–1871 (8.25 miles long), the St. Gotthard, 1872–1882 (9.26 miles), the Arlberg, 1880–1883 (6.2 miles), and the later struggle with water and rock pressure in the Simplon, 1895–1906 (which still holds the record of 12.4 miles with no intermediate shafts) to realize that here is a record of persistence and determination in meeting the antagonistic forces of nature unequaled in human experience.

The Simplon involved not a single, double-track bore, but two single-track tunnels. This plan proved to be most advantageous from the construction standpoint and may be regarded as having established what has become known as the "pioneer tunnel or heading" method since used on many longer tunnels where no intermediate shafts were employed. These include the American work in which this method was first developed, the Rogers Pass Tunnel on the Canadian Pacific in 1913–1916, the Moffat, west of Denver of 1923–1927, and the Cascade of 1925–1929 on the Great Northern Railroad. The greatest of recent tunneling operations, however, have been in connection with water supplies. The Colorado River–Los Angeles aqueduct has required 108 miles of tunnels while the West Catskill supply for New York is carried entirely in tunnel.

These are all land tunnels. During the latter years of the 19th century, two notable subaqueous works were built in Britain through rock and without the use of air. The Severn Tunnel, 4.3 miles from portal to portal, near Bristol, took no less than 13 years to complete, 1873–1886. Sir John Hawkshaw (1811–1891) of London "underground" fame and an equally famous British contractor, Thomas A. Walker, finally completed this remarkable work in spite of flooding and other obstacles. At the same time, 1879–1886, a similar work under the Mersey between Liverpool and Birkenhead was under construction.

It will be recalled that Brunel's Thames Tunnel of 1825–1843 was so difficult and costly to build that it discouraged for many years further subaqueous tunnels in porous materials. Barlow improved Brunel's shield in 1864, but it was not until 1879 that Cochrane's compressed-air method was combined with the shield and the technique of modern subaqueous tunneling thus established. British workers pioneered in perfecting this technique in connection with the building of London's underground transportation system.

The Hudson–Manhattan Tunnels in New York were begun in 1879 but in 1880 a sudden "blow" occurred and the work filled so rapidly with water that 20 "sand hogs," as the tunnel workers are called, were trapped behind the air lock and lost their lives. Finally, in 1889, a firm of British contractors, Pearson and Sons, took up the task with two famous British experts, Sir Benjamin Baker (1840–

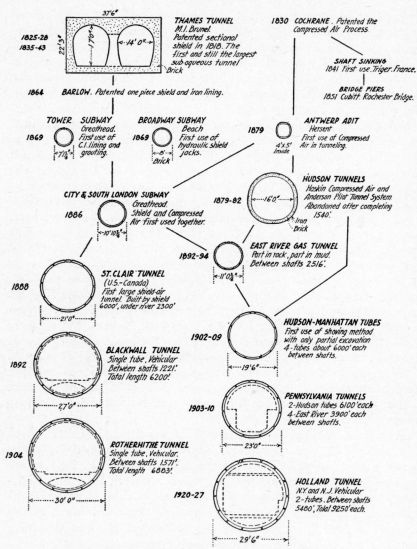

The Evolution of Subaqueous Tunneling

Showing Brunel's remarkable Thames tunnel of 1825–1843, built with a primitive type of shield but without the use of compressed air, the early rise of the pneumatic process, the first combination of shield and air in Greathead's London Subway, and some subsequent notable subaqueous tunnel constructions.

1907) and James H. Greathead (1844–1896) as consultants. After later financial difficulties, it was finally completed in 1905. It included the Hudson Terminal Building in New York, one of the most remarkable foundation constructions ever attempted, in which a series of caissons forming a caisson-cofferdam were sunk, completely enclosing the terminal station and serving as foundations for the terminal building above.

Design Techniques. The above notes deal with actual constructions and the forces and factors which have influenced construction methods and practices. All modern construction works are designed and planned in the greatest detail before a sod is turned, and these final plans, plus detailed specifications describing all the conditions of the work, the quality of materials, the methods to be followed, and the workmanship, form the basis on which the engineering-contractor estimates the cost and contracts to undertake the construction.[7] Back of these advances in construction methods, therefore, there have been corresponding improvements and developments in the techniques of design. The engineer, as someone has remarked, is a man who always makes the right decision even when he has insufficient evidence. He has successfully dared to meet current problems by building greater works, often without having full and complete knowledge on which to base his designs. Failures have thus been unavoidable, and understanding in structural design is continually in the process of catching up with practice. In short, construction has been in many cases unable to wait for complete understanding. Arch bridges were built before we thoroughly understood the mechanics of the arch, dams before we knew with any quantitative certainty how they acted, truss bridges came before truss analysis, reinforced concrete antedated the theory of concrete design, even the steam engine came before the modern theory of heat. The 20th century has been preeminently an era in which theory has been catching up with practice, certainly in the domain of civil engineering. Greater understanding has, of course, made possible bigger and better works, but, until well into the 20th century, it had not revealed the possibility of new types of structures, of designs of a fundamentally new and different character.

[7] In comparison with the simple outline drawings and brief specifications calling simply for "first-class materials and workmanship," the multiplicity and detail of modern plans and specifications are simply astonishing. It is possible, for example, for the total number of drawings for a large bridge—every rivet is shown and located to the nearest $\frac{1}{16}$ in.—to run up to 5,000 or 10,000, and it is said that the total required for the Bank of the Manhattan Company Building exceeded 30,000.

One of the important first steps in this direction was brought about largely by the advent of reinforced concrete. Earlier timber, iron, and steel structures were of a unit type of construction— assemblies of independent beams, columns, and tension members, "simple" structures. Reinforced concrete, on the other hand, was built in place. Joints were not necessary, "continuity" was not only a "natural" to such construction but provided a factor which, if properly evaluated in the design, resulted in a more economical use of this new material. In a rough way, one may say that in a simple structure individual members support the load while in a continuous design the entire structure plays a part in this process; it all "works" and, accordingly, the individual parts may be made less strong.[8]

But due allowance for continuity in design required far more advanced understanding of structural mechanics than was commonly available in American textbooks before World War I. European workers had, however, tackled these problems, and just about this time these new ideas were beginning to influence structural design in the United States. Witness, for example, Lindenthal's continuous truss at Sciotoville of 1917, and note also that its designer was an engineer whose education had been secured abroad. American engineering teachers took a leading part in simplifying, as far as possible, these new theories, making them intelligible and easier of application. The advent of the airplane speeded this process for it is a flying structure in the design of which full advantage of continuity is taken. There are, indeed, few structures today which, although they may not appear to the uninitiated to differ radically from earlier works, are not designed with special regard to this principle. In fact, there are probably very few people who realize that the rigid-frame bridge, widely used for parkway and railroad crossings, is not a simple arch structure but a completely new structural form in which the side walls as well as the overhead span form one continuous unit.

New and more exact methods of analysis have also been developed in the design of arch and suspension bridges. The suspension bridge, for example, had, until recent years, been a combination structure; it was in effect a suspended truss, the truss acting to stiffen the otherwise very flexible cables and to distribute any concentrated load over a sufficient distance to prevent excessive local deflections. Rankine,

[8] It has been jestingly but nevertheless truthfully, if inelegantly, remarked that if a man standing on a continuous truss bridge should expectorate into the river below, this would change the stresses in every member of the structure.

the Scotch analyst, had offered an approximate solution of the problem of the division of the stresses between the truss and the suspending cables, but it was not until 1903 with the construction of the Manhattan Suspension over the East River in New York that the first really scientifically designed suspension bridge appeared, almost a century after Finley's first successful suspension spans had been built.

A curious and interesting chapter in suspension-bridge history was revealed with the failure in 1940 of the Tacoma, Washington, suspension bridge. As spans increase, the "live" load—that is, the moving vehicular or similar load which the bridge is planned to carry—contributes proportionately less and less to the total stresses for which the structure must be designed. Dead load, the weight of the bridge itself, becomes the dominating factor. Furthermore, highway loads are rather light and, as a result of these conditions, the stiffening truss became, in these modern highway bridges, of less importance as a load-distributing device. In fact, in many of the later long-span highway suspensions it almost disappeared—their floors became a series of suspended platforms. The fact that a cross wind could cause a twisting type of undulation in such "platform" structures—had, indeed, done so and caused the failure of a number of the earliest suspension bridges—was lost to sight or was regarded as not possible with a modern relatively heavy concrete roadway. Yet, at Tacoma, a comparatively light cross wind (40 mph) set up unbelievable, astonishing undulations, "writhings" in the floor, which was finally broken and dropped into the river leaving only the towers and bare cables in place. The evolution of the suspension bridge brought the structural expert face to face with a new force, an aerodynamic phenomenon, and when a new and still longer suspension span is erected, we may feel sure that due provision will be made to resist, or preferably to prevent, the development of another "Galloping Gertie," as the Tacoma bridge was nicknamed.

The modern arch bridge may be regarded as an inverted suspension bridge. The cables become a compression chord, and the function of the stiffening truss may be met either by stiffening this chord, by providing this action in the floor system, by using trussing members between the floor and the arched chord, or by some combination of these methods. We, thus, may have a wide variety of arch forms varying from the arched rib or truss, through the spandrel braced arch to the apparently thin and daring arch of slender section with simple spandrel columns in which the floor is designed to serve the load-distributing function. Needless to say, the analysis of such structures is not a matter of simple mechanics.

Similarly, in the design of great modern dams, their huge size and the advent of combination forms have led to new and complicated design problems. Many of these structures, for example, are now built in curved form—arch-gravity dams, resisting the water pressure back of them in part through their weight but in part also as horizontal arches supported at each end by the sides of the valley in which they are built acting as abutments. Special and involved techniques of design have been developed in connection with such structures.

Thus the search for more complete understanding to the development of scientific, rational, quantitative techniques of analysis and design to replace the older, uncertain, empirical practices stemming from experience, goes forward, and at an ever greater tempo, for such design is more safe and certain and, especially, usually effects saving in cost. Mechanical engineers also face similar problems of stress analysis in the design of machines and machine parts, often in very complicated (from the stress-analysis standpoint) forms but requiring the same methods of advanced mechanics for their analysis. In fact, there are many machine as well as structural and other parts which, even today, still defy such scientific analysis. Recourse must be had to such techniques as the photoelastic study of transparent models or to actual tests of models or even of full-sized parts.

To one who can look back to close to fifty years of progress in design and construction, the changes and improvements which have been made seem truly astounding, but there are still many questions remaining to be solved which will undoubtedly provide equally interesting and stimulating problems for the civil engineer in the years to come.

Chapter 14. ENGINEERING AND
WESTERN CIVILIZATION

If there was no grand design in the beginning of the universe, fragments of one are now evident, and mankind can complete the picture. A knowledge of the good life is our certain philosophic heritage, and technology has given us a power over nature which enables us to provide the conditions of the good life for all the earth's multitudes.

Charles A. Beard.[1]

A SUMMARY AND AN ANALYSIS

The story of engineering, as we have outlined it in the preceding pages, has been that of an activity which, in earlier eras a powerful and important instrumentality in the rise of Western civilization, has now become the dominant force in shaping the lives and interests of ever greater numbers of mankind. The identification of engineering with industry, the dependence of our modern economy and means of producing the needs of life on engineering, have been major factors in bringing about this change in the status of engineering in human affairs. But the history of engineering also reveals the story of successive early periods of remarkable technological promise which, because of the lack of various essential stimulating influences, of a progressive spirit, and of favorable environment, have ended in stagnation and decline.

The United States is today embarked on the most recent and greatest of these eras of engineering promise. It has become the heir to the accumulated engineering experiences of fifty centuries. It has won this position of leadership for itself through an unparalleled development of its natural and technological resources in establishing the highest level of industrialized life yet attained by man and, because World War II has effectively eliminated its nearest competitors, the nations of Western Europe. Will this remarkable American

---

[1] Quoted in *On the Meaning of Life,* by Will Durant, 1932.

technological development also end in stagnation and decline, in a failure to integrate technological advances and change with continued progress and evolution in the democratic, Western way of life?

Such a failure would mean far more than America's loss of technological leadership. It has become clear in recent years that technology is no longer a mere instrumentality of material progress, a mere tool subject to the will of man. It has become a dominating force, not alone dictating the form of our economic life and social order but determining also the trends and possibilities, the hopes and aspirations, of our political thinking, and is fundamental to our faith in continued progress. We are today in an Engineering Age, and the further evolution of Western life will be determined not by wishful thinking or pious hopes, not by efforts to control or direct technological progress, but by our ability to understand and take optimum advantage of the potentialities for continued advances which stem from a dynamic and progressive technology. The future of Western civilization is at stake. The fate of the Western World is in our hands.

There can be no turning back. We could not return to the old economic order, an agricultural-home, a craftsmanship economy, even if we so desired. Such an economy could no longer support our millions even if modern standards of living were sacrificed to nostalgic yearnings for a way of life which, upon careful analysis, is seen to have been hard and uncertain with little idyllic about it. In spite of poets and storytellers, it was, in fact, for most of the earth's millions, a "hand-to-mouth" life of unremitting toil and labor.

Further, we could not turn back unless, through some magic power, we could cancel the advances in knowledge of the past hundred years and prevent further search by man for new understandings. "All men by nature are actuated with the desire of knowledge," wrote Aristotle over twenty centuries ago.

This desire of knowledge and the wonder which it hopes to satisfy are the driving power behind all the changes that we, with careless, question-begging inference, call progress. They and their reactions upon man's other wants and needs have, since history began, wholly altered the appearance of the dwelling place of man as well as man's relation to his dwelling place.[2]

As well attempt to stay the hand of time as to bring about such a fundamental change in human nature.

We cannot turn back, for our security as a nation and our power

[2] *Philosophy*, by Nicholas Murray Butler, New York, Columbia University Press, 1911.

for peace in the world of today depend upon our continued leadership in science and technology. The human aspirations of the centuries, our faith in human values and in free institutions, depend upon our success in meeting the challenge we face to use such leadership in carrying forward the Western Way of life. We must, it seems clear, recognize that we are dealing with no mere tool of man but with a self-evolving, an evolutionary force in human affairs which cannot be cribbed, cabined, or confined. For better or for worse, we are in the grip of a relentless evolution dominated by this thing we call technology, and there is no escape from it.

The prophets of doom claim that in technology man has created a Frankenstein which will destroy the human race. In more cheerful mood, we preach medical and engineering science as making possible "Man's Redemption of Man" and advise that we maintain our faith in human progress, seek to understand the implications of this new force in life, and courageously face the many difficult and perplexing problems of a future which will bring ever more rapid technological change.

Historians usually insist that history does not teach, or rather that one may, by judicious selection, find in history facts and analogies to support almost any preconceived thesis or favorite bias. This need not prevent us, however, from seeking to understand history. It seems quite clear, for example, that engineering has played a constructive part in stimulating man's faith in human progress. Says Dean Inge:

Until quite modern times, there was little or no faith in human history as having any meaning. We were sent into the world to save our own souls and to help other people save theirs. But there was so little belief in the life of man as having any meaning or value, that if God chose to "shatter to bits the whole sorry scheme of things entire" the day after tomorrow, that would be a quite satisfactory end to the entire business.[3]

Yet, continues the Dean, "It seems quite clear that whether we call the world good or evil, it is within our power to make it better." "Man is capable if he will but exercise the required courage, intelligence, and effort," writes a modern philosopher, "of shaping his own fate. Physical conditions offer no insurmountable obstacle. The patient and experimental study of nature, bearing fruit in inventions which control nature and subdue her forces to social uses, is the method by which progress is made."[4] Technology thus offers the

[3] *Labels and Libels,* by W. R. Inge, New York, Harper & Brothers, 1929.
[4] *Reconstruction in Philosophy,* by John Dewey, New York, Henry Holt & Company, Inc., 1920.

means to progress if we can but provide the essential environment to "make it work."

The over-all general lesson of technology also seems to be clear. It has been a powerful force in the spread of democratic principles, equalizing inequalities of environment and forcing man out to ever more intimate relationships with his fellow man and to more inclusive economic understandings and cooperations. Like every evolutionary force in nature, it has been neither kind nor gentle, moral nor immoral, in its action. The airplane and the radio, gunpowder in the Middle Ages, the atomic bomb in ours, bring us face to face with an imperative command to seek "one world." Either men must increasingly find a way to live together in amity and cooperation, enjoying the fruits of knowledge or, ultimately, the misdirected power of such knowledge will result in the extermination of the human race —or in its decimation to the point where the survivors realize that they must, after all, work together, let live to live.

But engineering also offers us means to intelligent action and understanding, a reliable method to guide us in steering our course through the struggles of this Technological Evolution. It has been remarked that "great movements are seldom directed by reason; the gentlemen in black robes come in afterwards to prove that what has been done is wise and good." Needless to say, this has never been the method of science and engineering. That we need more of the unbiased search for truth characteristic of science and engineering if we are to solve the problems of a technological adaptive society in the modern world is clear. Engineers in demonstrating the power of their methods through example are making an important contribution in clearing the path to a better way of life. As the late Robert E. Doherty, President of the Carnegie Institute of Technology, puts it:

Let me suggest that the hope that the comparative freedom of the American people may endure does not lie alone in such things as freedom of speech and of the press, congressional debates, and popular suffrage; these are merely the manifestations of such freedom. It lies in the ultimate attainment in public affairs of scholarly and professional thought, pursued under the discipline of the scientific spirit, and motivated by a philosophy of public good.

Thus the problem which America faces in meeting the challenge of this Engineering Age is not, as we have indicated, solely that of maintaining technological leadership. The modern problem of the Western World is not simply that of grafting successive technological changes to an older stable and static way of life. Engineering has created a totally new and different kind of world, a world of new values, of new economic relationships, of a new social order, of new habits of mind and interests. It is a world in which many older ideas, older standards and yardsticks, no longer are valid. It is a highly interdependent world of complex human relationships, of many baffling variables—a dynamic, ever-changing world and, thus, one subject to unavoidable risks and uncertainties.

As Sir Norman Angell observes:

> However cruel the automatic decisions of the older *laissez-faire* society, the "laws of supply and demand," they were at least automatic . . . made for man by impersonal forces, regarded as belonging almost to nature. . . . We of the West have very rightly rejected the dictatorship method of ensuring the necessary disciplines and collective action. But the harder way, the democratic way, in which responsibility rests with the individual, demands on his part much higher intellectual standards than are needed in a society where the government relieves the individual of his responsibility for decision.[5]

The future of engineering is thus tied up with the future evolution of our Western way of life. It will depend upon our success in building and maintaining, through widespread understanding and intelligent group action by a nation of free citizens, a dynamic, progressive, adaptive way of life based upon, favorable to and integrated with continued technological development. It will depend upon our success in meeting not only the problems which, as history reveals, have led to the downfall of great nations in the past, but also a host of new problems of human relationships which technology is continually creating. We turn, therefore, to a brief study of some of the relationships which must be clarified and developed if the Western World is to meet successfully, under these difficult conditions, the burdens and opportunities, the challenge, it faces today.

[5] *The Steep Places*, New York, Harper & Brothers, 1947, pp. 22 and 24.

Chapter 15. ENGINEERING AND ECONOMIC CHANGE 1: SCIENCE, TECHNOLOGY, AND AGRICULTURE

> In the time even of our great grandfathers, each village was self-sufficient. If impassable roads suddenly cut it off from the outside world, the village life, or life on the remote farm, went on much as before. Its water came from its own wells, its food from its own fields, its clothing woven from the wool of its own sheep, its fuel from the forest, its light from candles made at home . . . the producer was also the consumer of the goods he produced . . . he could adjust consumption to production and vice versa. The processes of the economy were visible to those who lived by them, and relatively under their control.
>
> Sir Norman Angell, *The Steep Places.*

ENGINEERING AND THE FARMER

We have outlined in earlier chapters, very briefly, some of the major historical accomplishments of the engineering of the 20th century, the "era of bigger and better engineering works and more of them" which began to take shape with the turn of the century but did not reach notable proportions until about 1910. We turn now to the impact of engineering on modern life.

In the last decade of the 19th century, 1890–1900, there was, at least in the United States, a strong feeling of transition. A *fin de siècle* conviction was widespread. America, it was felt, was approaching the end of an era. We faced "changing times," with a new period of new trends, of uncertain, in fact of disturbing and difficult, adjustment and readjustment coming upon us. Although this period is sometimes referred to as the "Mauve Decade"—an allusion to its nostalgic adherence to the passing practices and values of the Victorian era and its lack of any sharply colored convictions as to the future—it is quite obvious that this was, indeed, the end of an era.

The geographic frontiers of the American continent had been reached. East and West had been joined by rail in 1869. Custer's attempt to overcome the Sioux Indians at the Little Big Horn in 1876 had been unsuccessful, but these and other troublesome tribes had been at last subdued. The day of unlimited economic opportunity, when almost any active and aggressive citizen of initiative could become a property holder was passing. It began to be realized that the man who did not get ahead in this new age in the Land of Promise might actually be unfortunate, have missed a chance, rather than be simply lazy and sinful.

The basic movement then under way was, of course, that of completing the transformation of American productive processes, a change which had been slowly taking place through the latter part of the 19th century. We were following in Britain's footsteps. The old, relatively stable, laborious, but resourceful and resilient way of life of our grandparents, so clearly pictured in the quotation at the head of this chapter, was rapidly crumbling in the face of advancing industrialization, mechanization, and specialization. The basic productive economy of the country, the way in which we live and earn our living and which, in turn, determines not alone our physical well-being but our cultural and social interests—all was changing, as it had earlier in Britain, in a very fundamental way.

We can now look back over this adjustment with the perspective of half a century of experience with this new way of life. There have been two major changes involved. The first is reflected in the impact of increasing scientific knowledge and technological improvements on our old way of life, notably in agriculture. The second has been the increasing burden which manufacturing and the services growing out of technological advances have had to carry in providing gainful employment for increasing millions of our people. We turn first to a brief review of the agricultural situation.

In Britain as late as 1851, after more than half a century of industrialization, one quarter of the grown men, or 1 in 6 of the males over 10 years of age, were still linked with agriculture. By 1881, this had fallen to 1 in 10 or about 12 per cent of those gainfully employed. Thirty years later in 1911, it had dropped still further to 1 in 20, or 8 per cent. Agriculture had become so relatively unimportant an activity that Britain was almost entirely dependent on outside sources for her food needs, to the Low Countries for dairy products, to Canada for wheat, and to South America and far-off Australia for meat.

The trend in the United States, although similar, as is revealed in Table 2, was the result of quite a different development.

TABLE 2. AGRICULTURAL EMPLOYMENT IN THE UNITED STATES 1840–1940

Year	Total population*	Total gainfully employed*	Total agriculture*	Per cent of gain-fully employed
1840	17.0	4.8	3.7	77.5
1900	76.0	28.3	11.1†	39.0
1930	123.0	49.0	10.5	21.5
1940	132.0	53.3	9.1	17.1

* In millions.
† A maximum of 11.5 was reached in 1910.

In Britain agriculture was not only displaced to a major degree by manufacturing but was in the end almost abandoned as an industry. In the United States, on the contrary, agricultural production continued to grow, but technological improvements made it possible to accomplish this result with a smaller number of workers.[1] Thus, while there had been a steady increase in the total employed in agricultural pursuits in the United States throughout the 19th century, it was at a rate far less than the rate of increase in population, so that, in 1900, only two American workers in five were engaged in agriculture whereas in 1840 almost four out of five had been so employed. Not only has this ratio continued to fall since 1900, until, in 1940, it was less than one in five, but the actual number engaged in agriculture has decreased since 1910 by over 2 million. In other words, more than 2 million American workers who formerly looked to agriculture for a livelihood have turned to other pursuits. Yet, even with this great decrease, the productivity of American farms has so increased that, under normal conditions, there is an overbundance of food. This remarkable performance has been brought about by the rise of scientific agriculture and especially by mechanization.

Agriculture was the first American industry to benefit from government-supported research. Agricultural experiment stations and

[1] This raises an interesting point. Assume an old and completely agricultural economy, as, for example, the Chinese, where it takes the entire labors of the people to produce the essentials of life—enough food to keep alive. A rapid development of industrialization would not be possible without outside aid or an increase in production through improved agricultural methods. The nation would starve if any great number of workers were withdrawn from the task of providing food. While the Industrial Revolution in Britain was a gradual development, it is possible that the change from open "commons" to the more effectively cultivated compact areas, the enclosure of lands, was, as we have noted, one of the factors which prepared the way for the birth of industrialization in the century which followed.

schools dot our country, and many of the first Yankee inventions were in farm equipment. American agriculture has, in fact, had the full benefit both of improvements in agricultural products and methods and also in ever-increasing mechanization. It has been through the resulting spectacular changes that a smaller number of workers have been able to supply the needs of ever-greater millions.

Earlier farming methods were wasteful and laborious but, until the earlier days of the 19th century, farmers both here and abroad still used ancient hand methods. Between 1820 and 1830 the iron plow came into general use. The hayrake and the first threshing machine followed, while the Civil War, through reduction of manpower on the farms, gave impetus to new inventions and the improvement of such devices as mowing machines, reapers, and grain separators and stimulated the use of steam power. The combine, a harvester-thresher, also was a great laborsaving device. In recent years the introduction of the internal-combustion engine has marked a new era in farm operations, and tractors, trucks, and new machines have been continually developed and improved in adaptability to farm needs, in reliability, and in operating costs. In addition, the use of electricity on the farm has increased, bringing relief not only from the physical burdens of the barn but also of the farm home. The isolation of the farm has likewise, in large measure, been made a thing of the past through the motorcar, while the radio has been a powerful factor in farm education and the enrichment of farm life.

The U.S. Department of Agriculture was established in 1862, a major period in the introduction of farm machinery, for the promotion of agriculture in all its phases.[2] Research in agriculture is not only the oldest organized activity of this kind in the United States but has been liberally supported with public funds. Efforts to increase the productivity of the farm, control pests, and improve the quality of seeds and stock have been continuous and remarkably successful.

As a result of all these advances, there has been a constant decrease in the man-hours of work required for farm products. In the period around 1880, it required an average of 1.29 man-hours to produce a bushel of wheat, and this was a revolutionary improvement over earlier productivity. By 1900 this had dropped to 0.86, and by 1930 it had been cut to less than 0.5 man-hour. This increase in efficiency

[2] The Morrill Act of 1861 establishing the so-called "land-grant" colleges for the encouragement of agriculture and the mechanic arts, many of which are now important engineering schools, was part of this movement.

Mechanization in Agriculture

Part of a group of combines, *i.e.*, reaper-threshers, in operation on a Texas wheat field. Harvesting crews of this kind using the most modern equipment follow the wheat harvest from Texas, through Kansas, and on north to Canada. (*Courtesy of Life & Time, Inc.*)

affected grain and hay crops especially, while there has been much slower improvement in other products.

Needless to say, a decreasing but considerable part of farm produce is still consumed on the farm. When the Union was formed (1789), it required the surplus food produced by 19 farmers to maintain 1 city dweller. In recent years it is estimated that 1 farm worker can produce enough food to provide for between 3 and 4 nonfarm people. In fact, productivity per farm worker has increased at least as rapidly as that of the industrial worker, one estimate indicating that between 1910 and 1930 this increase averaged 41 per cent on the farm as compared with 39 per cent in manufacturing.

While older and marginal areas have been abandoned, new lands have been added. Our farm population has moved westward to new and richer areas as the fertility of older lands has declined, successively robbing each area of its mineral and organic resources and leaving it open to scour and wash from wind, rain, and storm. In recent years, however, attention has turned to the conservation of the soil from the standpoint of soil life, its chemistry and biology, the maintenance of its productivity, and the reduction of the erosive effects of water and wind.

In 1902 the Bureau of Reclamation was established to bring the benefits of water to those arid lands which had not yet been developed. It came too late in our history to make a very important contribution. Not only was agriculture on the decline, but the lands most easily and economically irrigated had already been provided for, largely through individual efforts or partnerships or by cooperative ventures. Less than 10 per cent was added by the Bureau to the total of over 24 million acres which were actually irrigated in 1939, out of the 28 million which could have been supplied that year with water and the 31 million which, it is estimated, can be irrigated. Compared with our total of over a billion acres of American farms, the relative general unimportance of irrigation is clear, although its vital importance to the states irrigated, some 19 in number, cannot be questioned.

One asks, therefore, Why, with all of this attention, expenditure, and remarkable development, was the agricultural situation in the United States in prewar years a problem of major importance— practically a continuous and unsolved headache? There appear to be two principal answers:

In the first place, there is little or no elasticity to the market for many farm products, and we had reached the saturation point. "Consumption of food and, to a lesser degree, demand for clothing, are inelastic." We all need farm products, but few of us can consume or use as much as our agricultural life can provide.[3]

The war and postwar needs of Europe have, it is true, brought about a complete change in the farm situation. Owing to this demand, plus subsidies and inflationary effects, farm prices have soared to unheard-of levels. Under these conditions and with bumper crops, American agriculture is at present riding high on a wave of unparalleled prosperity. War with its temporary demands on manpower and its destruction of productive areas has always been a major but temporary stimulant to American agriculture, but it has not permanently solved our farm problem. Under normal conditions, we can probably produce 15 to 25 per cent more of *present* farm products than we can consume.

This situation has led to the suggestion that we have concentrated our efforts on making two blades of grass grow where only one grew before, whereas we should seek new products which our farms could supply. This idea is reflected in the so-called chemurgic movement which was sponsored by the Chemical Foundation of New York. The criticism is warranted that, while this is undoubtedly a step in the right direction, many difficult problems are involved. The agricultural market is normally a consumers' market with wide fluctuations in prices, depending upon supply and demand and the vagaries of weather and of crops. At low prices, many farm products can compete in supplying raw materials for our present and future chemical industries, but the uncertainties of prices tend to force the development of chemical processes toward the utilization of our more stable mineral rather than our agricultural raw materials.

In only one field of farm operations has a basic change in recent years been encouraging. The production and consumption of milk increased materially in predepression years—25 per cent in the 5 years preceding the depression and, it might be noted, with an increase of only 15 per cent in feed. But even in dairy products, the making of butter and cheese, once a farm operation, has now become a town factory job.

While the value of certain crops was maintained through prewar days, some older crops became of decreasing importance. The older farm was a producer not only of carbohydrates: the starch group

[3] Recent experiences, especially with meats, fruits, and vegetables, indicate that, in certain areas, the market, under the stimulus of higher living standards, may be more elastic than has been suspected.

(corn, wheat, etc.), the tubers (potatoes), the sugars (cane, beet, and corn), and the celluloses (cotton, grass, and forest products) but also of the proteins (meat and milk, the vegetable proteins, and hides and wool); of the fats (butter, lard, tallow, and oils, including those derived from seeds); and, last but not least, of power. Before World War I, the major part of the power used in the United States, outside the railway or mill, was furnished by horses and mules. It has been estimated that over 20 million horses and mules were in use. Today a horse is rarely seen.

There have been other changes in the importance of older farm crops. Cotton has been and is the largest employer of agricultural labor although the grains greatly exceed it in acreage. The rise of cotton growing is, of course, directly attributable to the development of low-cost textiles. There has, however, been relatively little mechanization in cotton farming although quite recently a picker has been developed which may displace many of the low-cost laborers, mainly women and children, who have eked out a precarious living on tenant farms. For a while it appeared that we lived in a cellulose age, but recent developments of synthetic fibers also reflect a far from bright outlook for the cotton industry.

The second major effect has been in the loss of independent economic status by the farm home, its increasing dependence on the purchase of many of the necessities of life from other groups, notably the manufacturing industries. When the horse was king, the farmer actually produced power machines and the fuel required on the farm. The replacement of the horse and mule by the gas engine and tractor made it necessary for the farmer not only to purchase his power units and the fuel to run them from other more favored groups but to replace by purchases of chemical fertilizers the loss of millions of tons annually of organic fertilizer in the form of manure. It is estimated that 9 million horses and mules were "retired" from our farms between 1918 and 1932, "releasing over 30 million acres each of cropland and pastures," thus forcing these areas into other production. In 1929, it was estimated that more than 80 per cent of all farm products were sold or traded, and farmers were purchasing products they formerly provided to meet the needs of their own families.

What is the answer?

Before the war the agricultural market was saturated; it was limited and could not be materially expanded. The use of farm products cannot be increased through the process that created the textile and other industries, that is, by a reduction in prices. It is doubtful whether a 25 or even 50 per cent decrease in the price of farm products, if it were possible, would increase consumption by more than 10 per cent except in a few products.

Until the postwar boom began to affect farm operations, the answer had been decline. Government subsidies, still in force, are essentially a tax on all our people to aid our less-favored farm population but, when they result, as they did in prewar years and are doing today, in piling up useless surpluses, they are simply postponing the inevitable.

Marginal areas, the farms less favorably situated for modern operations, have been abandoned. Technological developments also tend toward the replacement of many small units by larger areas which are suitable for larger and more efficient machines and justify their use. In other words, we are tending toward the factory system of farm operation, and this would mean the further abandonment of small farms, those not favorable to mechanized operations, and the encouragement of larger operations by those who can secure the capital necessary for the purchase of modern equipment. On the other hand, as living costs continue to mount in our larger cities, we may see a return, particularly by older workers, to the more self-sufficient life of the small farm.

One of the striking factors in the farm situation, as it has developed, has been the loss of year-round employment. In older days, the farmer was kept busy throughout the year in providing many of his needs which are now met by purchase from others. Agriculture has become in some areas a seasonal operation with, in the harvesting of certain crops, transient workers moving from one state to another as their services are required.[4] The stabilization of production is a major problem of all American industry and can be achieved in large measure in many industries. We cannot, however, change the seasons, and the only hope along these lines for the farmer appears to rest on a combination of manufacturing or other service with farm operations.

Those nations of the world whose economy is, as yet, agricultural and who thus must face industrialization, still have this problem to meet. In China, in particular, a rapid industrialization in urban centers, such as has occurred in the United States, would result in untold misery and confusion. The only hope that this revolutionary change can be accomplished with a minimum of dislocation seems to rest in the decentralization of industry and a combination of agricul-

---

[4] The numbers involved should decrease, indeed, may have decreased in recent years, with the replacement of hand harvesting by machines.

tural and manufacturing life. This may well be the solution of this problem toward which we shall gradually move in the United States. Industry is turning toward decentralization, toward the village factory where each worker may lead an established life, have his own home, and be less apt to take the risks of change and strikes. Technological change has, in all directions, destroyed our older social order and family life. This movement may create the new, the fuller, freer, and more stable life we so much desire and so greatly need.

It would be interesting, if we could, to look ahead to the final solution or, more probably, solutions of this problem. In later years, increasing farm productivity per unit of area and decreasing need for farm labor are certain again to present a major problem. The long hours of farm labor, estimated at 60 to 70 weekly, or almost 50 per cent more than those of the industrial worker, make it difficult to secure labor at wages the farmer can normally afford to pay. Production was maintained during the war by granting special exemptions to farm workers. When they are free to move to industrial centers, however, the farm-labor situation again becomes increasingly critical.

While, as we have noted, war and postwar demands have thus pulled the American farmer out of a slough of despond into an important position of monetary affluence, the farm problem is still unresolved. As we shall later note, the purchasing power of the American farmer had steadily declined in prewar years when there was a surplus of farm products and when manufacturing labor, through unionization, had forced upward the wages of manufacturing workers. It has been solely through destruction of other farm operations during the war, creating a seller's market plus the artificial stimulation of subsidies, that the farmer occupies his present position in American life. How long he will hold it is uncertain.

Chapter 16. ENGINEERING AND ECONOMIC CHANGE II: MANUFACTURING AND THE TECHNOLOGICAL SERVICES

Beginning with management, where unquestionably mass production methods take their rise, there has been a notable increase in industrial control, as distinguished from financial control. The engineer's point of view has gained the ascendancy. . . . Such control has been marked by the instant adoption of the better method to the exclusion of the old, in the interests of production. . . . It has been engineering control, entrenched in mass production methods, that brought in this new readiness to advance.

Henry Ford, "Mass Production," *Encyclopaedia Britannica.*

MASS PRODUCTION AND EMPLOYMENT

Recalling that employment in agriculture in America declined from a maximum of 11.5 million in 1910 to 9.1 million in 1940 and that in the meantime the population of the United States, in the age group over 14, almost doubled between 1900 and 1940, we see quite clearly that new activities not only absorbed this displacement of 2.4 million agricultural workers but must also have provided for the many more millions who were added to our working ranks in these years. Table 3 gives the main figures of this tremendous shift and expansion in the American employment picture.

In other words employment has been found for an increase in working population of 25 million since 1900, and we have been able to maintain an even better ratio of gainfully employed to total population than prevailed in 1900, although the "over 14" ratio shows a slight decline.

Fortunately, data are available which enable us to determine in what areas of activity these new millions secured a livelihood. A very interesting and revealing study of this changing employment situation is given in chart form in the accompanying diagram.

It is to be noted that the year 1920 seems to mark a new era in the trends indicated, the period of post-World War I adjustment. Thereafter agricultural employment declined. Mining, which had increased up to 1920, simply held its own, and this same situation is especially noticeable in manufacturing. Between 1900 and 1920 manufacturing had played an important part, together with some of the services resulting from an expanding economy, in providing employment for new millions of workers. But between 1920 and 1940 there was relatively little further increase in manufacturing employment. It was the service areas—trade, finance, public service, amusement, etc.—which carried the major share of the burden.

TABLE 3. COMPARISON OF TOTAL POPULATION AND THOSE GAINFULLY EMPLOYED, 1900–1940

	1900	1940	Per cent increase
Total population, millions............................	76.0	131.7	75
Those 14 years of age and over.....................	51.4	101.1	97
Ditto in per cent of total population................	68	77	
Gainfully employed................................	28.3	53.3	90
Ditto in per cent of total population................	37.2	40.5	
Ditto in per cent of those 14 and over..............	55.0	52.7	

This fact was the basis for some of the dire predictions which were made as a result of attempts to explain our errors during the '20s and the causes which led to the Great Depression. It was argued that these service activities constituted an unnecessary "overhead load" on the American economy, that we spent so large a share of our income on such unproductive activities that we thereby curtailed our ability to absorb the increased output of the really basic essentials produced by American industry. This diversion of purchasing power, it was said, resulted in overproduction and unemployment.[1] It is difficult to follow this argument, however, when we recall that this is not a case of the reduction of purchasing power through hoarding but actually an expansion of such power, through the creation of a new and major group of ultimate consumers.

If, for example, three-quarters of our labor force was, in 1940, occupied in manufacturing as it had been in 1900, there can be little

[1] See, for example, *Who Gets the Money?* by Walter Rautenstrauch, New York, Harper & Brothers, 1929; or *The New Deal,* by Stuart Chase, New York, The Macmillan Company, 1932.

question that we would have had overproduction. Actually the shift of our people from agricultural work to manufacturing activities seems to have been quite completely accomplished by 1920. By that time 10.8 million were employed in manufacturing, and this number has varied but little during the years of subsequent change. It in-

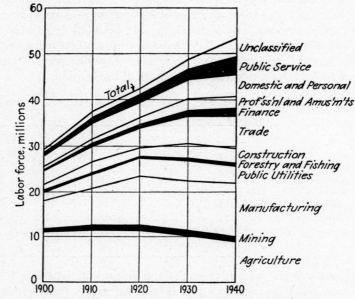

The Changing Composition of American Labor

The rise in manufacturing accounts for the major part of the increase in employment from 1900 to 1920. Since 1920 there has been little change in manufacturing employment while trends, evident even as early as 1900–1910, in public, domestic, personal, and professional services and amusements, construction, and public utilities, but, especially trade, have absorbed the increase in our labor force. Data from an unpublished report by Daniel Carson, submitted to the Conference on National Income and Wealth. (*Courtesy of National Bureau of Economic Research, Inc., New York.*)

creased less than 1 per cent during the '20's and totaled only 11.9 million in 1940, an increase of less than 10 per cent, and this increase undoubtedly reflected foreign war demands and our own prewar "preparedness" or defense movement. In short, we have been too prone to think of manufacturing as our major stand-by in providing employment for new millions of our people; this it did up to 1920 but, since that date, other occupations have been carrying the load.

The accompanying chart shows that this same observation holds for another technological activity, public utilities, while construction has tended to increase somewhat in its claims for labor.

When we turn to these newer activities, the first point to be noted is that many of them are not new. Public service, personal services, professional services and amusements, finance, and, especially, trade have been steadily increasing in their employment claims since 1900, and probably earlier records, if available, would show that this has been a long-time trend.

What are the new services?

A vast number of these new service jobs have been created by our manufacturing development. For example, the half million workers employed in the automobile industry is but a small part of the employment created by the rise of automotive transportation, not only in other industries which furnish basic materials such as steel, rubber, and gasoline, but in new services. We have all heard of "the thousands of dealers from coast to coast" who supply gasoline to motorcars and trucks. Many of these stations are not only distributors of gasoline but are also garage and repair shops. The distribution of cars, tires, batteries, and even licenses employs other thousands. Truck and bus drivers are also needed. Our modern Highway Era, a creation of the motorcar, supports a major industrial and also constructive activity. It has been estimated that "five million *extra* jobs have been created by the advent of the automobile."

Another important factor has been the increase in services made necessary by the mass manufacture of products formerly produced in the home. For example, in a comparison of employment over the years in question, it has been noted that one of the largest increases has been in the baking industry. In 1899 this former home industry gave employment to 60,200 persons. By 1937 this had risen to about 240,000, a fourfold increase. We are apt also to forget that such changes involve not only production but also the problem of distribution. Labor is not limited to manufacturing alone but is a factor also in an increasingly important element of product cost, that is, distribution and sales.

Another item among these expansions in services is that connected with our urban problems. There has been a tremendous expansion in the activities of municipal government in recent years, with similar increases in taxes and per capita debt. For example, Detroit was incorporated in 1824 with, perhaps, a dozen major municipal functions, including police, fire protection, streets, elementary education, elec-tions, etc. After the Civil War about one new responsibility was added per year until, by 1900 there was a total of 102 new activities. From 1910 to 1922 some 70 more were added. These included a number of health services, nutrition of school children, women police, city planning, vice control, etc. In this same period, 1910–1922, taxes per capita increased 350 per cent and bonded indebtedness 500 per cent.[2] Yet it has been stated that "the accelerated rate of growth of the American city, particularly of the large cities, has necessarily left municipal governments far behind in their programs to provide the equipment required by an increasing population." As a matter of fact, the period of most rapid urban growth appears to have been before 1922 at which time we had 261 cities of over 30,000 population.

Thus, what has been happening has apparently been a tremendous increase in the services which modern man deems essential to modern life. We are no longer satisfied with reasonable provision for food and shelter, for warmth and clothing, but have come also to regard our motorcar, telephone, radio (and, now, television!) and greatly increased facilities for lighting, heating, ventilation, refrigeration, cooking, etc., as essentials.

Perhaps, in this picture, the most disturbing factor is distribution. The special packaging of all sorts of supplies and needs plus their passage through many hands in their path from producer to consumer, very often adds, with advertising, tremendous increases in cost without creating any commensurable increase in employment or services rendered. Our efforts are also too often directed toward increasing sales volume with little or no improvement from the consumer standpoint or consideration of the waste involved and the unnecessary burden it imposes.

All this is of vital importance in a technological-industrial age for increased production with less labor is a basic characteristic of such an economy. This demands a constantly increasing purchasing ability by constantly increasing numbers of our people. A wide distribution of our national income is, unquestionably, an important factor in meeting this basic technological-economic need, but, in the long run, bringing goods within the citizens' purchasing power through lower real prices is the basic factor in creating an expanding market. Distribution costs are an important element in this respect. America has

[2] See "The Growth of Municipal Functions," by L. D. Upson in *Recent Trends in American Municipal Government,* Chicago, International City Managers' Association, 1930.

become a nation of workers, and there is a remarkably widespread material prosperity; but our economy is also burdened with some passengers who toil not neither do they spin. Yet the opportunities for progress—greater production distributed among greater numbers of our people, higher standards of living for all—are everywhere apparent.

The major source of increased productivity in the United States has, of course, been the mechanization of industry. In every branch of American industry for which there is reliable information—from agriculture and mining to transportation and manufacturing—there has been a continued reduction in the man-hours of labor required to produce a unit of product. While scattered earlier data are available, a comparison of actual trends since 1900 shows the wide scope of this trend. Furthermore, it reveals that improvement appears to have been distributed among various industrial activities with a remarkable degree of uniformity.

TABLE 4. PERCENTAGE REDUCTION IN LABOR REQUIRED TO PRODUCE A UNIT OF PRODUCT IN THE UNITED STATES, 1900–1940 *

Area	Total reduction	Average annual reduction
Agriculture.	44	1.5
Mining.	52	2.0
Manufacturing.	48	1.6
Transportation and public utilities.	45	1.5
Average.	47	1.7

* See *Labor Savings in American Industry, 1899–1939*, by Solomon Fabricant, Occasional Paper 23, National Bureau of Economic Research, Inc., New York, 1945. It should be noted that this tabulation covers somewhat less than half the total national product and that, in other areas, largely services and trade, the percentage improvement probably was somewhat less.

In other words in these areas we produced a unit of product in 1940 using approximately one-half the labor required 39 years earlier. Such a comparison makes no allowance for the improvements, which have been great, in the quality of the product or service produced.

Within the fields noted, however, there have been wide variations. In manufacturing, for example, Table 5 shows some of the changes in wage earners per unit of product in certain major industries, which makes it clear that various influences—the nature of the process, the possibilities and extent of mechanization, the pressure of rising labor costs, the market demand—undoubtedly have had an important effect.[3]

TABLE 5. PERCENTAGE REDUCTION IN NUMBER OF WAGE EARNERS REQUIRED PER UNIT OF PRODUCT PRODUCED, 1899–1939

	Total reduction	Average annual reduction
Forest products	2	0.1
Leather products	24	0.7
Foods	34	1.0
Iron and steel products	50	1.7
Beverages	51	1.8
Textile products	54	1.9
Paper products	62	2.4
Chemical products	63	2.5
Printing and publishing	71	3.0
Transportation equipment	74	3.3
Petroleum and coal products	77	3.6
Tobacco products	83	4.4

It should also be noted that the rate of such decrease has not been uniform over the years. In years of extensive industrial shifts and readjustments, such as prevail during war and postwar periods, the rate has fallen markedly. For example, improvement between 1939 and 1947 in the manufacturing industries as a whole was at an average of about 1 per cent per year and again reveals a marked irregularity of occurrence among various branches of manufacturing. Clearly an important factor of increased production has been the rate at which funds for new and better equipment have become available as witness the annual average changes in three great eras of expansion: 1899–1914, 2.5 per cent; 1921–1929, 5.6 per cent, and 1931–1939, 3.1 per cent. Since World War II there has been a decline in the efficiency of labor—a letdown in the will to work—but this is apparently on the mend, and war-brought gains in technical knowledge, in forcing also improved management and organization, better equipment, and processing, plus the spur of high labor costs, will undoubtedly be reflected in increased future gains in productivity.[4]

[3] From *Labor Savings in American Industry, 1899–1939,* by Dr. Fabricant, Occasional Paper 23, National Bureau of Economic Research Inc., New York, 1945. Some 60 to 70 manufacturing activities are listed in this study.

[4] See *The Structure of Postwar Prices,* by Frederick C. Mills, Occasional Paper 27, National Bureau of Economic Research, Inc., New York, 1948.

The constant growth in the power of labor to produce is reflected also in the increase in the value of the laborsaving tools with which technology has made it possible to supply labor. In early days the worker was expected to supply his own tools while today he is furnished with tools totaling in many cases $5,000 to $7,000 per

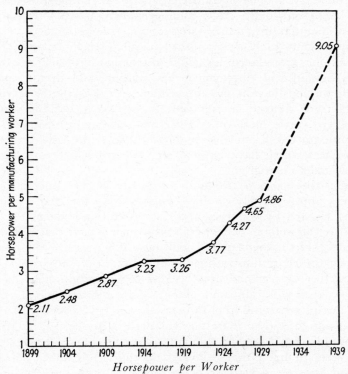

Horsepower per Worker

Chart illustrating the growth in the power equipment provided per worker over the past half century. Assuming 1 hp equivalent to 6 manpower, the modern worker has 25 or more "silent slaves" to relieve him of physical toil and effort. Data not available between 1929 and 1939. (*From "U.S. Census of Manufacturers," 1929, Vol. 2., p. 14, and 1939, Vol. 2., Part 1, p. 20.*)

worker. Data on the horsepower provided per worker reflect this same trend. The U.S. Census gives some interesting statistics along these lines, as shown in the accompanying chart.

Assuming 6 to 10 manpower as equivalent to a horsepower, it is evident that the American wage earner is actually aided by 25 or more helpers. The manufacturing worker, in particular, is primarily, a power user, producing through his operation of a machine rather than through the exertion of muscular effort. At the same time, this new type of power economy has brought about radical changes in the life of the wage earner and in his relationship to the economic and social order of which he is a part.

In summary, it may be said that the major employment adjustments from our older American agriculture-craftmanship to our modern manufacturing mass-production economy appear to have been quite completely accomplished by 1920. In more recent years, while mining, manufacturing, and construction have held reasonably steady, agricultural employment has continued to decline and increasing millions have found employment in providing the services—utilities, trade, finance, amusements, public—of modern life. Many of these services arise, on the one hand, from the management, sales, and distribution needs of our mass-manufacturing enterprises. Others are new services which have become not only conveniences but necessities of modern living.

During the war, the productive capacity of the American economy was approximately doubled. In postwar years the backlog of demand created by war shortages has raised employment to a new level—over 60 million. Some minor adjustments have taken place but a high level of employment still continues. When data, similar to that shown in the chart illustrating the distribution of employment over the past 10 years (complicated because of war production), become available, they will, thus, undoubtedly show a sharp general upturn. Also veterans returning from military service have frequently turned to other activities than those they followed in prewar years. Mining, for example, has found it difficult to recruit essential workers. It would seem probable that a reversal of the trends above noted has occurred, that is, an increase has taken place in manufacturing employment as contrasted with other occupations.

Chapter 17. ENGINEERING AND THE WORKER

It is a mistaken and romantic notion to believe that everything was rosy when industry operated in small-scale units, and
that all our troubles are due to the fact that the owner no
longer has a personal contact with his men. Intense bitterness
often existed between the employees and the owners of small,
family-owned plants in England and in Germany. The small
family enterprise is, in a way, somewhat analogous to the old
feudal ownership and is not so much in keeping with the spirit
of our national life as are the large depersonalized institutions.
Stressing the advantages of small-scale units sounds suspiciously
like the customary romantic reminiscences about "the good old
times."

Sam A. Lewisohn, *Human Leadership in Industry.*

CHANGES IN INDUSTRIAL CONDITIONS AND EMPLOYMENT

In 1848, a century ago, John Stuart Mill wrote: "Hitherto it is
questionable if all the mechanical inventions yet made have lightened
the day's toil of any human being."[1] Even in 1866 a note of doubt
as to the promise which technological advances held for real progress
was voiced by Professor Thomas Henry Huxley: "If the wealth resulting from prosperous industry is to be spent for unworthy desires,
if the increasing perfection of manufacturing processes is to be accompanied by an increasing debasement of those who carry them on,
I do not see the good of industry and prosperity."[2]

The rise of industrialization, notably in Britain in the earlier 19th
century before the passage of the Factory Act of 1850, had, as we
have seen, provided a new and powerful means of exploiting the
labors of factory workers on a hitherto unparalleled scale. In the age
in which Mill and Huxley were writing, industrialization had simply
opened a new way to secure greater returns from human toil, and its
possibilities in lightening the hours and burdens of labor were yet to
be realized.

Social and economic writers are apt, however, to put the entire

[1] *Principles of Political Economy,* Book IV, Chap. VI.
[2] *Science and Culture.*

271

blame for such abuses on the Industrial Revolution. The fact that
men who held the upper hand had, since civilization began, exploited
their less powerful and fortunate fellows is usually lost to sight in
the surge of indignation and horror which wells up when we read
of the almost unbelievable abuses, the cruel and inhuman treatment
of men, women, and children—man's inhumanity to man—which
was brought to light by the new power which industrialization
created. These were not all new abuses as Mr. Lewisohn notes, in the
quotation heading this chapter. But the new industry did bring them
out where they could be seen while it also, of course, created new
opportunities for their further growth. World War II clearly demonstrated that the beast in man is very near the surface, ready to break
out at the first opportunity—if any such demonstration is necessary.
It is also agreed that the one certain thing in this world is that we
cannot change human nature. Nevertheless the experiences of the
past century have clearly demonstrated that we can change human
behavior. This change in behavior and viewpoint has nowhere been
more marked than in the United States. Practices, which, while not
perhaps approved, were at least condoned and permitted to exist,
even tacitly accepted, by the majority of our people little more than
a half century ago, would today be regarded as completely inex-
cusable and impossible under any conditions.

Looking back to the latter years of the 19th century, for example,
to the group of forceful men in America who exploited in their own
immediate and selfish interests the technological developments which
were then creating new "industrial empires" one wonders at the
patience and forebearance of the American people. These "malefactors of great wealth," as President Theodore Roosevelt characterized
them, gave little thought to the human tragedies and economic waste
involved in their struggles for industrial supremacy. Yet again, one
should not judge this group by modern standards or in the light of
present-day public opinion. Many of them had themselves risen from
the ranks and were playing the game under the rules of the day,
rules that public opinion had not yet been aroused to modify.

There have been two directions which improvements in the status
of labor have taken in more recent years: improvement in the conditions of employment and hours of labor and an increase in the
share which labor has received of the proceeds of production.

The major change which industrialization has brought about has,
of course, been in the way man secures a living—in the productive
process. While the farmer often is still an independent operator, the

average factory worker has become a mere pawn in the mass-manu-facturing process. The older era of pride of craftsmanship, of the days when a worker actually produced practically a completed product, has given way to a division of labor in which the individual performs but one operation in a productive series. The rise of technology has thus forced man into new and far more inclusive cooperations. Man no longer stands alone, relatively self-sufficient and independent. He lives an interdependent life; he is one of a nation of workers in a widespread, a national, economic organization.

A nostalgic yearning for "the good old days" is, of course, futile. We know no way of achieving increased per capita production, the foundation on which our higher standards of living are built, other than through the division and specialization of labor. We cannot have the one without the other. This means, that we cannot expect to find in our daily labors the individual rewards of the creative spirit which were a marked characteristic of the earlier days of "craftsmanship" economy. Such personal interests, satisfactions, and conditions must be met through home sources, the hobby shop, or through club or other interests. The late President Eliot of Harvard once remarked that it was the aim of modern technology to make it unnecessary for man to do any work which could be done by a machine. We are rapidly approaching, if we have not already reached, an age when it will be impossible for any large numbers of men to afford any service or product which cannot be provided through machine production. The "handmade" heirlooms of the future, labors of love, examples of patient craftsmanship and creative art, will be the products of leisure hours rather than the rewards of our efforts to earn a living.

It might be further remarked that those who so earnestly deplore the passing of the craftsmanship era seldom realize that, after all, the able and really gifted craftsman is a rare individual. The modern ma-chine and the production line, so widely condemned for their deaden-ing monotony, have made it possible for millions, who could never find useful employment in any craftsmanship economy, to lead pro-ductive lives and to secure rewards in standards of living which the mere exploitation of their physical prowess could never have afforded. Similarly many men and women neither possess the capacity for, nor have any desire to accept the responsibilities of, independent thought and action. While we seek through education to improve the mental development of our people and their capacities for responsible leader-ship, we also face the problem of adapting a machine age to the exist-ing capacities and abilities of great masses of citizens who, while they may in the large be more gifted than any other similar group in the world, are, nevertheless, limited in abilities and interests. The task of modern democracy is to increase the productive capacities not alone of the specially gifted but of all citizens. This implies the creation of employments, of a production economy, which will use ever more effectively a wide variety of abilities and interests. This Modern Technology has accomplished.

It seems quite clear, therefore, that we must "adjust certain habits of mind and a scale of values developed in one kind of a world to life in quite another kind of a world." Such satisfactions as may be found in modern industrial life must largely stem from a spirit of teamwork and cooperative effort, from group rather than individual accomplishments. This fact has been clearly realized in recent studies of industrial efficiency, and many of our large industries have given special attention to building up this feeling of group action and group rewards. The team spirit not only in production but in sports and other "extracurricular" activities is encouraged through company contests and awards.

In earlier days the passage of laws relating to the improvement of working conditions had been the major factor—apparently the only effective means in many cases—in securing proper sanitary and health conditions for industrial workers. But there has in this respect also been a remarkable change in viewpoint and understanding on the part of industrial management in recent years. This change is not to be attributed to the growth of a more compassionate and humane approach to labor problems, although there have been a few industrialists who have undoubtedly been inspired by such motives to create almost ideal industrial communities. In our highly competitive system, however, efficiency and economy must be the controlling factors. What has happened is that it has been realized at long last that unhealthy working conditions and long hours of labor do not lead to increased production—that, in addition to the efficient use of materials and machines, we must seek the most efficient use of our human resources if optimum production is to be achieved. A wave of interest in "human engineering" has spread over the country and, through the cooperation of engineers, industrial and medical experts, problems of working conditions, from sanitation and safety to lighting and fatigue, are being studied scientifically and the results applied with understanding and skill.

One of the most recent developments has stemmed from the observation that the efficiency of the worker is influenced not only by his physical health but also by his mental well-being. There is a well-defined movement today away from the huge urban factory employing thousands of workers, who too often must live under crowded conditions, lack any stable family life or social status, own no property, and look forward only to bigger and bigger pay envelopes. The decentralization of industry, the division of manufacturing plants into smaller units, the location of these units in smaller cities under conditions more favorable to stable home life, to real citizenship and social interests, are rapidly gaining wide attention. Here again, these are the results of a movement which is based on sound technological reasoning—a reduction of labor turnover through more stable home attachments and responsible citizenship, increased opportunities for both a physically and mentally healthier life and hence better industrial efficiency, greater opportunity for closer personal contacts between management and the worker developing better understandings and a more responsive and responsible productive organization—all these factors, rather than the risks of strikes or a charitable or paternalistic interest in the worker, tend to correct some of the errors inevitable in the far too rapid, and, thus, shortsighted, earlier rise of modern industrial civilization.[3]

Indeed the question may well be asked: If all these developments are now in process, why has it taken industry and the engineering profession so long to discover them? This is a movement which gives promise of adapting the machine to man rather than the much discussed earlier trend which seemed destined to make man a slave of the machine. Has it not long been obvious that improved productive capacity did not depend alone on the provision of better tools, more machines?

The engineer has, of course, always been concerned with the use of our human as well as our material resources. But it was probably inevitable that, with the advent of mechanical and electrical power and the rapid development of machine tools, he should concentrate on perfecting the machine and too often neglect the human side of this problem. As a matter of fact, human engineering has lacked the scientific studies and thus the rationalized approach to its problems which have been so generously lavished on inanimate engineering. It

[3] The desirable size for such isolated plants depends upon the type of industry involved. Where operations can be broken down into unit parts or where single products do not require a larger force, a labor force as low as 500 or 600 has been deemed desirable. It should also be noted that another problem arises in the fact that a "one-industry town" is generally vulnerable to change and is thus undesirable.

has been possible to throw some light on the many variables in the behavior of the human machine only by bringing into the problem groups of experts whose fields have seldom crossed in the past, such as men of medicine and psychologists as well as industrialists and engineers.

The major problem we face in the further development of better employment and worker conditions is that of the small manufacturing establishment. Our larger industries can and must look forward to their longer range stability, needs, and interests. They can afford to take the long-range viewpoint. They realize that, in the long run, what is best for industry must be best for the American people. On the other hand, the small establishment which may be set up simply to take advantage of a temporary market for some short-lived product or service—here today and gone tomorrow—offers an opportunity for abuses which it is indeed difficult to control.

Turning to the problem of wages and hours of labor, it is to be noted that it was in the same year, 1848, that Mill made the statement quoted earlier in this chapter, that Karl Marx published his famous *Das Kapital*. He wrote before the abuses growing out of the first half century of rapid industrialization in Britain had been corrected and when America had not yet come of age. Marx predicted that, owing to technological advances, the working class would inevitably receive less and less for their labors while capitalists, through ruthless competition, would continually decrease in numbers and increase in power. The last century of progress in America has effectively demonstrated quite the reverse, and the process of attaining an ever more widespread material prosperity still goes forward; it is an essential factor in continued technological progress and development.

A study of the position of the American worker and his purchasing power in the economy in which he works, shows that there was relatively little change in dollar wages throughout the 19th century. The ranks of common labor in the United States had been swelled by immigration, notably Irish and then Italian, and, even as late as 1900, rates of $1 to $1.25 per day, or 15 to 17 cents an hour and a 60-hour week—the *semaine anglaise* of a half century earlier—still prevailed. On the other hand, skilled labor, always scarce, had experienced a doubling in wages in the expansion period after the Civil War. By 1900 masons were receiving $3 to $4 a day or 30 to 40 cents an hour. Both groups had, however, as we have said, benefited to some extent in real wages through declines in the cost of the necessities of life.

Nevertheless, with the creation of the new industrial empires, there was a great increase in industrial workers, and it became obvious that these workers could not rely on the sense of fair play or an interest in human welfare on the part of the existing management of these enterprises either for improved working conditions or a more reasonable share in the increased productivity of the new era which technology had created. Labor was too often considered to be a mere commodity to be purchased at the lowest possible price.

The Homestead Strike of 1892, during Cleveland's second administration, was a knockdown and drag-out battle between the newly created steel industry and one of the most powerful of the earlier labor unions which sought fairer conditions for labor and a greater share in the profits which the new era was creating. Bargeloads of Pinkerton guards and strikebreakers moving up the Monongahela to break the strike were met by 5,000 strikers who killed 10, wounded 60, and forced their surrender. State militia came to the aid of the steel interests, and the strike was broken although the sympathy of the public was with the union.

The Pullman Strike during the gloomy winter of 1894 was the result of a series of cuts in wages at a time when the company was making 7 per cent on their capital and had a surplus of 70 per cent. The attitude of an industrial leader of the day is reflected in the remark of Mr. Pullman that "it was simply a matter of business." It also appeared that the company's model village, highly praised by sociologists, was operated at a handsome profit by this paternalistic corporate despot. Following general misrepresentation by the press and the riots of the Bloody Fourth of July in Chicago, with 12 killed and 6 World's Fair buildings burned, this strike was also broken. Here, however, the report of Cleveland's commission exposed the policy of the company and the railroads, and the strike added another milestone in the struggle of labor for adequate wages and recognition.

The Anthracite Strike of May, 1902, in Theodore Roosevelt's era, again emphasized the determination of "the Interests" to break the union movement at all costs. A coal famine followed, schools were closed, but the operators refused to budge. In this case, however, organized labor achieved a direct victory for "fair play and working conditions." Public opinion was coming around to the labor viewpoint.

As a result of this change in viewpoint—and, it should be noted, probably because the American economy was rapidly expanding and, when there is more to go around, all groups are usually benefited—there was a steady rise in wages of both common and skilled labor and a decline in the work hours after 1900. Labor took advantage of the pressures of World War I in the administration of Woodrow Wilson to establish the 8-hour day as standard. Immigration was being restrained, common labor becoming less available, and new opportunities were being constantly found for better employment in the rising manufacturing and service occupations. By 1928 common labor had, in the urban Northeastern states, reached 75 cents to $1 an hour and a 44-hour week was standard. Skilled labor had risen to $1.40 or more.

All this appears to be quite favorable for these groups of workers. But these are money wages, and money wages are subject to price changes in the necessities of life. The actual purchasing power of money, "real wages," is a more revealing indication of actual improvement in the position of the worker. It was becoming evident that the terms "skilled" and "common" were far from sufficiently inclusive; America had, in fact, become a nation of workers. The "gainfully employed," that is, those working for remuneration, either self-employed or hired, included, by 1930, 97 per cent of the male population in the age group between 25 and 50 years, and in the entire population over 10 years of age, 76.2 per cent of the men and boys and 22 per cent of the women and girls were workers. In other words, the position of the worker in the American economy could no longer be measured in terms of any one group; only a study of the relative status of a wide number of groups from agriculture to manufacturing and white-collar workers would reveal the actual position of the worker in this new era.

Chapter 18. THE DISTRIBUTION OF
TECHNOLOGICAL GAINS

> The struggle about money-wages primarily affects the distribution of the aggregate real wage between different labor groups. The effect of combination on the part of a group of workers is to protect their relative real wage. The *general* level of real wages depends on other forces of the economic system.
>
> Lord Keynes, *General Theory of Employment, Interest, and Money.*

WHO GETS THE PROFITS?

The principal problem of life in a modern industrial economy seems to have become that of answering the question: Who gets the profits? Organized labor has insisted, and successfully, that it is entitled to a larger share of the profits and that wages must be increased. Management has claimed that it is the American people rather than a small group of capitalists who invest savings in industrial enterprise and that they are entitled to a fair return on their investment. Also in order to maintain a healthy, progressive, industrial economy a major share of profits must be plowed back into new plant and equipment to overcome obsolescence and provide for expansions. Government is put to it to secure through the added burden of taxes the funds needed to support its many activities. The shifts and changes in this struggle affect practically the entire population for, as has been said, the majority of our people are both workers and investors. The battle is no longer between a handful of "malefactors of great wealth" and the common man but one of the changing fortunes of great groups of American citizens as the ups and downs of supply and demand and government burdens, or the pressure tactics of other more effectively organized groups, cause shifts in their relative bargaining positions.[1]

These shifts and changes are of special importance in the United

[1] Yet many writers and teachers continue to emphasize the sins of the earlier independent ruthless capitalist, forgetting that the errors of their ways are now acknowledged and that the perpetrators of these evils are now dead.

States because our economy is based primarily in internal trade, on the exchange of goods and services between many groups which constitute the American people. Exports have, in the past, been an important means of disposing of certain surpluses, but since the United States has become the creditor nation of the world, foreign countries can pay for our exports only by our acceptance of imports from those countries. Certain of these imports, such as essential raw materials which we do not possess, furnish an important exchange for our manufactured goods and are, thus, doubly valuable to our economy. Recent technological advances, however, have tended to reduce the importance of many of these raw materials, the struggle to control which has long been a factor in the economic warfare among nations.

The exchange of our manufactured goods for foreign goods that we also manufacture raises another and very controversial problem. Theoretically, at least, what experts regard as one of the few well-established principles of economics should apply, namely the so-called law of comparative costs. "The essence of it is that it pays a person or a country to devote resources to those activities in which the person or country has a relative advantage, not necessarily to those in which there is an absolute advantage." In other words, if we can purchase certain goods abroad on which our margin of profit is small or which may even cost less than we can make them for at home, and if, in exchange, we can find abroad favorable markets for goods in the production of which we excel—and thus make a larger margin of profit—it is to our advantage to encourage such export-import activity. While the soundness of this viewpoint may not be questioned, the present trend in world affairs appears to be in the contrary direction.

The struggle today seems to center in an effort by the leading nations of the world to attain the highest possible degree of self-sufficiency. The rest of the world, of course, needs American products very sorely today while we have little need for foreign goods. Furthermore, the rest of the world, as we have said, is short of American dollars, and they can pay for our products only if we, in turn, accept theirs. Both American business and American labor appear to be opposed to the idea of removing tariff barriers which prevent the flow of goods from foreign countries with lower standards of living into the United States. Unlike Britain, which has long been dependent on imports to meet the necessities of life, the United States, with its largely self-sufficient economy, has never faced this problem. The chances of developing an extensive export-import trade thus seem rather remote. Whether we go forward or decline depends, therefore, almost entirely on how successful we are in distributing, within our own borders and among all our people, the proceeds of technological gains, that is, on a healthy internal trade.

When we recall that the basic characteristic of modern engineered industry is the production of more goods with less labor, it is obvious that an expanding internal economy is also essential to a healthy dynamic America. The American economy will work only if a constantly increasing market for the products of our industries can be maintained—only if there is a widespread increase in purchasing power among all groups of our people. It has been through the increasingly wider distribution of the profits of industrial progress that American standards of living have been raised to a level never known in the past and unequaled in the world of today. Two major factors affect the extent and uniformity with which the American people share the profits of industrial progress: the concentration of our manufacturing industries in certain sections of the country and the varying fortunes, which Lord Keynes notes, of the different groups of workers in the struggle with other groups for a greater share in profits, for increased purchasing power.

As we have indicated, technological advances making for increased productivity have been shared with remarkable uniformity among all major American industries. Owing to the fact, however, that agriculture has declined in its economic position while the manufacturing industries have risen, and that these activities are centered in certain areas or states, there has been and still is a marked geographical difference in the relative prosperity and progress among different groups of our people. Thus a comparison of the states of highest and lowest incomes shows that the highest is New York with an average per capita of $1,579, closely followed by California, Connecticut, and other manufacturing states. The lowest is Mississippi with only $519 followed by South Carolina and Alabama—the Southeastern states with the addition of one or two western areas such as Arkansas and New Mexico. There is, of course, some equalization of this great difference due to differences in the way of living. Real income, purchasing power, is more nearly uniform, but many products produced in a national scale, such as automobiles, radios, and clothing, are beyond the pocketbooks of these areas. The Rev. Edward A. Keller in a recent summary points out that those who used similar studies of the National Resources Committee during the early days of the New Deal as a basis for the statement that of the American people there was "one-third ill-fed, ill-clothed, and ill-housed" failed to note that about 73 per cent of this third were on farms and rural areas and 40 per cent were in the South.[2] The trend, however, has been, and undoubtedly is, toward wider industrialization and, thus, toward an increasing equalization of income.

Thus New England was the birthplace of American manufactures, but New England's younger sons were moving westward through the Mohawk Valley to the Ohio and North Central states even before the Revolution. They carried Yankee ingenuity with them. That this group of states, covering roughly the northern half of the northeast quarter of our country, some "fourteen in number and with only 14 per cent of the land area of our country," have long been the center of America's industrial empire and are often referred to as "the Industrial United States" is, thus, no mystery. The great machine-tool building centers of the country are in this area, and the majority of the great manufacturing plants of the country are located within its borders. These states include almost two-thirds of our manufactures, support almost half of our population, and enjoy 60 per cent of our national income—another example of the truth that industrialized areas are the richest, offer the highest wages, and provide the highest standards of living.

When the American Union was formed in 1789, Virginia was the wealthiest and most prosperous state while New York stood fifth. Today the income and bank deposits of New York are over thirty times those of Virginia. The answer is not to be found in natural advantages for Virginia has excellent coal and other resources, which New York does not enjoy. Among other factors, however, New York has become a great financial center and New York's manufactures are some fifteen times those of Virginia. A similar observation would apply to the other industrialized states.

In more recent years there has been a marked trend, as we have noted, toward wider industrialization and thus a more equitable distribution of the proceeds of technological progress. The series of maps of the United States, earlier presented, showing the location of our industries, reveal very clearly this spread of industry over our country. During the war, West Coast industries, in particular, a major power area of notable resources, expanded at a far more rapid rate than the older industrial regions. Texas, long an agricultural state, has, because of her remarkable resources of oil and

[2] *The National Income and Its Distribution,* published by the Bureau of Economic Research, University of Notre Dame, Notre Dame, Indiana, 1947.

natural gas, forged rapidly ahead in industrial importance. The textile industry, operating with cotton from the South but long centered in New England, has been moving southward thus adding to the rapid expansion of Southern industry. Many factors influence such changes—natural resources, the availability of cheap power, the transportation costs of raw materials and manufactured products, the attitude of labor, and the burdens of taxation. But the trend is unquestionably toward an ever more widespread industrialization in the states and, thus, toward a more uniform distribution of the industrial wealth, the technological gains, of the nation.

Yet, in addition to the still evident geographical inequality in income, another and far more disturbing factor has operated to bring about widely varying fortunes among various groups of our people. Up to World War I the fruits of technological gains, increased real wages and purchasing power, were shared with remarkable uniformity among the American people. The primary producers, farmers, miners, producers of raw or processed-raw materials as groups, fared about the same as the fabricators of these products, that is, those who manufactured them into consumers' goods, semidurable products, or those who operated the equipment and construction industries.

Since World War I there has been a remarkable change in this picture. The relative trading position of various groups has been subject to violent changes. Certain favored industries have vastly improved their status. Workers in certain favored groups have, in fact, claimed a larger share in the increased profits of our economy than advances in productivity would justify. They have moved ahead at the expense of other groups. This raises a fundamental problem which affects not only the status of particular workers but the general economic stability and welfare of our whole country.

The effects and importance of these trends are, of course, obscured by the fact that we have no definite and accepted criterion as to what constitutes the optimum distribution of the proceeds of American productivity; that is, what kind of distribution of technological and industrial gains makes for the best general economic health of the country. What has happened, as we have said, is that some groups have found it possible to enhance their position at the expense of other groups, but the question as to how importantly this affects the general economic welfare cannot, at least at present, be answered on a factual basis. Perhaps the best that can be done is to examine some of the evidence and endeavor to draw from it such lessons as it appears to offer. Fortunately, reliable data have been made available through the efforts of experts in the analysis of economic statistics which make it possible to measure with reasonable accuracy some of the changes in real wages, in the relative purchasing position of various groups in American life.

Because certain influences lag in their effect—such as conditions of supply, changes in the consumption habits of our people, fluctuations in money values—year-by-year comparisons do not reveal these major trends so reliably or clearly as a comparison of longer periods in which data for each period are based on the average of several years. It is also true that the periods compared must be selected at reasonably comparable times in the major cyclical changes which have affected the tempo of American economic life.

This procedure has been followed by Professor Frederick C. Mills in a recent study, "The Anatomy of Prices," from which the data in Table 6 have been derived.[3] We begin with showing certain general price comparisons for three major periods.

TABLE 6. PRICE TRENDS IN VARIOUS MARKETS

	1891–1894	1912–1914	1912–1914	1933–1938
Wholesale prices................	100	132	100	113
Cost of living, industrial workers....	100	136	100	142
Construction costs...............	100	137	100	170
Per capita earnings, manufacturing industries.....................	100	134	100	183
Hourly earnings, manufacturing industries.......................	100	142	100	257

As this table indicates, all prices in the areas noted advanced with surprising uniformity in the 20-year period from the early '90's to World War I. During these same years, the productivity of the country also increased a like amount, namely about 30 per cent. In other words, the gains of our economic life, of technological and industrial improvements, were passed on to all groups of our people with remarkable impartiality. Gains in the prices secured by the various groups kept pace with gains in production, and more goods went to more people. This is not to say, of course, that any inequalities which may have existed in the purchasing position, the economic status, of any of these groups were corrected or improved. Quite the contrary.

[3] *Bulletin* 80, National Bureau of Economic Research, Inc., New York, September, 1940.

While they all shared equally in the advances which were made, their earlier relative positions remained unchanged.

Quite a reverse distribution of the advantages stemming from advances is evident, however, in the next 20 years, in 1933–1938 as compared with 1912–1914. Increases ranged from 13 per cent in wholesale prices to 157 in the manufacturing industries. "The evidence of an extraordinary reversal of prewar tendencies and accompanying alterations in the price structure is," as Professor Mills observes, "impressive." Instead of equal shares for all, what had happened was a marked increase in the position of the manufacturing industries—owners, management, and workers—as compared with the other classifications.

A further extension of this study to provide more detailed information shows that this increase in the prices received by, and thus in the purchasing power of, those concerned in manufacturing was far from uniform. A classification of all commodities as producers' goods, that is, as either raw or processed goods not yet in form for final consumption, and consumers' goods, goods that are ready for consumption or use without further fabrication, indicates where the major price changes had occurred.

TABLE 7

	1891–1894	1912–1914	1912–1914	1933–1938
Consumers' goods...............	100	117	100	139
Raw.......................	100	122	100	116
Processed...................	100	117	100	132
Producers' goods...............	100	122	100	117
Raw.......................	100	143	100	106
Processed...................	100	110	100	127
For consumption..............	100	123	100	95
For construction and capital equipment.................	100	122	100	139
Raw farm products..............	100	134	100	100
All other products..............	100	118	100	127

While changes in the relative productivity of certain of these groups might offset some of these price differences, it seems clear that the prices realized by the processors and fabricators, the manufacturing industries, had risen more rapidly than those of the groups which provided raw materials. Since, however, the incidence of technological gains had been remarkably uniform, as we have noted, among all branches of American industry, it seems clear, for example, that if the price of farm products remained stationary while the price of all the other products, presumably the goods bought by farmers, increased 27 per cent, there had been a decline in the purchasing position of farmers of a like amount.

A further study of Table 7 shows clearly who had gained by the farmers' loss. Clearly the processors and fabricators, the manufacturing industries, and the capital goods, construction industries had gone ahead at the expense of the miners, farmers, and similar producers of raw materials. Data are not available which will permit more detailed comparisons in all lines of activity, but Professor Mills has made a study of three periods in the manufacturing industries themselves which is very revealing (see Table 8).

TABLE 8. PERCENTAGE CHANGE PER WORKER OR PER MAN-HOUR WORKED*

	1899–1914	1914–1929	1929–1937
Change in output.............................	29.6	49.7	24.1
Change in real returns:			
All agents of fabrication...................	2.8	51.9	17.8
Wage earners.............................	0.7	31.3	34.9
Ownership, management, and other claimants.	4.5	67.5	8.2

* This table shows increments in output per worker or, when data are available, in hours worked, and corresponding changes in the real returns of manufacturing producers. These later figures were estimated by dividing the total of monetary returns of the groups noted by the number of wage earners or man-hours worked and deflating the quotient by appropriate indexes of the prices for which the money returns of these groups were expended. In the case of wage earners, the index is their cost of living. In the mixed class of ownership, salaried workers, and other claimants, the index was based on a weighted proportion of living costs, wholesale prices, and prices of capital goods. It should also be noted that data up to 1929 are given on a per worker basis, whereas those for 1929–1937 are on a man-hour basis.

This study permits us to secure at least some idea of the distribution of gains within the manufacturing industries themselves, as between the wage worker and the owners, managers, and other claimants, the so-called "white-collar" group. The previously noted gain in production of 30 per cent between 1899 and 1914 is indicated. In this period, while there had been a negligible gain among workers and a modest advance among the ownership and management group, it seems quite clear, as above stated, that the major gains in output had been passed on to the ultimate consumer in the form of more goods for less money. But between 1914 and 1929 the gain of almost 50 per cent in manufacturing output was a bit more than absorbed by the manufacturing industries themselves. Furthermore it was not the wage earner who secured the lion's share of it, he claimed a bit better than 30 per cent increase, but it was the ownership-management group that captured a two-thirds advance—an advance in excess of the gain in output.

The effects of these changes on the trading positions of groups other than manufacturing are reflected in other available data. For example, our previous statement of a quite uniform and widespread sharing of gains in the period 1912–1914 is illustrated by the fact that producers of raw materials in general had received, for a unit of their output, 22 per cent more in manufactured and 19 per cent more in consumers' goods at this time than they had in 1891–1894. The mineral industries did not fare quite so well (17 and 14 per cent, respectively) and the farmers were in about the same position (14 and 15 per cent). In sharp contrast, the 1914–1929 period, marked by the greatly increased claims of "ownership, management, and other claimants," naturally resulted in reducing the relative purchasing value of farm products (the decline was from 6 to 9 per cent) and mineral products also declined (5 to 6 per cent).

Now, as we have previously remarked, we cannot assume that the economic position of the various groups of producers in the United States in 1899, or at any time for that matter, was fair, just, and equitable and such as to encourage the most effective and productive American economic life. While there is, thus, no absolute criterion, it would seem reasonable to assume that such changes as that here indicated do have an effect on the equilibrium, the stability of our economy. From 1914 to 1929, for example, the relative economic fortunes of some 10 million mineral and farm workers—involving probably a fifth of our people—were declining, and the workers were, presumably, unable to purchase, at least as freely as in the past, the products which our manufacturing industries were turning out.

This is not to say that this one factor alone caused the Panic of 1929 and the Decade of Depression and Doubt which followed it. But, if we recall two of the most discussed ideas of the earlier New Deal era, it appears that there is some relationship between the way in which we share the productive gains of technology and industry and the stability of our economy. Thus, recall the so-called paradox so widely quoted in the early '30's, of unemployment, want, and starvation in the midst of plenty. Was this due to overproduction or simply to the fact that a large segment of our people had been robbed of their purchasing power by the ownership, management, and other claimants of the manufacturing industries? The farmer was, of course, producing more than he could market—he was advised to "plow under" his little pigs—but one could, with equal reason, have suggested plowing under much of our manufactures. Great numbers of our people were not in a position where they could buy them.

The second New Deal idea reflected another situation: too much of our income, it was said, had become "frozen" in the hands of a relatively small group, presumably the ownership, management, and other claimants of the manufacturing industries. They could not proportionately increase their purchases of consumers' goods, and there was, necessarily, no demand for increased capital commitments. We had productive capacity and had ample funds, but the latter were in the hands of too few people.

Of course the effects of such unbalance were greatly exaggerated in the Panic of 1929 by the attempts made to postpone the inevitable adjustment by encouraging possible purchasers to mortgage their future through installment buying. Everything from fur coats and automobiles to refrigerators and radios was bought "on tick." Those presumably best qualified to express opinions assured us, however, that America had reached a new level of productivity and economic life and that we should forget the outmoded economics of an earlier era. The explainers decided that our troubles were due to the lagging population curve, the closing of frontiers, the failure of foreign creditors to make good on our generous war loans, and too rapid scientific and technological progress. A moratorium on science and technology was seriously proposed. The lesson, however, seems to have been that we must have an ever more widespread and increasing market for American goods and services if we are to absorb the ever-greater production stemming from technological improvements and industrial know-how. A nation of a few millionaires, or of a few pressure groups, with a great host of other workers who earn no more than they need for food, heat, and clothing cannot sustain modern technological-industrial life. When the increased purchasing power resulting from gains in productivity is not widely distributed but is claimed by relatively small groups of our people, or when these relatively small groups even enhance their position at the expense of larger groups, it seems inevitable that the makings of a major economic upset are at hand.

It we refer again to Table 8 and note the further changes which took place in the later, 1929–1937, period we find that, while the workers in the manufacturing industries continued to improve their position (a further gain of about 35 per cent as compared with a gain in output of only 24 per cent), this time the advance was at the expense of the "ownership, management, and other claimants" contingent. A further analysis reveals, as might be expected, that the trading position of the producers of raw materials under these conditions did not enjoy comparable advances; in short, their furtunes also declined. An output which would have exchanged for 100 units of manufactured and consumers' goods in 1912–1914 was good now for only 82 or 83 such units. This means that in 1933–1938 the primary producer received 16 to 18 per cent less than he had received a quarter century earlier in exchange for the same quantity of his produce. The mineral industries fared somewhat better than this group as a whole. They stood, in 1933–1938, almost even with their position in 1912–1914.

Professor Mills certainly puts the case very mildly when he summarizes his analysis in the statement:

The general picture, as of 1940, is that of an economy in which primary producers give more in physical goods than they gave in 1910 or in 1900 for a constant quantity of the goods they require, in which fabricators give less time and effort for a constant quantity of the goods they require, and in which costs to the mass of final consumers (other than those in certain favorably placed groups) have not been lowered to a degree commensurate with the great productivity gains of recent years.

This disequalization in economic position may be ascribed largely to the activities of organized labor, plus the tax burden imposed by government. While in the '20's the merchants of debt had a holiday, in the '30's organized labor and the taxes of the New Deal were having their inning. Earlier labor leaders, like Samuel Gompers, would have given some thought to the effects of these changes on our economy. As a top labor leader of recent days put it, however, "I do not give a d——n about economics. All I'm interested in is higher wages."

Then World War II came into the picture. Unemployment was a thing of the past, wage increases continued, and the farmer suddenly experienced a remarkable comeback. The unprecedented demands of the war, the unfilled backlog of consumer needs created by concentration on war products, and the demand for food by the countries overrun by war have not only kept the American economy operating at full blast since 1940 but shortages have led to inflation, and prices in all areas have risen. The old laws of supply and demand have been at work. What further changes have taken place in the relative purchasing position of the various groups of our economy?

Professor Mills summarizes in a more recent study the current situation as compared with 1938–1939 as follows:[4]

1. Prices in wholesale markets have doubled and living costs have risen two-thirds.

2. Uneven advances in prices have further altered the terms on which various groups exchange their products.

3. Farmers have gained substantially. In aggregated terms of their gains in purchasing power over gains in output, the relative gains of farmers may be estimated at 47 per cent, with due allowance for subsidy factors as well as prices, their real per capita income had gone up about 100 per cent.

4. Among other primary producers those turning out forest products have gained about the same as farmers while price indices have moved against producers of metals and hard coal.

5. Manufacturing labor increased its total input of working time about 80 per cent and its aggregate rewards were about doubled. The real per capita gain of manufacturing labor was about 34 per cent. This, superimposed on earlier gains, meant a total gain, 1924–1927 to 1948, in real hourly earnings of 85 per cent.

6. For four groups of nonmanufacturing labor—soft-coal miners, hotel workers, quarrying workers, and common road labor—the gains were even greater. But for telephone, electric-light and power, and skilled construction workers, real hourly wages declined.

As a consequence of these changes material and labor costs constituted a larger percentage of the total value of manufactured product in 1947 than for any other year of recent record. Farmers were blessed, after a long period of declining purchasing power, with undreamed-of prosperity. Management had also taken advantage of a sellers' market, and industrial profits were high although in part this was due to inflation, to high inventory estimates. Industrial productivity, however, had declined, especially in the letdown following the end of the war, and white-collar workers and those dependent on income from investments were the main groups of sufferers.

In attempting to summarize this story, the first question which comes to mind is: Why should the problem here outlined be of special interest to the engineer? The answer is that he is the principal pro-

[4] *The Structure of Post War Prices,* by Frederick C. Mills, Occasional Paper 27, National Bureau of Economic Research, Inc., New York, 1948.

fessional man of our modern technological industries. This is a problem of interest to all American citizens but especially so to the engineer, the future of whose position and professional interests is so closely tied up with the health and prosperity of American industry. As Professor Mills makes clear, wide price movements in the economy are a vital factor affecting its equilibrium and growth. Such modifications not only militate against a wide and equitable distribution of the proceeds of increased productivity but act artificially to encourage or unnecessarily to discourage new investments or capital improvements, may raise or lower the break-even point in industrial operations, and may contribute to major economic dislocations. We have had occasion elsewhere to note the important part played in the growth of our way of life by ample provision for the replacement of old equipment by new and better tools and machines. We may easily run into a situation where the claims of pressure groups plus those of government seriously curtail the maintenance of an up-to-date, truly progressive industrial plant.

The inequalities above noted doubtless tend, in the long run, toward adjustment but, temporarily at least, they are extremely dangerous. Workers tend to switch from less favored to favored groups. Lack of labor forces up wages in neglected areas. Overproduction ultimately leads to reduction of output. But the reduction in violence of these fluctuations is a major problem in the avoidance of "boom or bust," in the maintenance of a reasonable stability in our American life, as well as in the steady growth and development of American engineering and industry. To such extent as organized pressure activities of any kind are involved, they must ultimately be curbed. As Lord Keynes observes of certain groups of labor, "Once the oppressed, they are now the tyrants, whose selfish and sectional schemes need to be bravely opposed." A similar observation might be made in regard to many other selfish groups—political distributors of other people's money and wishful thinkers as well as those who specialize in financial legerdemain.

Chapter 19. TECHNOLOGICAL CHANGE
AND CAPITAL GOODS

> Of the physical survivals of earlier eras only an infinitesimal remnant survives today . . . save for the vintage of very recent periods it represents but a tithe of the "durable" goods originally produced. The life of most such goods falls far short of the three score years and ten the psalmist has allotted to the human span. Indeed, in the United States at least, a typical year's output of durable commodities and structures has an average life expectancy less than half as long. The hand of time lies heavy on the works of man, whether ancient or modern.
>
> George Terborgh, *Dynamic Equipment Policy.*

PRODUCTIVE CAPACITY, OBSOLESCENCE, AND REPLACEMENT

Up to this point in this brief discussion of some of the economic and social problems which have been brought about by engineering and industrial advances, we have noted the impact of technological change on the character of employment and the status of the worker. The questions naturally arise: What of the problems of providing the worker with the modern tools of production? How does technological change affect our capital investment in productive equipment?

On the one hand, the conclusions to be drawn from the employment situation seem to be that the obsolescence of older employment skills tends to become of less importance as the development of machines makes the acquisition of new techniques less difficult. The necessity for an exceptional manual dexterity which can be achieved only through long apprenticeship and experience is reduced as machines are made more fully automatic and production processes more fully routinized.

On the other hand, the continued improvement of the tools and machines of production, the capital commitments of economic life, resulting from technological and industrial developments, brings not only increasingly rapid displacement of older products, processes, and methods but, especially, a heavy burden of plant and equipment obsolescence or replacement. Few of our capital investments in the so-called durable goods of modern life—plants, structures, machines —ever terminate through what might be called a natural death, through complete physical decay and collapse. It is their useful, their effective, their economic life, which comes to an end and leads to their being discarded. As Mr. Terborgh puts it,

Capital goods live out their mortal span in an atmosphere of combat, a struggle for life as bitter, as intolerant of weakness, as the tooth and claw of biological competition. In principle, this mechanical warfare surpasses in depravity the carnage of the jungle; the beasts respect their own kind, but machines destroy their own species and others indiscriminately.

The problem is, thus, one not only of providing the initial productive capacity through capital outlay but of maintaining this equipment in effective operating condition through replacement financed from current income.

This problem is, of course, vitally important also from the employment angle. Between 1900 and 1940 there was, as we have seen, an increase of 90 per cent in those gainfully employed in the United States. In other words, over these years jobs were found for an average of over 600,000 new workers per year. It has furthermore been noted that the investment in the modern tools of industry has been mounting upward to, perhaps, $5,000 to $6,000 or more per worker. Even if such per worker investment applies to only a part of the new jobs which must be created annually, it follows that a continual investment of large capital sums in extensions or new plants is essential if we are to provide the facilities necessary to maintain employment. In addition, funds must be found, as we have said, continually to modernize existing plants, to keep them in up-to-date condition, to replace not only worn-out but obsolete equipment which is no longer capable of effective and efficient use. Where are such funds to be secured? The answer is that they are part of the burden of a dynamic industrial life. They must come from earlier savings or from the current net profits of industry itself.

As we have noted elsewhere, the United States was an importer of capital from abroad, notably Britain, throughout the 19th century. World War I, however, reversed this situation and made us a capital exporter. Indeed one of the theories developed by the New Deal was that the United States had reached a condition of economic maturity and that this was the fundamental fact back of the collapse of 1929.

Briefly summarized, this theory held that the United States had ceased to grow, was no longer expanding. Population growth was tapering off. The geographical frontier with its opportunities for investment no longer existed. Technology was no longer creating new investment opportunities comparable to those of the past. Savings were accumulating, piling up as hoarded idle funds, thereby setting in motion a downward spiral of declining income and bringing about an era of stagnation. In other words, excess savings were poisoning the economy and, in this crippled state, it remained for government to step in and save the situation. This argument was quite completely answered in a book, *The Bogey of Economic Maturity*, by George Terborgh published in 1945. With taxes where they are today, with the many demands on the United States for dollars to speed European recovery, with the burdens of old-age pensions and unemployment insurance, one hears less of the problem of finding ways and means of disposing of our surplus dollars. It seems clearer that, if a widespread demand can be maintained through a widespread material well-being and purchasing power among our people, opportunities will be available for the investment of funds in extending old and creating new industries. Hoarding is usually "against a rainy day," and few people hoard who need and want more food and clothing, more of the conveniences and services of modern life. Investment opportunities expand as the demand for production expands, and it would appear that all the needs, wants, and desires of the American people are far from satisfied as yet.

New enterprises necessarily seek funds from various external sources, the capital market, through bonds or stock issues and similar devices. In the past there has usually been a very considerable amount of "venture capital" available for smaller enterprises of an admittedly risky, venturesome character. Much of this "speculative" spending has ended in failure but, in a few cases, new enterprises have been created in this way which have fertilized and strengthened our economy. In our efforts to protect the unwary investor through the Security Exchange Commission (SEC) we have, however, created such obstacles and introduced so much red tape in connection with the flotation of new ventures as to discourage many smaller undertakings of this type.

Existing enterprises secure funds for expansion either through turning to the same external sources or from the net income of their own operation. These two extremes are illustrated by the case of the Ford Motor Company and the American Telephone and Telegraph

Company. The former has financed its remarkable growth and development through internal funds, from the net income, after the first funds needed to start operations, of these operations themselves. The latter, a public service company under government supervision, has, on the other hand, resorted almost continuously to the capital market for its expansion needs. The whole problem of the basic economies of saving and investment is most complicated and difficult, one on which there is a wide difference of opinion among economists, and it cannot be fully discussed in these brief notes.

It has long been assumed, for example, that the creation of productive capacity in a free-competitive economy follows the law of supply and demand. A shortage of production, on the one hand, would lead to high prices and thus attract capital by offering an opportunity for profitable investment. Vice versa, overproduction would result in declining prices, plants unable to operate at a profit would shut down, and capital would, of course, look elsewhere for investment. Many enterprises exhibit a sequence of development and growth while maturity is often followed by decline. Productive capacity in many areas is, thus, constantly in process of change in character while, at the same time, its quality and use value are subject to constant deterioration.

Following the Panic of 1929 various attempts were, as we have remarked, made to explain the reasons for this collapse as a logical first step toward remedial action and recovery. Among the suggested errors to which our difficulties were attributed was that of having diverted far too much of our income during the 1920's to capital commitments, to the expansion of our productive facilities. All through the earlier history of our country there were efforts to encourage thrift and saving. Benjamin Franklin in his *Poor Richard's Almanac* was a leader in a preachment which emphasized industry and frugality, extolling self-denial and praising saving:

> For age and want, save while you may,
> No morning sun lasts a whole day.

One of the arguments advanced in explanation of the Collapse of 1929, however, took the reverse position. It was held that what was referred to as the "Dilemma of Thrift" had caused us to oversave and that not only had the saving habit led us to reduce our purchases of consumers' goods, but, seeking investment for our savings, we had continued to make capital investments, thus increasing our productive capacity not only far beyond our abilities to purchase but far beyond our needs. In short, it was held that thrift had led us to curtail our purchases of consumers' goods and, at the same time, to increase the volume of such goods by overbuilding our productive plant.

In 1934 a careful study, *America's Capacity to Produce,* showed quite conclusively that there had been no such overexpansion of our productive facilities during the years before 1929. There were of course, a few specific industries which had long been developed beyond our needs. World War I had also led to overexpansion in some areas, but, in general, it appeared that the estimates of those who claimed great overbuilding were based on a *theoretical* productive capacity rather than on the established, customary, or even the reasonably attainable capacities of American industry. For example, very few industries are operated 24 hours a day, as are power stations, certain steel and by-product coke plants, and other activities in which continuous operation is essential and frequent shutdowns are impracticable. In general, not only is the 8-hour day standard but in a number of industries there are slack periods needed for repairs. Furthermore, we have as yet been unable to avoid seasonal operation in some operations such as in agriculture, in fuel production where winter needs increase coal consumption while summer demands for gasoline are high, or in cement manufacture in which, owing to great summer construction activity, shipments in August may be three times those in February. Indeed, in the case of power plants where it is essential that capacity be provided to carry the peak load with, in addition, some stand-by, "spare" equipment in case of emergency, the average load is seldom over 40 per cent of the peak.

From the standpoint of maximum output and highest efficiency it would, theoretically, be desirable for us to operate our productive plant continuously at full capacity. There is no doubt, for example, that one of the problems we face in the improvement of the efficiency of our economy as a whole is that of devising economical ways and means of ironing out seasonal and similar variations, thus securing a higher use factor and more steady employment. On the other hand, the purpose of such increased efficiency in productive capacity is not to provide the opportunity to labor 24 hours a day and 365 days a year but to supply the needs, necessities, and conveniences of life to all our people with less labor. During the war the productive capacity of the United States was doubled not by doubling equipment (the increase has been estimated at about 50 to 60 per cent), but to a major degree by working overtime, "around the clock." These, however, were not normal, nor are they desired conditions.

It is now, of course, quite generally admitted that, since technological and industrial developments make greater production with less labor increasingly possible, in order to maintain an economy based on industrialization, an increasing capacity to use and purchase the products of production is essential. There are those who feel that such increased production must inevitably lead to overproduction, unemployment, loss of purchasing power, collapse, and the paradox of want in the midst of plenty. Yet it seems clear, as we have said, that our wants are far from the saturation point. There are a substantial number of our people who need more goods and services, and there are few who would not, if they could afford to, purchase and use more. Furthermore, new goods and services are being constantly developed and, while regarded today as conveniences or even luxuries, will, as has so frequently happened in the past, soon come to be regarded as necessities and essentials. In other words, the usefulness of increased production is apparent. The problem we face is that of making it possible for all our people to afford to purchase these services.

This problem has its implications, as we have seen, from the standpoint of the widespread distribution of the fruits of technological gains. It also raises a problem from the standpoint of the effect of enterprise obsolescence on the purchasing power of those involved in a declining industry. There has, always, been overbuilding in some industries. Hindsight is always easier and more certain than foresight. It is to be hoped that, as factual knowledge and understanding improve, the burdens of mistakes and failures which our economy has to absorb will decrease. The general economic danger of decay and obsolesence seems to center, however, primarily on the loss of purchasing power in the labor group involved.

For example, at the present time there can be no doubt that bituminous coal mining is a declining industry. A study of the past relationship of productive capacity and output shows that, while productive capacity had long been in excess of demand, there was a steady increase in production up to the end of World War I. Thereafter, while there was no further increase in demand, productive capacity continued to increase until, some five years later in 1923 a peak was reached variously estimated as between 800 and 950 million tons annually as compared wtih a demand averaging somewhat over 500. There followed a closing down of marginal mines and, between 1923 and 1930, over 200,000 men lost their jobs. Various temporary factors influenced the increase to the peak of 1923 while the competition of petroleum, increased efficiency in the use of coal in power plants, changes in the demand for coke (a major market), plus improvements and mechanization in coal mining itself, undoubtedly contributed to the decline in demand which followed.

The coke industry, closely tied up with coal, was also undergoing a transformation. Production in the old-fashioned and wasteful beehive ovens declined sharply after World War I, and within some 12 or 15 years, over 100 million dollars of older plant had been rendered useless by the rise of the by-product oven. Then a new competitor, natural gas, entered the field and demand further declined.[1]

We have no measure of the effect of such changes and obsolescence on the purchasing power of those most directly affected and, of course, none on the effect of such declines on the stability and prosperity of the American economy as a whole. All we can say is that such shifts and adjustments tend to destroy, temporarily at least, the power to purchase and, if they affect a sufficiently large segement of our people, are undoubtedly a disturbing factor in our economic stability.

In addition to these major shifts and changes which affect entire industries there is the constant problem of the obsolesence and need for replacement of the facilities and equipment used in any industry. A tendency to continue to use old plant and machines, that is, a failure to replace them with modern, up-to-date, and more efficient facilities, inevitably leads to reduced production, to a waste of manpower, and to higher costs. We have already noted the fact that the neglect of this problem of replacement—the prevalence of the idea that it is unnecessary to replace "good" tools or facilities or those which will still function after a fashion, by better equipment—has been an important factor in bringing about the collapse of some of the older industrial economies of Europe, notably in Great Britain. The burdens of obsolescence and replacement clearly increase as industrialization itself becomes older and more widespread. As the capital investment committed to plant and equipment grows, there is also a tendency to put off the fatal day. A new industry has, presumably, been skillfully designed for optimum production and is, thus "up-to-date" when built. The problem of keeping it so must be a continuing one with expeditures covered annually from current

[1] See the excellent analysis in *America's Capacity to Produce,* Chap. II, "Coal and Coke."

income. Its neglect in a competitive economy may lead to failure or, at least, become, through ill-advised postponement, a major operation involving almost a fresh start, almost the complete rehabilitation of an enterprise with major expenditures and difficult problems of refinancing.

Thus the destruction by the war in Europe, terrible and devastating as it has been, has, at least, "wiped off the books" many plants and much equipment which, under progressive and far-sighted management, should long ago have been replaced. It is probable, however, that these antiques could not have been liquidated by any less violent means. This war-induced European "house cleaning" has, therefore, left Europe with an unparalleled opportunity to modernize her facilities. It has also raised anew the question as to the present status of American industry. The challenge it imposes on America's industrial supremacy is very clearly stated in the report of the President's Scientific Research Board:

The future is certain to confront us with competition from other national economies of a sort we have not hitherto had to meet. Many of these will be state-directed in the interest of national policies. Many will be supported by new, highly efficient industrial plant and equipment—by the most modern technology. The destructiveness of the recent war makes it inevitable that much of Europe, in rebuilding its factories, will soon possess an industrial plant more modern than ours of today.

The importance of this problem not only from the standpoint of an individual enterprise but from that of the general economic health and industrial position of a modern industrialized nation, cannot, thus, be questioned. Yet there is probably no problem of engineering and investment economics which poses more difficult conditions for analysis. It is, in fact, difficult for any nation even to take stock of its present position and appraise the quality of its productive plant. The general viewpoint has been that the United States has led the world not only in the mechanization of production but in the speed with which we have adopted improved equipment, thus keeping our productive machinery constantly up to date.

The percentage of current earnings, "plowed back" annually into industry for the replacement and improvement of the facilities of production, is generally recognized as indicative of the general state of our productive plant. As has been noted, this percentage in Britain between the World Wars has been estimated at 3 per cent as compared with a similar estimate of 15 per cent in the United States.

Yet who can say whether an average of even 15 per cent over the years will maintain an optimum condition in our productive machinery or may not, on the other hand, represent an economic waste of still useful facilities through their too early retirement? It seems quite clear that, as the tempo of technological and industrial advances increases—as a result both of increased emphasis on research and efforts to reduce the time lag between the discovery of new knowledge and its application—there will be a tendency toward more rapid obsolescence of older equipment and, thus, an increasing burden if a backward condition of mechanization is to be avoided. Furthermore, we must always face the fact that errors in making provision for obsolescence or replacement result in inadequate financial provisions for depreciation and leave "on the books" assets of doubtful value for which the unrecovered cost is still high.

It is also true that, whereas in general the attitude toward replacement policies is usually liberal in times of prosperity when earnings are high, it seems also to be the practice, especially in such times, to require the recovery in savings of the full first cost of a replacement or improvement in an unreasonably short time. This unreasonable burden naturally leads to the postponement of the fatal day.

Finally the functional degradation and decline of most productive equipment are not clear and obvious. It does not suddenly fall apart "all at once and nothing first" like the famous one-horse shay.[2] The operator of a machine, for example, may know its weaknesses, but to "top management" it appears to be still operating satisfactorily. In short, it may be said that there are many factors which tend to lead to procrastination in the replacement of facilities which will still operate, albeit uneconomically, and, as Wellington might put it, constitute through an unceasing ooze of waste an unnecessary burden on our economic life.

On the constructive side of this story, however, it is stimulating to note the advances which have been made in the engineering technique of estimating the service life of engineering works or devices and in providing for future needs and requirements.

In all probability the longest lived works built by the engineer are the great dams constructed for water supply, power, or irrigation. In general, these are built of durable materials, their stability rests on properties such as weight or compressive strength, little affected by the heavy hand of time, and they also suffer little degradation in

[2] See the poem by Oliver Wendell Holmes, "The One Hoss Shay."

function. It may well be that new structures could be built to replace them at a lower first cost but the operating costs of these works are low and they may long retain their ability fully to meet the service for which they were designed and built. The best we can do is to regard their physical life as indefinite—the most enduring works of man. As far as we can see, so long as the service they provide retains its economic value, they will effectively and efficiently meet its demands. Maintenance and repairs they may require, but obsolescence of service rather than replacement will bring an end to their days.[3]

In general the works of the civil engineer fall in this long-life group. Many bridges, for example, have served long and useful lives. Recall Old London Bridge, built in 1209 and not replaced until about 1825, over 600 years of useful service carrying a cavalcade of British history from the Crusades through the Napoleonic Wars. On the other hand, the majority of American, 19th century railroad bridges have had to be replaced long before they reached the end of their physical lives because they could no longer carry the railroad locomotive loadings which came with the evolution of railroad service. At first sight, this need for replacement may appear to reflect a lack of foresight on the part of their designers. It was quite clear at the time they were built that locomotive weights were increasing. The decision as to the design load was largely a matter of balancing present costs against possible future needs but was based on judgment alone. As far as we know, no attempts were made to project this increase in loads and to plan for the most economic period of service, computed, as may be done, on the basis of the present worth of the replacement which would have to be made at the future date. Only a detailed study would in this case reveal whether the judgment these earlier designers exercised in always designing for loadings heavier than those current was, in fact, sufficiently in advance of current needs to be economically reasonable and sound.

Buildings and more permanent plant facilities used in industry

[3] In this connection it should be noted that probably the longest range attempts at forecasting made by man are in the design of water supplies for our large cities. For example, when the first Catskill water supply for New York was planned in 1903, the required total supply in 1930 was estimated on the basis of forecasts of per capita consumption and of population. In short, a forecast of 27 years was made, in this case with remarkable accuracy. Many public service enterprises, such as the telephone companies, are continually making and revising forecasts of future needs and developments, and there is an increasing volume of technical procedure under development in this important area.

clearly partake of some of this long-life security. The chance that their useful life may approximate their physical life depends primarily upon the survival of the enterprise of which they are a part. Indeed, even if this enterprise is rendered obsolete by technological advances, such facilities may still be of use for other purposes, may possess salvage value.

In the area of machine equipment and machine tools, the tempo of change is far more rapid. In many cases a machine, such as a locomotive, may, in its earlier days when it is highly efficient, be used in almost continuous service. As it grows older, it is relegated to less important and exacting use—if a locomotive, perhaps, to branch-line service. Finally, it may be given a lowly task where little is expected of it or it may end its life as a switch engine. Continual maintenance and the replacement of worn parts, a piecemeal rebuilding of a machine, which can almost indefinitely prolong its physical life, may, thus, if proper use is found for it in its years of declining efficiency, bring its useful and its physical life within close agreement.

Such practice, however, may lead to a tendency to retain obsolete and inefficient equipment. When does it become desirable from the investment standpoint to retire an old piece of equipment from "main line" service and replace it with a new, improved, and more efficient device?

Many attempts have been made to reduce the investment economics of replacement to mathematical terms, to develop formulas giving the answer in dollars and cents. On the one hand, certain basic assumptions must be made to bring the problem within the bounds of mathematical analysis. Furthermore, a large number of factors which cannot be evaluated enter the problem, so that, in the end, time and judgment still remain the major elements in bringing about a decision. As a result of these inherent difficulties, more or less arbitrary rules are usually followed.

Replacement is, of course, tied up with the depreciation policy and practice of the enterprise. Funds must be set aside annually, as we have said, from current earnings to provide for equipment replacement. Allowances for this purpose should involve the estimation in advance of the useful life of the asset, that is, its period of service, an estimation of its possible salvage value, and the planning of a program for the distribution of capital recovery over this period. Studies of 560 machine-tool users made in 1947 showed, however, that in practice this period seemed to be arbitrarily assumed and varied widely—from a requirement that the annual saving produced by a replacement permit the recovery of its cost in from 1 to 10 years with the median in the 3- to 5-year range.[4] Some variation is, of course, to be expected, for the tempo of technological change may affect the use value of the equipment of one enterprise more sharply than in another. Furthermore, there is clearly a tendency to seek rapid capital recovery when earnings are high and to postpone replacements in depression periods.

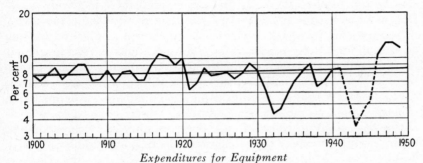

Expenditures for Equipment

Showing expenditures by private industry for equipment, not including building and similar improvements, expressed as a per cent of all physical production and on the basis of constant prices, namely, those of 1929. (*From "Capital Goods Review," February 15, 1950. Courtesy of Machinery and Allied Products Institute.*)

These variations in timing are well illustrated in a graph recently published by the Machinery and Allied Products Institute. This shows the variations in the annual expenditures for producers' equipment as a percentatge of the total value of production in the United States during the present century. The decline in such expenditures during depression years is immediately noted. While World War I brought a "tooling up," World War II evidently resulted in postponements which, together with the Depression of the '30's, created a backlog now in process of rapid correction. This is not to say that the war did not create demands for machine tools. What happened was that these went into new production while older equipment was continued in use—could not, in fact, have been effectively replaced because prewar models and designs were in many cases "frozen" for the duration. One of the striking features of this graph is the increasing violence of these fluctuations. Up to 1930 the

[4] See *Iron Age,* September 11, 1947.
[5] *Capital Goods Review,* No. 1, Machinery and Allied Products Institute, Chicago, February 15, 1950.

percentage variation is within 2 per cent. The Depression and World War II, however, brought about much more extreme fluctuations.

The situation as regards replacement may, therefore, be summarized by stating that the importance of the problem not only from the standpoint of the survival of a particular enterprise whose assets must, under competitive free enterprise, be operated for a profit, but also from that of the national economy as a whole, is becoming more clearly and fully realized. On the other hand, there is a wide variation in practice due not only to differences in viewpoint and policy but also to the financial condition of the enterprise plus the varying impact of improved machines on the operations of the particular industry. In general there is undoubtedly a tendency to hold fast to older equipment, especially when its book value, its unrecovered cost, is still high. Mistakes in forecasting and inadequate depreciation provisions hold up replacements. Similarly, there seems to be an inclination, especially in times of special uncertainty as to the course of future events, to expect the savings secured through a replacement to liquidate its cost in an unreasonably short period of time. All these trends naturally act to retard replacement, and the continued improvement and modernization of our productive plant thereby suffers. Furthermore, with the increasing tempo of technological change the adverse effect of these trends seems destined to become greater.

The problem of replacement is further complicated by the fact that, whether an enterprise does or does not possess up-to-date equipment, this is not necessarily the determining factor in its success or failure. A company may advance, in spite of inferior equipment, more rapidly than its competitors by reason of more effective advertising, more aggressive salesmanship, better financial position, product design, personnel, and other advantages. Furthermore, its success or failure may not depend upon any of these factors but upon its location. An industry once favorably located with regard to raw materials and market may, owing to changing conditions beyond its control, to rising taxes, to costs of transportation, and to other factors, find itself no longer in a position successfully to compete with more favorably located newcomers. The cotton textile industry of New England offers a case in point. Today these old established mills face the competition resulting from the growing industrialization of the South where new plants are not only new in equipment, and are more favorably located with respect to raw materials but also often have advantages of lower power, labor, and other costs.

Constant problems of replacement, major shifts and changes,

major industrial illnesses and even death, are, thus, an inevitable accompaniment of the ebb and flow of economic life and evolution in a dynamic, progressive, industrial nation. It has been said that there are three interests to be considered in any study of production and its distribution: the worker, the owner, and the public. To these should be added the health and condition of the instruments of production themselves, for a failure to set aside from profits the funds to build, to maintain, and to keep up to date our productive plant can lead to industrial stagnation and decay.

Chapter 20. ENGINEERING AND RESEARCH

> We have only begun to knock a few chips from the great quarry of knowledge that has been given us to dig out and use. We know .almost nothing about everything. That is why, with all conviction, I say that the future is boundless.
>
> Charles F. Kettering.[1]

KNOWLEDGE AND KNOW-HOW

It has been remarked that, in spite of the wonderful discoveries and inventions of the 18th and 19th centuries which ushered in our modern Engineering and Industrial Age, the most outstanding, the most important and far-reaching advance was the invention of invention itself—the discovery of a method of attack, a process of search, which would lead to the continued disclosure of new and useful knowledge, to never-ending invention and progress.

The history of research, the rise of this modern method of diligent systematic, directed inquiry has, apparently, paralleled the corresponding evolutionary sequences which have characterized the modernization of other scientific professions. Thus the attainment of the commanding position which research occupies today in the minds and hopes of men and the ambitions of nations has been largely the result of the application to this pursuit of the same methods of scientific study and analysis which have so greatly increased the power and service of medicine and engineering.

The basic idea of research certainly reaches far back in human history. We have already quoted Aristotle's statement that "All men by nature are activated with the desire for knowledge." It would also seem quite clear that, in its earlier stages, much new scientific knowledge was gained not only as a result of man's efforts to satisfy his curiosity but also through the teachings he secured in meeting the problems of gaining a livelihood and attempting to make use of the material resources of his environment. The empirical rules and pro-

[1] Dr. Kettering, after a long and outstanding career in the field of gas- and oil-engine development, recently retired as Director of the Research Laboratories of General Motors.

306

cedures of the Ancient Egyptians, for example, were undoubtedly not the product of diligent search but of oft-repeated experiences and slowly dawning truths stemming from observation.

The Greeks, however, were not, as we have noted, satisfied simply to observe and apply but began to inquire. With this approach to the acquisition of knowledge, the spirit of both modern science and modern research may be said to have been born. Indeed a new era in the evolution of man began to dawn—an era of creative intelligence.

But there is, coupled with intelligent observation, with search and inquiry, another technique fundamental to modern research—the creation of opportunities for study, observation, and analysis through experiment, through bringing about the conditions, isolating and artificially producing the phenomena, one desires to observe and study—in short, what is called the experimental method.

It may be argued that, here again, this is but a modern name for an ancient practice. The advances made in engineering during the many centuries when it was a practical art may, for example, be regarded as based on experiment—on a full-scale and costly method of try it and see. But while these early masters learned through such practice, through trial and failure, the works they built were planned not to advance knowledge but to serve more directly practical, immediately useful ends.

We have noted in an earlier chapter some of the biases which had to be overcome before science could be released from the restrictions of philosophy and the church, and the power and importance of the experimental method become fully recognized. The centuries of the dominance of Greek philosophical ideas and their later support by the early church long discouraged the rise of the experimental method. Finally, in the later Middle Ages and Renaissance, the pioneers of modern natural science—the Friar, Roger Bacon, Gilbert, the pioneer student of magnetism, that grand old man of astronomy and mechanics, Galileo, and others—made the power of the experimental method clear. Sir Francis Bacon (1561–1626), a contemporary of Galileo, is generally regarded as the Father of the Experimental Method. It is quite clear, however, that the did not himself experiment, that many of his ideas were ridiculous, and that his great and important service to science stemmed from the fact that a man of his outstanding position and prestige, his powerful pen and influence, strenuously advocated experimental procedures.

Freed from these earlier restrictions, the combination of inquiry and observation, plus experiment in the hands of specially gifted and inspired, experienced, and patient but individual and more or less isolated seekers, gave us the epoch-making discoveries of the 18th and 19th centuries. Newton, who, working alone and failing even to communicate his discoveries, was led into bitter controversies with Hooke and Leibnitz; the monk, Mendel, whose pioneer work in genetics was practically unknown until after his death; the more articulate but nevertheless solitary efforts of such giants as Faraday —these are but examples of the extent to which scientific knowledge relied in the past on the labors of the solitary genius of outstanding gifts. With this picture the systematic, orderly, organized teamwork of modern research stands in sharp contrast.

It is difficult to give a precise date or to attribute to a few men the invention of invention—the credit for this change which has taken place in the transformation of individual search into the organized teamwork of today. The genesis of organized research is probably to be found in the practices which gradually came into use during the late 19th century in graduate teaching in the universities of Europe, especially Germany. These involved the assigning to individual students of specific tasks in carrying out a research, that is, the application to research of production methods, the division of labor, and sequential operations. In short, research was being put on a production basis.

Certain it is that German industry was quick to realize the importance of this method and to take advantage of it—to see that systematic research offered promises for the continued development of industrial products and processes which justified its support on a sound, economic, business basis. The United States lagged far behind in the realization of the power and promise of such organized search. A few American teachers, primarily those whose graduate education was obtained abroad, struggled to implant these new ideas in American science. It was World War I, however, which made it clear not only that we were dependent upon Germany for many of our basic chemical needs, thus leading to the birth of the American chemical industry, but that the foundation of Germany's remarkable industrial growth was organized research. World War I was, thus, an important factor in directing American attention to industrial research, and the American chemical industries have been leaders in the growth of organized research in our country.

This is not to say that there was no industrial research in the United States until 1917. There were a few of the older American universities in which isolated workers were advancing the frontiers of basic knowledge. There were also a few larger American industries —du Pont, General Electric, the Bell Laboratories, for example— which pioneered in industrial research in America. But, by and large, America's position both in pure and applied scientific research was woefully weak. Even as late as 1932 a series of some dozen or more papers by a handful of pioneer American research specialists was published, as has been noted, under the title *Profitable Practice in Industrial Research*. Industry was beginning to realize that the tempo of industrial change and improvement was increasing and that, if a company hoped to develop new and improved processes and products, hoped, in fact, to keep in business, the best insurance for a prosperous future was to be found in the industrial research laboratory.

The importance of such research is strikingly revealed in the history of one of the American pioneers, E. I. du Pont de Nemours & Company. The first formal research laboratories of this long-established explosives manufacturer were organized in 1902, and were devoted to research in explosives—to the idea that, if bigger and better explosives were made, duPont wanted to make them. However, a new development laboratory was started in 1903, and the company began to branch out into other chemical fields, to seek a wider diversification of its products. A centralized chemical department took over all research activities in 1911, but, in 1921, the decentralized plan with research divisions in each manufacturing department was adopted. As a result of these activities, it was reported in 1942 that almost half (46 per cent) of the gross sales of this company consisted of products which either did not exist in 1928 (only fourteen years earlier) or were not then manufactured on a commercial scale.[2]

By 1929 it was estimated that something in the order of 75 million dollars was being spent in industrial and institutional research in the United States. Such research was, however, still confined to a small number of larger organizations. The depression years added impetus to this movement, for, as we have observed, in uncertain and pressing times man is forced to attempt to find new ways out of his difficulties. Then came World War II with its emphasis on technological warfare and research—not basic scientific research but a frantic struggle

[2] See "Du Pont Research," a paper presented by Dr. E. K. Bolton, Chemical Director of du Pont, when he was awarded the Perkin Medal of the American Section, Society of Chemical Industry, January, 1945.

to bring to the aid of our Armed Forces and Allies some of the accumulated scientific and technological knowledge which had been awaiting the pressure for development. Developmental research went rapidly forward. Economic considerations no longer controlled, cost was no longer an influencing factor; the only criterion was that, if it could be done and would aid in winning the war, it should be done quickly. Research expenditures during the years 1941–1945 jumped to over 600 million dollars, not including atomic research. The trends in and the distribution of research support are summarized in Table 9.

TABLE 9. PERCENTAGE DISTRIBUTION OF RESEARCH SUPPORT*

Sponsoring agency	1930	1940	1941–1945	1947
Industry	70	68	13	39
Federal government	14	19	83†	54†
Universities	12	9	2	4
Other, including states, etc.	4	4	2	4
Total	100	100	100	100
Total in millions	$166	$345	$600	$1,160

* From *Science and Public Policy*, Vol. I, Report of the President's Scientific Research Board, by John R. Steelman, Washington, D.C., U.S. Government Printing Office, 1947.

† Not including atomic research.

It is very obvious from these figures that one result of the war was to broaden the base of interest in research from our educational and industrial institutions into that of a national undertaking. We were passing beyond the earlier, stirringly romantic vision of modern research and opening a new and assured path to continued, never-ending material progress as we continued to knock more "chips from the great quarry of knowledge." Not only our material progress was at stake but our power and place in the world—even our survival as a nation. As President Truman put it in a message to Congress: "Progress in scientific research and development is an indispensable condition to the future welfare and security of our nation. . . . No nation can maintain a position of leadership in the world today unless it develops to the full its scientific and technological resources." The prophecy that man's greatest discovery had been the invention of invention was being fulfilled. Natural resources were being marshaled in support of this systematic, orderly, organized search for new knowledge.

It may, thus, be questioned whether the growth of scientific research in the United States should be attributed to an evolution from American university research or has been primarily due to the rise we have noted of American industrial research since World War I. Both sources have been important, but it would appear that the latter exercised the predominant influence. This situation naturally poses some interesting and important problems. What are the limitations of the organized teamwork method of research? Can it be effectively applied in carrying forward basic, fundamental, scientific inquiries? It has been questioned, for example, whether the teamwork method, which has unquestionably been proved effective and powerful in the type of applied research important to industry, can be expected to supersede the efforts of the inspired, individual worker in the realm of pure, scientific research.

The older generation of natural scientists—notably such British giants of the 19th century as Tyndall and Huxley—insisted that he who hopes to be successful in uncovering Nature's secrets must search in a humble spirit animated solely by a desire for truth and with no thought in mind of rewards or of the ultimate use, if any, to which the truths revealed may be put. As Tyndall stated it: "Science must be cultivated for its own sake, for the love of truth, rather than for the applause or profit it brings." Clearly, the motive back of industrial research is quite different from that which inspires this pure search for truth. Yet this does not necessarily mean, as some pure scientists seem to hold, that the methods which have proved so valuable in industrial research cannot be applied to research in pure science—that the latter must rely solely on the labors of the rare individual genius of outstanding gifts. Motives differ, but methods may have values which are independent of motive.

On the one hand, the industrial researcher seeks answers to specific industrial problems and cannot ignore the fact that he is expected to show a reasonable probability of—must, indeed, in the long run, produce—financial returns commensurate with the costs of his searches. It is clear that few, except, perhaps, some of our major industries, can afford to support free-roving individual workers and gamble on the remote possibility that, sooner or later, they may turn up with a discovery which will be of value to that particular industry.

When it comes to writing a prescription for research, therefore, the doctors differ. There is the apparently incurably romantic group which insists that scientific truths come to us as special revelations granted to the very rare, inspired, self-sacrificing, and faithful scientific worker in a magical "flash of genius." There are others who hold to the statement, attributed to Edison, that genius is 1 per cent inspiration and 99 per cent perspiration. Important discoveries both in pure science and in engineering science and industry have been made by both methods. For example, Langmuir's work with the General Electric Company in the development of the gas-filled electric lamp may be cited as an example of the value to industry of research which stemmed from a spirit of scientific curiosity, began as an inquiry in pure science. Morgan's epoch-making discoveries in genetics on the other hand, were made possible through organized teamwork. Industrial research, it is true, does aim to anticipate the possible discoveries of individuals through teamwork—but, here again, notable industrial advances—new products and processes—are still being developed by individual, independent inventors, although it seems certain that, as the equipment essential to productive research increases in scope and cost, the isolated inventor will face increasing difficulties.

We are reminded, in this connection, of an observation by the British author Hilaire Belloc, in his biography of the great French cardinal Richelieu. "The conquests of physical science," he observes, "have been due to the minute and extensive observations conducted by vast numbers of men," and, he concludes, "therefore, for the most part by the unintelligent." Belloc does not deny that there have been great men of science and engineering—men who had the breadth of vision to draw from this huge mass of observation the great generalizations of science or to synthesize this knowledge in the service of man. "This mass of observation," he observes, "has led to astounding results."

In this statement Belloc was contrasting this remarkable result stemming from the work of many with the great-man theory of history—the idea embodied in the famous statement of Marshall Foch, quoted earlier, that it was not an army that crossed the Alps, it was Hannibal. We may not like Belloc's use of the word "unintelligent," but he put his finger on a truth which constitutes the major element of strength and power in science and engineering—the power of an ever-growing body of scientific and technical knowledge and understanding, and the fact that not only the individual genius but vast numbers of men of less than extraordinary gifts can add, through organized research, their bit to this ever-accumulating power. Belloc may also be quite right in holding that, in the past, in military and political affairs it was the individual who dominated the picture. In science and engineering, thousands of workers, known and unknown, have played a part in building the huge accumulation of knowledge and experience from which the power of technology stems. It is precisely on this fact that modern organized and directed scientific and engineering research relies.

The best techniques and methods to follow in organized research have also been widely discussed. Edison was a strong advocate of a method frequently called Edisonian, which consisted in trying everything which might conceivably produce the desired answer, observing the results, and hoping to be led, more or less by chance but guided by an analysis of this mass of experimental data, to the desired end. Another approach, sometimes referred to as the Aristotelian, begins with the formulation of a theory and seeks facts to support it. This latter approach is reflected in the remark of the late Professor Michael I. Pupin to the effect that a good idea constitutes at least 50 per cent of a successful research. Again, both methods have been used in both pure and applied research and both have produced valuable results. The one basic observation which may be made is that researches are brought to successful conclusions only by men who have prepared themselves through intensive, exhaustive study of their problems and have become completely absorbed in their search. It should also be realized that the achievement of successful results through research, remarkable as such results have been, cannot be guaranteed. Victory is not assured. The element of gamble is still present. Research results cannot be purchased on an over-the-counter basis.

We should also note that continued technological and industrial progress depends upon maintaining a dynamic and progressive attitude in both fundamental and applied research. Fundamental research, whether in natural or in engineering science, seeks to extend the bounds of knowledge and understanding. In the former case, this pursuit is an end in itself. In the latter it is true, the ultimate, long-range, utilitarian value of such knowledge is constantly kept in mind but the search is, nevertheless, for basic understanding rather than for some limited, special, or immediately useful end. In sharp contrast also, applied research of the developmental type may be said to seek to reduce the time lag between the acquisition of basic knowledge and its practical application and use. Industrial research is clearly developmental research, but it also usually includes another vital industrial service which has been called "trouble shooting." This is a search for better ways and means of solving the details of production,

"ironing the bugs" out of a process or product, expediting manufacture, improving quality—of obtaining better quality-cost relationships. In the long run, therefore, we rely on fundamental research
not only for discoveries which may ultimately be developed into new
products or services through further applied research, but also for the
basic knowledge which will increase our power in solving developmental and other industrial problems. Basic research and applied or
industrial research are, thus, both essential to continued technological progress. They are not mutually exclusive but complementary
and mutually stimulating pursuits.

While both these types of research obviously have direct values to
industry, basic research, as we have noted, poses far greater uncertainties—it is a "luxury" few industries can afford. In large measure,
therefore, our more progressive educational institutions still retain
the responsibility for basic research, although both industry and
government have, in recent years, given increasing attention to such
basic searches. When the desirable scope and character of these basic
studies are reviewed, however, an important and still unresolved
problem comes to light.

The general situation the United States faces today in research
has been briefly and effectively set forth in a recent statement by the
Engineers' Joint Council in connection with the creation of a proposed National Research Foundation.

The American people have been foremost in technical ingenuity and
industrial organization. It is a well-acknowledged fact on the other hand,
that in the realm of basic sciences and basic scientific research the United
States did not keep pace with the principal nations of the old world. . . .
To a large extent practical applied research in the United States relied on
basic scientific material coming from overseas. The war has violently
upset this balance. Europe is in eclipse. For years to come in the intellectual and scientific realm the United States will have to depend
upon its own resources. . . . This brings this country face to face with a
problem of utmost gravity. Under the threat of losing its primacy, the
United States *must* speedily fill the void left open by the ravages of
Europe.

In other words, while World War I made the United States industrial-research conscious, World War II brought us face to face with
a challenge to quickly attend to our weaknesses in the area of basic,
fundamental research. "We must be prepared for any military event-
uality. Also this country must lead in science to assure national
health, prosperity, and welfare."

The reasons for our weakness in fundamental research are not difficult to understand. We have in the past been completely absorbed in the immediate and practical tasks involved in transforming in less than a century a virgin continent into an ever-improved dwelling place for ever-increasing millions. Fundamental research could play little part in this epic of human achievement. Basic research has been neglected, and its few adherents have fought an uphill battle until comparatively recent years, with little recognition and totally inadequate financial support. Not only has the force of events, among others the advent of the atomic fission, turned attention to this neglect but American science has secured increasing support through one of the most active promotion and propaganda campaigns ever inaugurated. Basic research in the domain of natural science is, thus, today receiving ever-increasing recognition and support.

There is, however, one phase of this movement which has been adverse in its effect on another vital area of basic research, namely, that in engineering science, and which, if allowed to continue, must ultimately prove disastrous to technological progress and will weaken the position of the natural sciences themselves. In engineering, as in the case of medicine, the work of natural scientists has never provided all the scientific knowledge and understandings which are essential to continued professional growth. In engineering the practical mechanics of heat (engineering thermodynamics), of electrical machines and circuits, of liquids and gases (hydraulics and fluid mechanics), of solids (elasticity and strength of materials), more recently of soils, foundations, and earth structures (soil mechanics) —all these and other basic engineering studies were, over a century ago, designated by the Germans as engineering science. They were based to be sure on the facts of natural science, but they have been developed by engineers in directions, scope, and understandings which would not claim the interest, time, and efforts of workers in pure science. Exactly the same situation has existed in the medical field, but here the scope, function, and importance of medical science is well understood and fully recognized. American engineering, on the other hand, faces today the task of making equally clear the place and importance in technological progress of research in engineering science.

The modern propaganda of natural science has, as we have said, been a major factor in bringing about this situation. In order to secure the admittedly much needed, essential support for research in pure science, natural science propaganda has attributed practically all past advances in engineering to research in natural science, and the notion has been widely broadcast that engineering is merely "applied science." It has thus been assumed that all that is needed to ensure continued American leadership not only in science but in engineering is support for research in the natural sciences alone. On every hand we are deluged with pronouncements not only that "science is remaking the world" but that the pure science of today becomes the applied science of tomorrow and the implication that the engineer is becoming an increasingly unnecessary and ineffective middleman in bringing science to the service of man. In view of the fact that engineering was a recognized profession long before modern science was born, these ideas strike the engineer as rather amusing, parvenu notions, but their adverse effect in securing support for research in engineering science is only too evident.

Furthermore, the implications of these misunderstandings and half truths were exaggerated by the war experiences of some American scientific workers. Many such workers were drawn into the struggle, previously noted, to develop and make available to our Armed Forces and those of our Allies any available scientific or technological knowledge possible of use in the shortest possible time and regardless of cost. This was not fundamental scientific research; neither were these activities limited by the conditions which normally control in engineering or industrial research. It was applied research and development of an uninhibited variety made mandatory by the emergencies of technological warfare. In such an emergency and under such abnormal conditions, scientific personnel, notably physicists and chemists, could and did provide very valuable services.

It thus came about, as above remarked, that some natural scientists began to regard the engineer as an unnecessary and incompetent middleman. Furthermore, once the war was over, these workers continued to embark on research projects which would hardly meet Tyndall's requirement that such searches be free of all utilitarian taint, pure seeking for truth.

Here again the answer is not to be found in either extreme position. Both the natural scientist and the engineer clearly have their parts to play in bringing about continued technological advances. Progress in natural science and progress in engineering science must, as we have said, go hand in hand.

Finally it must be recognized that engineering research cannot, must not, be limited to efforts directed solely to achieving greater understanding and improved use of the material resources of Nature.

There have been four factors which have conditioned engineering progress in the past, and a major one of these has been economic and social in origin.

For some forty-nine of the fifty centuries of human history the engineer was, as we have seen, limited in his activities to those works which could be accomplished in timber, stone, brick, and cement with the use of metal, notably iron and steel, confined to tools and fastenings. British developments of the late 18th and early 19th centuries greatly widened the scope of the engineer's power by providing iron, and later steel, at a cost and in such quantity that their use in machines and structures became possible. To these have been added new steel alloys of special quality and usefulness as well as new metals—aluminum, for example—and a host of plastics and other materials.

Much of the effort of producers of materials today is devoted to finding and exploiting, practically forcing a market for their particular product. "It is a technology of adaptation, and its success has been measured by the tonnage of materials sold by the companies financing such research." We are, however, already embarked on an era of composite construction. The modern automobile, once largely, like the wagon, a thing of wood and iron, has become a composite of composites—various metals and grades of metals, plastics, artificial cloth, upholstery and carpeting, natural and synthetic rubber, insulation, fiberboard, and a host of other newcomers. In such an era each material is used under those conditions to which by reason of its peculiar characteristics, qualities, and cost, it is especially adapted.

In the metal field steel is still king. It constitutes some 95 per cent of the total tonnage of metal used annually. There is little likelihood that any other metal will dispute this position, but it is quite clear that the usefulness of our steel output is being many times increased by employing steel in thin sheets in combination with other materials. It seems certain, therefore, that in the area of materials the trend today is toward the development through research of the particular materials, which, having special qualities by nature or through processing, are needed to meet particular, highly specialized uses and needs.

In the area of power production, the remarkable improvements which have been made in efficiency and performance have been noted. For centuries man was dependent solely on his own physical strength or that of animals, helped out by the uncertain gifts of wind and water—the windmill and the water wheel. A new era opened with the development of the steam engine and especially with the electrical utilization of steam power and the advent of easily portable gas and oil engines. The steam turbine followed, and today the gas turbine is on its way. In fact the possibility of tapping a new power source on a large scale, atomic power, has been revealed through research. Jet engines and gas turbines are today in the early stages of development. The ever-increasing demand and increasing cost of fuel must inevitably lead to a search both for more efficient engines and for less expensive means of securing, preparing, and transporting fuel.

Perhaps the most astounding revelation of engineering history is that of the remarkable accomplishments of earlier workers who not only had at their command none of the great array of modern tools but lacked also the understanding, knowledge, and methods which have been developed through engineering science. Here again, the vastly increased power which the new engineering of the past century has given the engineer is obvious. Furthermore, the prospects of still further advances through research are, apparently, limitless.

If to these we add a fourth vital influence in engineering development—a widespread, economic, and social demand—it is notable that the present age is the first in the history of the world in which there has been simultaneously present dynamic and progressive growth in all four of these elements of progress—materials, power, understanding, and demand. Research promises to provide continued development in the first three of these areas—materials, power, and technical understanding.

We need similar research: the statistical approach of basic, scientific fact finding, the careful analysis of forces and factors, the clarification of alternate possibilities, their evaluation on a long-range, rather than a narrowly opportunistic, expediency basis, if we are to solve our present day economic problems. We progress through evolution not revolution. The pursuit of ideologies, the search for the end of the rainbow, will never help us to understand and adapt our civilization to the evolution in human life of which the present day is but a passing stage. The know-how of the engineer, drawing its "know" not from natural science alone but from many sources— from economics and business, from the practical arts, and from ages of human experience—continues to grow in power through the continued rationalization of its problems by the application of the scientific method. We need far more of this method in other areas of human endeavor if we are successfully to meet the perplexing problems of the modern world. Will we be able to solve, through such research and understanding, the problems which have been discussed in some of the previous chapters on which the maintenance of a growing economic and social life depends—be able to provide the favorable environment, the dynamic spirit, the progressive conditions, and the expanding market essential to continued technological advances? Sound, scientific research, a search for factual knowledge and for full understanding in the areas of economic and social affairs, is fully as essential to progress as is research in natural and engineering science.

Chapter 21. CONCLUSION

> The first foundation of Western freedom is one that has been the chief support of every great civilization until our day—the belief that underlying the ebb and flow of historical events and human happenings there exists a moral order of right and wrong, and good and evil, which transcends every particular interest and which, far from being created by men and events, is the yardstick by which they are judged.
>
> Barbara Ward, *The West at Bay*.

DEMOCRACY AND PROGRESS

Professor Grant Showerman begins a most interesting study of the Roman poet, entitled *Horace and His Influence,* with the observation:

To those who stand in the midst of times and attempt to grasp their meaning, civilization often seems hopelessly complicated. The myriad and mysterious interthreading of motive and action, of cause and effect, presents to the near vision no semblance of a pattern, and the whole web is so confused and meaningless that the mind grows to doubt the presence of design, and becomes skeptical of the necessity, or even of the importance, of any single strand.

In all ages men have been confused by current trends and worried about future prospects. In fact the uncertainties of life are often so discouraging that we are apt to abandon attempts to look ahead and, thus, to accept Carlyle's advice: "Our main business is not to see what lies dimly at a distance, but to do what lies clearly at hand."

This attitude, however, is impossible in the present age. It is clear that no nation can expect to muddle through from one expedient to another and hope to maintain a leading position in the modern world. To such extent at least as alternatives are available we must seek to appraise their long-range as well as their immediate possibilities and to select those paths which give the greatest promise for continued progress.

It may be true that each new generation, as has been true of youth through the ages, must learn from its own mistakes rather than from those of generations past. Yet the industrialized way of life which the British-speaking people have evolved and have been struggling with for two centuries or more, is now in process of encompassing the earth. Time may come when our advantages stemming from having been first may no longer carry as great weight in the maintenance of our position. The newer areas now seeking industrialization have, indeed, the advantage of taking well-developed methods and ideas from us without having, as we have done, either to originate them, discover and develop them, or bear the trials and burdens of their adaptation to man's needs. Foresight as well as inventive skill and industrial ability will be an increasing factor to national stability and continued progress in the future.

We have pictured man in these pages as caught in the toils of an evolutionary force, a natural law, an inevitable process of human development, that, willingly or unwillingly, he must carry forward. The heavy hand of fate thus seems to determine his destiny, and one may well ask what part foresight or human desires may play in such a picture. The answer is that we live within and are part of the structure of Nature and Nature's laws, laws which we cannot change and must, perforce, learn to understand and work with. Yet man is free within this cosmic net to chart his path understandingly, making the most of his opportunities while accepting the great mystery of purpose, a mystery which is beyond his power to penetrate. We would believe, as Galsworthy would have us believe of his fellow novelist Conrad, that although "mystery enwraps the cause, the origin, the end of life, yea, even of human life . . . our acceptance of that mystery brings a certain dignity to existence" and a purpose to life.

The engineer thus has faith in his work and in the ultimate beneficence of the forces he serves. Listen to the words of Dr. Henry Emerson Fosdick:

From our apelike progenitors in the forest we have come to our modern era of international hopes and, as the stars count time, we have done it in a few ticks of the astral clock. To say that we did it of ourselves is nonsense. It was the necessity of our being. . . . Something in the marrow of the cosmic life from which we came laid this necessity upon us. We have been under a drastic mastery greater than our own. Looked at in the large, man, with his stupidities, his cruelties, his wanton frivolities and wars, appears across the ages desperately struggling to escape from an imperious necessity which will not let him go. This necessity has lifted us up from the ape-man to the present day, although no ape-man ever dreamed of planning such a consequence. It has swung us up the long spiral of human ascent, bringing us ever back to old problems, but forcing us to face them upon higher levels, and driving us out, whether we would or not, to larger cooperations and more inclusive human fellowships. At times we can fairly see man digging in his heels as though resolutely refusing to go on. Something stronger than humanity— call it what you will, necessity, fate, God—has laid hold on humanity and will not loose its grasp.[1]

Such faith in progress is particularly characteristic of the American mind—of "the land of hope and promise." To few Europeans has life, apparently, held similar promise or work meant more than a means of living. The rungs of the ladder have appeared far apart, or the ladder itself has been but a misty uncertain vision to those people of the older, largely static, overpopulated areas of the earth.

Various attempts have been made to explain the phenomenal rise of the United States to its present outstanding position in the Western World. Unquestionably in part it has been due to the fact that the American people had before them a new continent of unparalleled natural resources—all the advantages of great areas of fertile soil, of an abundant supply of essential mineral and other materials; open spaces waiting only for settlement. But, as Sir Norman Angell points out in a provocative study of modern world affairs from which we have already quoted:

The North America of the United States and Canada, which now supports a hundred and fifty million souls at the highest standard of living ever achieved for such a mass of men anywhere in the world, or in history, is the same North America, in which, for perhaps twenty thousand years, less than a million primitive men found only the means of semistarvation and fought each other in deadly wars for the meagre resources of the hunting grounds. The Europeans who replaced the original Indians did not bring a new climate or a new soil, new external conditions; nor a human brain which differed physiologically from that of the Indian. What the European brought was a new way of thought in using the soil and the climate as a means of sustenance, new skills in the use of thought as a tool for the achievement of that end.

While the new skills which made this achievement possible were those of technology, one cannot explain man's conduct, as Sir Norman remarks, by his reactions to his environment. One cannot attribute solely to resources and technology, or to the fact that the United States is one economic unit with no trade barriers, the largest free-

[1] *As I See Religion*, New York, Harper & Brothers, 1932, p. 24.

trade area in the world, her rise to a foremost position in Western life. The unwavering faith of the American people in progress, a conviction that the future holds in store still greater opportunities, still greater promise, has been a vital factor to our success. Similarly, there can be no question that this faith has been fortified in the American mind, strengthened and reinforced, by the past material accomplishments of our people. We have quoted that typical Yankee, Dave Harum, "It's a sight easier to have faith on meat and taters than on corn mush." Benjamin Franklin in the person of Poor Richard had long ago remarked in similar vein: "It's hard for an empty sack to stand upright." Yet, when depression asails us, doubt comes in the door and we are prone to turn to other, supposedly easier, safer, and more active means of conducting our economic affairs—until we realize, again to quote Franklin, that "Those who would give up essential liberty to purchase a little temporary safety deserve neither liberty nor safety."

All this is not to say that our American democratic, free way of life is a cure-all, applicable at all stages in a nation's growth to the solution of all its ills. "Confident of the success of his methods the American wants to apply them all over the world and sees in a refusal to apply them willful and sinful blindness. American life is a product of American experience." When we recall the difficulties which we face in carrying forward democratic ideals, the new and difficult problems we continually encounter in a prosperous country of widespread education and material well-being, it seems clear that many other less fortunate peoples have a long way to go before they will be ready to bear the burdens and responsibilities of the democratic way of life. There are three basic essentials in this American way: patience, cooperation, and understanding. No nation, not even our own, has them in full measure. No industrially and educationally backward nation can achieve them overnight.

As to patience, it seems strange that a people which has been blessed with such rapid material advances—a 250 per cent increase, as we have noted, in the past 50 years, in the goods and services their labors command—could, as we did in the early '30s lose patience with the rate of such progress. Free enterprise had failed, we were told, because one-third of our people were still ill-housed, ill-fed, and ill-clothed. It should be noted that this is a comparison not with the condition of the poor of other nations but with the status of the other two-thirds of the American people. It was natural that Americans, whose hearts and pocketbooks have been touched by human misfortunes all over the earth, should wish to raise to higher levels these fellow citizens. Yet what country has done more to improve the status of all its people, to provide widespread material welfare for all its millions? What economy in the history of the world has ever borne even a small part of the burden of social betterment and aid that has been placed on that of the United States? Someone must pay the bill, must earn through productive labor every dollar that goes to social welfare, to relief, to health, and to similar services both at home and abroad. Our economy is expected to carry, through taxes, not only the essential services of government, Federal, state, and local, not only the debts of war, but provisions for the aged and the unemployed, for the so-called underprivileged man, woman, and child—an ever-increasing burden of social and welfare commitments which must be met, sooner or later, from the net proceeds of our economy. The millenium cannot be achieved overnight.

Certainly one of the major factors which has brought about the collapse of earlier great nations has been the overburdening of their economic life with the expenses resulting from military ambitions, from the demands of their rulers, or from attempts to maintain standards of living beyond their capacities to support. Rome's attempted "New Deal" measures brought but temporary relief and failed to stimulate her economic revival.[2] The king's sponsorship of French industries failed to offset his contributions to her bankruptcy. War, on top of a declining economy, has brought Britain to her knees. In the end social welfare and human well-being are not brought about through revolution or relief, but through the growing capacity of the country's economic system to raise all its people to a higher level of production. Charity, private or public, is not a permanent cure for unemployment or a low level of social and economic life.

In an economic system which is becoming ever more complex and interrelated, it is obvious that cooperation among various groups of workers must be secured, either freely or by compulsion. When it is possible for a pressure group comprising but a small fraction of a larger group which in turn represents but a small fraction of our people, as was the case with some 10,000 railway workers a year or so ago, to threaten to completely disrupt our entire economy and bring starvation and distress to millions, the need for cooperation in our complex interrelated life becomes evident. "If the conflicting

[2] See an interesting study, *The New Deal in Old Rome*, by J. H. Haskell, New York, Alfred A. Knopf, Inc., 1939.

claims of organized groups cannot be settled voluntarily, by consent, give and take, then compulsion will increase."

It is this question—Can the necessary degree of forbearance and cooperation, essential to the maintenance of an umpired but otherwise relatively free and competitive technological economy, be secured by voluntary action, or is ever-increasing government planning and control to be forced upon us?—that constitutes the major issue today not only in the United States, but in the conflict of political and social ideologies which encompass the earth. Problems of monopoly vs. competition, of labor vs. management, of depression and inflation, of economic and military conflict, of social security, subsidies, and foreign aid, of profits and taxes, of unemployment and depression, and of uncertainty and doubt—these and other problems of cooperation press upon us from all sides. At the same time, we have been brought face to face with the fact that technology is the major force not only in creating this multiplicity of problems but that it is basically a self-evolving process in human life which we cannot stop and which does not permit us to stand still.

Man undoubtedly has in all ages, as we have noted, been confused and disturbed by conflicting trends and uncertain prospects, but the older generation of today is passing on to modern youth a very much more troubled and difficult world than it received from its elders of a generation ago. The modern student will, facing the deluge of conflicting ideas and interpretations, viewpoints, and opinions, which these changes have brought about, find need for a firm and sound backbone of faith in human values and a keen ability to discriminate between wishful thinking and a really constructive, long-range viewpoint. He will have need of "the faith that at the base of things we shall not find mere arbitrary mystery," as Professor Whitehead puts it, "faith in reason, the trust that the ultimate natures of things lie together in a harmony which excludes mere arbitrariness." He will need the engineering method of calm unbiased fact finding and analysis as a prerequisite to the evaluation of possible alternatives and, thus, to intelligent action.

We have selected a few from the multitude of modern works on economic and social matters in relation to technology which are noted in the Bibliography. The student will find that the factual, statistical, and other technological information set forth in these volumes is usually reliable, although limitations of sources and assumptions are not always noted or made clear. Such books are also seldom engineering products. They are usually prepared by economic or social workers who have only a superficial knowledge of engineering methods and needs and whose various suggestions thus frequently lack engineering understanding.

He will find, in general, two major fields of thought in these works. On the one hand, there are those who, while they may profess to uphold free enterprise and competition, argue that we must seek to forecast the future and plan our economy, and that this can, *ipso facto*, be undertaken only at the national, Federal government level. This idea has not lacked many supporters, and the great majority of publications offer proposals along these lines. As pointed out in a small book by Professor F. A. Hayek, it is difficult to see how this proposal can lead to any other end than state socialism and probably ultimately to some totalitarian form of government.[3] The arguments against such planning seem, to the writer, convincing. In the first place, all progressive industries which hope to keep in business have long been attempting to forecast future needs. Production undertaken today will not usually reach the market for some weeks or months. What reason do we have to believe that government agents possess greater special abilities in foreseeing future needs and requirements? Government can, through its various agencies, give valuable and important aid in collecting and disseminating information, but, as is only too apparent, it is difficult if not impossible to eliminate political considerations from even such activities.

Second, there is obviously little use in government planning unless there is coupled with it the power of controlling industry and enterprise in order to give effect to such plans. With such control the end of free enterprise is inevitable. Our ultimate arrival at a static condition, a society lacking the stimulus or even the will to adventure, and thus at technological stagnation and decay, seems certain. Bureaucrats are not noted for their interest in living dangerously, and we must be willing to live dangerously, to adventure and take risks, if we are to have continued technological progress. As Professor Whitehead puts it: "A race preserves its vigor as long as it harbours a real contrast between what has been and what may be; and so long as it is nerved by vigour to adventure beyond the safeties of the past. Without adventure civilization is in full decay."

In sharp contrast with the "wishful planners" there are the "old-time businessmen" who insist that the government should keep out of business and who seem to have a nostalgic yearning for the good old days of a laissez-faire world. Needless to say this attitude is

[3] *The Road to Serfdom,* Chicago, University of Chicago Press, 1944.

equally unreasonable and unrealistic. There is and can be no such thing as pure and complete free enterprise or unrestricted competition. Our railroads, although privately owned, came into being through public action. In order to give birth to railroad and more recently highway transportation, the government exercises the right of eminent domain, recognizing that the public interest may transcend individual rights. The superior economy of monopoly over competition is recognized in such fields of public service as water supply, electric light and power, the telephone, and the telegraph.

We have, thus, long ago embarked on what may be called the middle way, recognizing that in certain areas government grants certain privileges in the public interest and must likewise in the public interest exercise as an umpire certain reasonable controls, that is, controls which attempt to equalize the threefold interests of owners, workers, and consumers.

It seems clear, however, that such controls will, perforce, be extended if voluntary cooperation fails. A major direction is in the field of labor-management relations. The costs of the battle between labor and management, even between conflicting labor groups themselves, are one of the major burdens our economy is being asked to carry. The interests of capital and labor are, in the long run, identical. They cannot, in the long run, be settled by continual warfare. There must be a recognition that, in the long run, what is best for the American people will have to be best both for capital and for labor. At the present time government is attempting to set up rules for the game of collective bargaining and to act as referee. It is to be hoped that both labor and capital will ultimately decide they prefer to work on a basis of mutual understanding and respect in solving their common problems. If they cannot reach agreement and put their house in order, the American people will ultimately insist that government attend to the matter.

But there is also another direction in which government will be forced to move, namely, in anticipating the shocks and dislocations to which a dynamic technological economy is inevitably subject. The National Resources Committee Report of 1937 pointed out that there is a major time lag between inventions and their development and marketing—between discoveries and their economic and social effects. It is argued that this lag affords time for the government to plan for adjustments which will aid in cushioning the shocks of obsolescence and overproduction, of depression and inflation. It is yet to be demonstrated, however, that government can either develop such foresight or exercise any greater or more intelligent restraint or control over public expenditures than is currently exhibited in competitive enterprise by our business or industrial leaders. Certainly another answer is to be found in efforts to uncover and avoid those economic maladjustments which creep into our lives as the result of our too-frequent tendency to get rid of a problem by adopting the immediate expedient instead of making a real effort to seek a long-range cure. The shortsighted, selfish actions of pressure minorities also, taking advantage of the passing ills or temporary weaknesses of their fellow citizens, are another source of economic instability. We no longer stand alone. In the modern industrial state the great majority of the people must be prosperous if, as individuals, we are to enjoy prosperity.

Commenting on the almost complete interdependence of a machine civilization and the necessity for controls, Professor Wright remarks,

One answer would run in terms of character, self-restraint, humaneness, and certain instincts of workmanship. But the world has not yet, at least, been able to rely on moral persuasion alone. In the background must be an additional factor: the fear of the consequences of reprisal. We are thus brought up against another problem of delicate balance in the task of achieving and maintaining democratic freedom. The state must be strong enough to punish a minority acting in an anti-social fashion. Yet no ruling group can be allowed to become so powerful as to be no longer adequately responsive to the public will. For such an unresponsive clique, possessing in addition to political influence or control, the technological rule over the very basis of human life which modern science makes possible, would hold one of the most absolute powers known to history.[4]

The American way has thus necessarily made government the umpire in the interplay of our economic forces. The rules government seeks to enforce stem from public opinion. In order that the freedom which we regard as essential may be maintained, we must as a people agree to play the game of life under rules which will compel honesty, fairness, and an equality of opportunity. Absolute individual freedom is anarchy. Full and complete government control is totalitarianism—the denial of all freedoms. We seek the middle way.

We of the West have very rightly rejected the dictatorship method of insuring these necessary disciplines and collective action. But the

[4] *Democracy and Progress,* by David McCord Wright, New York, The Macmillan Company, 1948.

harder way, the democratic way, in which responsibility rests with the individual demands on his part much higher moral and intellectual standards than are needed in a society where the government relieves the individual of his responsibilties for decision.[5]

Knowledge alone is not enough. Education, says Professor Whitehead, is not the mere accumulation of knowledge, "it is the acquisition of the art of the utilization of knowledge." The future of America, with which the future of engineering is indissolubly linked, will depend upon the ability of our people to maintain faith in progress and in human values, and voluntarily to put aside narrow, immediate, personal gain in the interest of those essential cooperations without which freedom and progress are impossible. It is not a simple, restful world we hand on to generations to come. "Absolute certainty is an illusion," observed the late Justice Oliver Wendell Holmes, "repose is not the destiny of man."

> We sail a changeful sea through halcyon days and storm,
> And when the ship laboureth, our steadfast purpose
> Trembles like as the compass in a binnacle,
> Our stability is but balance, and wisdom lies
> In masterful administration of the unforseen.[6]

[5] *The Steep Places,* by Norman Angell, New York, Harper & Brothers, 1947, p. 24.
[6] Robert Bridges, "A Testament of Beauty."

BIBLIOGRAPHY

This is not intended to be, neither does space permit it to be, a complete or exhaustive bibliography. Its purpose is twofold. Those interested in the history of engineering will desire to fill out the very sketchy outlines given in the preceding pages by referring to source material. Teachers who may use this book as an outline for a course in the history of engineering will also find it desirable to give assigned readings to their students and, perhaps, to require them to prepare brief papers for presentation in class. Those books which, in the opinion of the author, would be especially desirable for a small reference collection for this purpose are marked with an asterisk (*).

A word of caution seems desirable. Few engineers would venture an opinion on any engineering problem without careful investigation. Yet they apparently have no such inhibitions where history is involved. As a result, the brief historical statements given in many engineering papers and texts are too often incorrect or misleading. The student of engineering history will find it necessary to refer to original sources and will accept with caution, or discard, the often exaggerated or erroneous statements which are too commonly encountered.

Certainly the most important of such original sources are engineering books themselves. The number becomes rapidly greater, of course, after the invention of printing—especially in the late 16th century and thereafter—but a number of earlier works—Hero of Alexandria, Vitruvius, Frontinus—have survived. Here another word of warning is necessary. One cannot assume that the engineering devices or methods described in these early works faithfully portray the engineering practice of their day. Many of these records of the past were in the nature of notebooks, not only filled with descriptions of current methods and designs but also including the various proposed inventions and speculations of their authors. The progress of engineering is measured by the actual conditions of practice rather than the state of research of theoretical speculations. One must learn, therefore, to discriminate in these records as he must also evaluate or interpret the reported observation of archaeologists and other researchers who have studied especially the records of Ancient Times but whose interests are too often in art rather than in engineering. When, however, we approach Modern Times—say, the 18th century and later—engineering texts appear to lose this speculative character progressively and can be generally accepted as reflecting current view-points and practices.

The student of engineering history will also find it desirable to review, or at least refer to from time to time, a good general history, or to histories of the nation under study. He will thus secure some perspective of the great tree of history and its main branches to which he may attach his engineering information.

Engineering, as we have attempted to show and as the late President Butler once remarked of the modern university, is not apart from the affairs of men, but in them and of them. For this purpose we know of no better general reference than the following:

Outlines of European History, by James H. Breasted and James H. Robinson, Boston, Ginn & Company, 1914, 2 vols.

As each nation is studied in turn, however, other, more detailed, historical studies will be of interest in attempting to relate the engineering achievements of a period to the economic and social problems and changes of the day. We have added, therefore, to each chapter list at least one or two texts of an economic, social nature. This part of our bibliography could also be almost indefinitely extended. There are many excellent books in this area but, unfortunately, usually too extensive and detailed for our needs.

CHAPTER 1. ANCIENT ENGINEERING

General

Ancient Times: A History of the Ancient World, by James H. Breasted, New York, Charles Scribner's Sons, 1905. A standard work in more detail than the *Outlines of European History.*

Engineering

The Technical Arts and Sciences of the Ancients, by Alfred Neuburger, New York, The Macmillan Company, 1930. A translation by H. L. Brose of the well-known German work, *Die Technik des Altertums.*

Egypt

Ancient Egyptian Masonry, by Somers Clark and R. Engelbach, New York, Oxford University Press, 1930. A fascinating story written by expert investigators.

The Problem of the Obelisks, by R. Engelbach, London, T. Fisher Unwin, 1923. A small book but a most interesting study.

Ancient Egyptian Materials, by A. Lucas, London, Edward Arnold & Co., 1926. By the chemist of the Egyptian Department of Antiquities.

Ancient Egyptian Metallurgy, by H. Garland and C. O. Bannister, London, Charles Griffin & Co., Ltd., 1927.

Imhotep, by J. B. Hurry, New York, Oxford University Press, 1926. A study of this ancient wise man and universal genius, the so-called Father of Masonry Construction.

Some older works, although no longer regarded as reflecting modern discoveries or viewpoints, are of interest. For example,

The Pyramids and Temples of Gizeh, by W. M. Flinders Petrie, London, Field and Frier, 1883.

Tools and Weapons, by W. M. Flinders Petrie, London, University College, 1917, which presents clearly the surprisingly ancient origin of many hand tools still in use today. Beautifully illustrated.

Mesopotamia

The Civilization of Babylonia and Assyria, by Morris Jastrow, Philadelphia, J. B. Lippincott Company, 1915. A standard modern text.

There are a number of earlier works containing items of engineering interest, such as those by Layard and by King.

The Code of Hammurabi, by R. F. Harper, Chicago, University of Chicago Press, 1904, contains the earliest known building code. This was abstracted in *Eng. News-Record,* June 5, 1930, p. 944.

Sennacherib's Aqueduct at Jerwan, a paper by Thorkild Jacobsen and Seaton Loyd, Oriental Publications, No. 24, University of Chicago, 1935. Describes a remarkable pioneer public water supply.

Greece

The Life of Greece, by Will Durant, New York, Simon and Schuster, Inc., 1939. A popular and interesting story of Greek life and thought.

The Legacy of Greece, edited by R. W. Livingstone, New York, Oxford Univeristy Press, 1921. A series of essays including studies of the natural sciences.

Engineering, by A. P. Gest, New York, Longmans, Green & Co., Inc., 1930. A small volume in the series "Our Debt to Greece and Rome."

Unfortunately there is no general work on Greek engineering in English although there are several German books:

Die Ingenieurtechnik in Altertums, by Curt Merkel, Berlin, 1899. Covers Greek and Roman works.

Antike Technik, by Herman Diels, Berlin, B. G. Teubner, 1914. Deals primarily with machines.

Technologie und Terminologie der Gewerbe und Kunste bei Greichen und Romern, Leipzig, Blümmer, 1875–1887, 4 vols. An old but standard work.

There are also numerous, isolated articles on special subjects but these are, unfortunately, scattered in various publications not available in many libraries. For a paper on water supplies, see an account of the ancient supply of Athens in

The Engineer (London), Vol. 101 (1906), p. 215.

A famous Greek work, "The Drainage of Lake Copias," is described (in French) by M. L. Kambanis in

Bulletin de correspondence hellénique, Vols. 16 and 17 (1892), pp. 121 and 322.

Also in French,

Les Mines du Laurion dans l'antiquité, by Eduard Ardaillon, Paris, 1897, and

Les Origines de méchanique, Part I of *Lectures de méchanique* by Emile Jouguet, Paris, 1908, are also of interest.

The Works of Archimedes, edited by T. L. Heath, and

The Method of Archimedes by the same author are of special interest.

Hero's Works (in German and Greek), edited by Wilhelm Schmidt and others, Leipzig, B. G. Teubner, have been translated in part (Pneumatics) by Bennet Woodcroft, London, Taylor, Walton and Maberly, 1857.

Rome

Books on Roman history are almost without number, but many of the studies dealing with engineering works are in foreign or other publications not generally available. There are no general engineering works other than those contained in references noted above.

Ingegneria Romana, by Gius Cozzo, Rome, 1928, is available only in Italian.

Roman Architecture and Its Principles of Construction, translated from the Italian of G. T. Rivoira, Oxford, The Clarendon Press, 1925. A modern, authoritative work on construction methods and practices.

Among French works are

Essai sur la science et l'art de l'ingénieur aux premières siècles de l'empire romain, by C. Germain de Montauzan, Paris, Leroux, 1908.

Vitruvius on Architecture is, of course, an engineering classic and has been translated into many languages. See that by M. H. Morgan, Cambridge, Harvard University Press, 1914.

Similarly, another equally famous survival is available in English with notes and comments by a famous American hydraulic engineer:

Frontinus: The Water Supply of the City of Rome, translated with notes by Clemens Herschel, Boston, Dana Estes and Co., 1899.

The Building of the Roman Aqueducts, by E. B. Van Deman, Monograph 423, Carnegie Institution, Washington, 1934. A recent and exhaustive study.

Two or three Roman bridges are described in

Old Bridges of France, published by the American Institute of Architects, New York, 1925. Contains drawings, etc., of several early Roman works.

An interesting study of Roman mining methods is given in

The Rio Tinto Mine, Its History and Romance, by Wm. G. Nash, London, Kent and Co., 1904.

See also

"Notes on Some Ancient Mine Equipments and Systems," by R. E. Palmer, *Trans. Inst. Mining Met. (London)*, Vol. 36 (1927), p. 299.

"The Eastern Iron Trade of the Roman Empire," by W. H. Schoff, Boston, *J. Am. Oriental Soc.*, Vol. 35, Part III, December, 1915.

History of the Iron Trade (from the earliest records to the present period) by Henry Scrivenor, London, Longman, Brown, Green and Longman, 1854.

Also, among the special project studies see

"The Ancient Roman Aqueduct at Athens," by J. F. Case, *Trans. Am. Soc. Civil Engrs.*, Vol. 91 (1927), p. 281.

Descriptions of later Empire works in the colonies are difficult to obtain and available only in French. See, for example,

Étude sur les travaux hydrauliques des Romains en Tunisie, by Dr. Cardon, Tunis, 1897.

Les Aqueducs antiques de Lyon, by C. Germain de Montauzan, Paris, Leroux, 1908.

The standard work on surveying is in German,

Die Romischen agrimensoren, by Moritz Cantor, 1875.

The Drainage of Lake Fucinus, by Alex. Brisse and Leon de Rotrou, Rome, Propaganda Press, 1876, 2 vols. Describes a famous later work with text in both French and English.

The Letters of Pliny, translated by Melmoth and Besanquet, include a number dealing with engineering matters. See Nos. 46, 47, 51, 52, 69, 70, 91, 92, 99, and 100.

CHAPTER 2. THE MIDDLE AGES AND THE RENAISSANCE

Middle Ages

The Middle Ages by Dana C. Munroe, New York, Century Company, 1922, and

*An Economic and Social History of the Middle Ages, by Jas. W. Thompson, New York, Century Company, 1928. Excellent but gives little attention to engineering matters.

*Dictionnaire raisonné de l'architecture française en XIe à XVIe *siècle,* by Violett-le-Duc, Paris, 1854. A monumental, illustrated work in 11 volumes covering all phases of architecture and engineering. See especially articles on Architecture Militaire, Chateau, Donjon, Engin, Siège, Tour, etc.

Numerous architectural books are also of interest such as

Byzantine and Romanesque Architecture and

Gothic Architecture in France, England, and Italy, both by T. G. Jackson, New York, Cambridge University Press, 1913 and 1915.

*Old Bridges of France, published by the American Institute of

Architects, New York, 1915. Gives measured drawings of some notable early French works.

The Ancient Bridges of England, by Edwyn Jervoise, a series of studies for the Society for the Preservation of Ancient Buildings, London, The Architectural Press, 1930–1936.

The Architect in History, by M. S. Briggs, New York, Oxford University Press, 1927. Reveals the position and methods of the medieval master builder.

Facsimile of the Sketchbook of Wilars de Honecourt, translated and edited by Rev. Robert Willis, London, 1859. Describes a fascinating survival, the manuscript notebook of a master builder of c. 1230.

Renaissance

Engineers and Engineering in the Renaissance, by William Barclay Parsons, Baltimore, The Williams & Wilkins Company, 1939. Contains data not otherwise available in English and is well illustrated.

"Leonarda da Vinci, Natural Philosopher and Engineer," a brief paper by John W. Lieb, *J. Franklin Inst.,* Vol. 191, July, 1921. Of special interest. There are, of course, many other studies of Leonardo and his notebooks.

There are numerous foreign works on architecture, military engineering, and mechanisms. A number of beautifully illustrated, early notebooks were printed in the 16th century, which, together with early surveying books, mark the beginning of printed engineering texts. These include

Théâtre des instruments mathématiques et méchaniques, by Jacques Besson, Lyon, 1579.

Novo theatro di machine et edificii, by Vittorio Zonca, Padua, 1607.

La diverse et artificiose Machine, by Augustino Ramelli, Paris, 1588.

The most famous of all late Renaissance works was

De re metallica, by Georg Agricola, published in 1556, which has been translated by ex-President and Mrs. Hoover. (The Mining Magazine, London, 1912) in a beautiful volume with all the woodcuts and with many interesting notes.

Surveying Instruments, Their History and Their Classroom Use, by Edmond R. Kiely, New York, Bureau of Publications, Teachers College, Columbia University, 1947. Issued as the Nineteenth Yearbook of the National Council of Teachers of Mathematics, this exhaustive and comprehensive study of the rise of modern surveying and early surveying instruments (up to 1700) is well illustrated and provides an extensive bibliography on this subject. No attempt will be made here, therefore, to list the many original works in this field.

CHAPTER 3. THE AGE OF FRENCH LEADERSHIP

A Short History of France, by Victor Duruy. A translation has been published in two volumes in the Everyman's Library (Nos. 737–738) New York, E. P. Dutton & Co., Inc., 1917.

Economic and Social Conditions in France during the Eighteenth Century, by Henri Sée, translated by E. H. Zeydel, New York, Alfred A. Knopf, Inc., 1927. A brief summary with many references to more detailed studies.

A large amount of material is available on French engineering, particularly in the 18th century. Many engineering books of the period not only offer a revealing picture of methods and practices but include some of the most beautiful engineering volumes ever published. With very few exceptions, however, these publications are available only in French.

Architecture hydraulique (ou l'art de conduire, d'élever, et de ménager les eaux pour les différents besoins de la vie), by Bertrand Forest de Belidor, Paris, 1737–1754. A remarkable work in four volumes with numerous engraved plans describing many notable hydraulic works of all types, from pumps and water wheels to canals and harbors. His other works on *"architecture militaire et civile"* also clearly reveal the methods, practices, and state of technical knowledge of his day.

Roads

Les Voies terrestres, by H. Heude, Paris, Libraire Polytechnique, 1927. A brief review.

Études historiques sur l'administration des voies publiques en France, by E. J. M. Vignon, Paris, 1862–1864.

Bridges

Old Bridges of France, published by the American Institute of Architects, New York, 1925. A brief résumé with dimensioned drawings.

* *Études sur les ponts en pierre,* by Fernand de Dartein, Paris, Librairie Polytechnique, 1907–1912. A monumental work in four volumes, offering a most complete and detailed study of stone-arch bridges.

There are numerous other works, including

Traité des ponts, by Émile-Marie Gauthey, Paris, 1809–1816. A classical work in three volumes, the last dealing with canals, published posthumously by his nephew, Navier.

Gautier and others also wrote on this subject but the most outstanding of these publications is

Description des projects et de la construction des ponts (de Neuilly, de Mantes, d'Orléans, et autres: du project du canal de Bourgogne, pour la communication des deux Mers par Dijon; et de celui de la conduite des eaux de l'Yvette et de Bièvre à Paris), Paris, Imprimerie Royal, 1782. In two folio volumes with 67 pictorial engravings and plans, this work is a memorial to the last and the greatest of French stone-arch bridge builders, J. R. Perronet. Published before the construction of the Pont de la Concorde, a supplement gives the plans for this work.

Histoire général des ponts de Paris, by Charles Duplomb, Paris, 1913, 2 vols. Tells the story of these most interesting works.

Engineers and Engineering of the Renaissance, by Parsons, includes descriptions of several earlier French bridges.

Canals

Des canaux de navigation (et spécialement du canal de Languedoc), by M. De la Lande, Paris, Desaint, 1778. A well-known work.

Among special books is

Histoire du Canal de Languedoc, by the descendants of P.-P. Riquet de Bonrepos, Paris, 1805. A brief story of this work in English is given as an appendix in Smile's *Lives of the Engineers,* Vol. 1 (Brindley and Smeaton).

Hydraulics and Hydraulic Engineering

"Henri Pitot, Pioneer in Practical Hydraulics," by R. S. Kirby, *Civil Eng.* (Am. Soc. Civil Engrs.), December, 1939, p. 738.

"On the Origin of the Chézy Formula," by Clemens Herschel, *J. Assoc. Eng. Soc.,* Vol. 18 (1897), p. 363.

See also Belidor's *Architecture hydraulique* already noted.

Les Fontaines de Paris, anciennnes et nouvelles, by C. A. A. P. Duval, Paris, 1813.

Les grandes Eaux de Versailles, by L. A. Barbet, Paris, 1907.

Description des travaux hydrauliques de L-A de Cessart, Paris, 1806–1809. In two volumes with 67 plans, this describes Cessart's famous digue, or breakwater, at Cherbourg, as well as the harbors of Havre, Dieppe, etc.

The Theory, Formation and Construction of British and Foreign Harbours, by Sir John Rennie (son of the more famous John Rennie of London Bridge fame), London, John Weale, 1854, in two large folio volumes with 123 engravings. Describes some French works.

Surveying

See Kiely, *Surveying Instruments,* previously noted (Chap. 2).

French Engineers

The standard French encyclopedias give some brief notes.
See also,

Notices biographiques (*sur les ingénieurs des ponts et chaussées depuis la création du corps, en 1716, jusqu'a nos jours*) by F.P.H. de St. Hardouin, Paris, Baudry et Cie, 1884. A series of brief biographies.

There are also numerous scattered "memoirs."

* *Vauban, Builder of Fortresses,* by Daniel Halévy, translated by Major C. J. C. Street, New York, The Dial Press, 1925. Gives an enthusiastic and interesting picture of this great engineer and patriot.

Sébastien le Prestre de Vauban, 1633–1707, by Sir Reginald Blomfield, London, Methuen & Co., Ltd., 1938. Offers a more conservative appraisal of the man and his work and is fully and beautifully illustrated.

"French Pioneers in Engineering," by J. K. Finch, *Eng. News-Record,* April 24, 1930.

CHAPTER 4. EARLY BRITISH ENGINEERING

Britain

The Making of Modern England, by Gilbert Slater (new rev. ed.), New York, Houghton Mifflin Company, 1920. A standard work on the Industrial Revolution, its economic, social, and political aspects. Includes chronological table and excellent bibliography.

*English Social History: A Survey of Six Centuries, Chaucer to Queen Victoria, by G. M. Trevelyan, New York, Longmans, Green & Co., Inc., 1942. A most interesting and unbiased analysis of the economic and social forces which made ready the way for, were concurrent with, and have resulted from the Industrial Revolution.

*A History of Engineering, by A. P. M. Fleming and H. J. Brockle-hurst, London, A. and C. Black, Ltd., 1925. Not a general history but does outline the development of British engineering and industry.

Transactions of the Newcomen Society, London. A society devoted to the study of the history of engineering and publisher of a number of valuable papers and bibliographies.

*Lives of the Engineers, by Samuel Smiles, London, John Murray, 1855–1860. Appearing originally in single volumes, this standard work was reprinted in 1904 under the above title and includes Vol. 1, Vermuyden, Myddleton, Perry, and Brindley; Vol. 2, Smeaton and Rennie; Vol. 3, Metcalf and Telford; Vol. 4, Boulton and Watt; Vol. 5, George and Robert Stephenson.

Surveying

Surveying Instruments, by Kiely, previously noted (Chap. 2).

Among many interesting books on this subject, the following deserve special notice:

A Geometrical Practise, Named Pantometria, "framed by Leonard Digges, Gentleman, lately finished by his sonne," London, 1571. A small, quaint black-letter book describing Digges's "theodolitus," the origin of our present theodolite.

* The Surveyor in Four Bookes, by Aaron Rathborne, London, 1616. A most interesting story of the surveying of the day.

Surveying Improv'd, or the Whole Art, Both in Theory and Practice, Fully Demonstrated, by Henry Wilson, London, 1731. The first description of modern methods of computation in land surveying.

Iron

"Dud Dudley and the Early Coal-Iron Industry," by R. A. Mott, *Trans. Newcomen Soc. (London)*, Vol. 15 (1934–1935), p. 17.

Textiles

The Story of Textiles, by Perry Walton, New York, Tudor Publishing Co., 1925. A brief outline of British and American developments.

The History of the English Woolen and Worsted Industries, by E. Lipson, London, A. & C. Black, Ltd.

Steam

Anecdotes of the Steam Engine, by Robert Stuart, London, Wightman and Cramp, 1829.

**James Watt and the Steam Engine*, by W. H. Dickinson and Rhys Jenkins, Oxford, The Clarendon Press, 1928. The centenary memorial volume.

Lives of the Engineers, Smiles (see above). Boulton and Watt.

**A History of the Growth of the Steam-Engine*, by Robt. H. Thurston, Ithaca, Cornell University Press, 1939. A reprint of the original publication of 1878.

Railroads

The Life of Richard Trevithick, by Francis Trevithick, London, Spon, 1872, 2 vols.

Lives of the Engineers, Smiles (see above). George and Robert Stephenson.

The Life of Joseph Locke, by Joseph Devey, London, Richard Bentley, 1862. A contemporary and associate of George Stephenson.

A Century of Locomotive Building by Stephenson and Co., 1823–1923, by C. F. D. Marshall, London, The Locomotive Publishing Co., 1931.

Centenary History of the Liverpool and Manchester Railway, by J. G. H. Warren, Newcastle, Reid and Co., 1923.

Railway Literature, by R. A. Peddie, London, Grafton and Co., 1931. Gives a most valuable bibliography of early works up to 1830.

The Tool Builders

**English and American Tool Builders*, by J. W. Roe, New York, McGraw-Hill Book Company, Inc., 1926.

**Memoir of the Life of Sir Marc Isambard Brunel*, by Richard Beamish, London, Longmans Green, 1862.

Canals

Lives of the Engineers, Smiles (see above). Brindley, Telford.

Roads

Lives of the Engineers, Smiles (see above). Metcalf and Telford.

The Life of Thomas Telford, Civil Engineer, Written by Himself, Ed. John Rickman, London, 1838, 2 vols. Folio with plates.

*The Story of Telford, by Sir Alexander Gibb, London, Maclehouse and Co., 1935.

Harbors

*A Narrative of the Building of the Eddystone Lighthouse, by John Smeaton, London, 1791, 2 vols. An engineering classic.

The Theory, Formation and Construction of British and Foreign Harbours, by Sir John Rennie, London, John Weale, 1854. See also Smiles: Smeaton and Rennie.

Bridges

A Practical Treatise on Bridge-building, by Edw. Cresy, London, John Williams, 1839. See also Smiles: Telford, Rennie, Robert Stephenson.

Drainage

Sir Cornelius Vermuyden, the Life Work of a Great Anglo-Dutchman in Land Reclamation and Drainage, by J. K. Altes, London, Williams and Norgate, 1925.

See also Smiles: Perry

CHAPTER 5. THE VICTORIAN ERA

*An Economic History of Modern Britain, by J. H. Clapham, New York, Cambridge University Press, 1938. The standard work on the economic problems of 19th century Britain, in three volumes. Crowded with information but lacking in summaries. The following chapters are of special interest: Vol. 1. The Early Railway Age, 1820–1850: Chap. I, The Face of the Country; Chap. IX, The Railways and Railway Policy. Vol. 2. Free Trade and Steel, 1850–1886: Chap. II, The Industrial Field in 1851; Chap. III, The Course of Industrial Change. Vol. 3: Chap. I, The Industrial State, Its Neighbours and Vicissitudes.

A History of Engineering, by Fleming and Brocklehurst. Gives in outline many data on this period. See also Kirby, The Early Years of Modern Civil Engineering.

Railroads and Bridges

The Life of Robert Stephenson, by J. C. Jeaffreson, London, Longman, 1864. Includes descriptions of some of his most important works by Wm. Pole.

An Account of the Construction of the Britannia and Conway Tubular Bridges, by W. Fairbairn, London, John Weale, 1849.

*The Britannia and Conway Tubular Bridges, by Edwin Clark, London, Day and Son, 1850.

Construction of the Great Victoria Bridge in Canada, by Jas. Hodges, London, John Weale, 1860.

The Life of Isambard Kingdom Brunel, by his son, Isambard Brunel, London, 1870.

History of the Great Western Railway, by E. T. MacDermot, London, Great Western Railway, 1927.

"Construction of the Center Pier of the Saltash Bridge," Proc. Inst. Civil Engrs. (London), Vol. 21 (1861–1862), p. 268. This description of a pioneer pneumatic foundation is but one of many papers of historical interest in the Proceedings.

The New Tay Bridge, by Crawford Barlow, London, Spon, 1889.

*The Forth Bridge in Its Various Stages of Construction, by Philip Phillips, Edinburgh, R. Grant and Son, 1885. A beautiful volume.

Tunnels and Subways

The Severn Tunnel, by Thos. A. Walker, London, Rich, Bentley and Son, 1888.

*Tunnel Shields and the Use of Compressed Air in Subaqueous Works, by Wm. C. Copperthwaite, New York, D. Van Nostrand Company, Inc., 1906.

*Life of Sir John Fowler, by T. Mackay, 1900. Covers tunnel and other works by an outstanding British engineer, the partner of Sir Benjamin Baker.

Die Londoner Untergrundbohnen, by L. Troske, Berlin, Verlag-Julius Springer, 1892. In German.

Hydraulic and Sanitary Works

Irrigation Works in India and Egypt, by R. B. Buckley, London, Spon, 1893. Describes many of the outstanding British colonial works.

A series of paper in the Minutes of Proc. Inst. Civil Engrs., of Great Britain review some of the notable sanitary works of this era:

"The Drainage of Paris," Vol. 24 (1865).

"The Main Drainage of Paris," Vol. 53 (1878).

"The Main Drainage of London and the Interception of Sewage from the River Thames," Vol. 24 (1865).

* Report on the Filtration of River Waters for the Supply of Cities, as Practiced in Europe, by J. P. Kirkwood, New York, D. Van Nostrand Company, Inc. A pioneer work by a pioneer American water-supply engineer.

An interesting French work is

M. de Montricher et le Canal de Marseille by Felix Martin, Paris, Gallet et Branc, 1878.

CHAPTER 6. AMERICAN ENGINEERING IN THE 19TH CENTURY

There is no brief outline of American economic-engineering development such as Slater. The nearest approach is to be found in

A History of American Economic Life, by Edward C. Kirkland, New York, Appleton-Century-Crofts, Inc., rev. ed., 1946. A large volume of over 800 pages which emphasizes the close relationships of technical, economic, social, and political changes.

Earlier Works

*The Early Years of Modern Civil Engineering, by R. S. Kirby and P. G. Laurson, New Haven, Yale University Press, 1932. Contains a large amount of data and numerous references.

*A Sketch of the Civil Engineering of North America (comprising remarks on the Harbours, River and Lake Navigations, Lighthouses, Steam-Navigation, Water-works, Canals, Roads, Railways, Bridges, and other works in that Country), by David Stevenson, London, John Wheale, 1838. A most interesting review of a number of early (before 1838) works by an observant and understanding British engineer.

Yankee Science in the Making, by D. J. Struik, Boston, Little, Brown & Company, 1948. Includes not only natural science but observations on many New England engineering ventures.

Pioneer American Bridgebuilders

"A History of the Development of Wooden Bridges," by Robert Fletcher and J. P. Snow, *Trans. Am. Soc. Civil Engrs.,* Vol. 99 (1934) p.

"The Evolution of Early American Bridges," by L. N. Edwards, *Trans. Newcomen Soc. (London),* Vol. 13 (1932–1933), p. 95.

Early Transportation

Historic Highways of America, by A. B. Hulbert, Cleveland, A. H. Clark Co., 1904. A monumental work in fourteen volumes which, however, does not give special attention to matters of engineering design.

A History of Travel in America, by Seymour Dunbar, Indianapolis, Bobbs-Merrill Company, 1915. In four volumes, especially rich in illustrations.

A History of Transportation in the U.S. before 1860, directed by B. H. Meyer, Washington, D.C., Carnegie Institution, 1917. There are numerous books and papers dealing with specific projects.

Canals

A History of the Canal System of N.Y. State, by N. E. Whitford, 1905. Includes not only the Erie Canal but brief notes of the other canals of the United States and Canada.

* *A Century of Progress, the History of the Delaware and Hudson Co.,* by L. F. Loree, Albany, J. B. Lyon Co., 1925.

"The Morris Canal," by C. C. Vermeule, *Trans. Newcomen Soc. (London)*, Vol. 15 (1934–1935), p. 195. See also Final Report by same author to Morris Canal and Banking Co. on dismantling of canal, Trenton, 1929.

Old Towpaths—The Story of the American Canal Era, by A. F. Harlow, New York, Appleton and Co., 1926. Gives an interesting account of the economic and social aspects of the Canal Era.

Early Railroads

A History of the First Locomotives in America, by W. H. Brown, New York, 1874.

*Iron Horses, by E. P. Alexander, New York, W. W. Norton & Company, 1941. Includes a remarkable group of colored plates.

*The Story of the Baltimore and Ohio Railroad, 1827–1927, by Edward Hungerford, New York, Putnam, 1928.

The Story of Erie, by E. H. Mott, New York, J. S. Collins, 1899.

"A Memoir of American Engineering," by J. B. Jervis, *Trans. Am. Soc. Civil Engrs.,* Vol. 6 (1877), p. 39. Covers many early works, including the first railroads in New York State.

*John Stevens, An American Record, by A. D. Turnbull, New York, Century Co., 1928. The pioneer engineer of the Camden and Amboy R.R.

Centennial History of the South Carolina Railroad, by S. M. Derrick, Columbia, South Carolina, 1930.

The Allegheny Portage Railroad, Information Pamphlet, Vol. 2, No. 1. of the Pennsylvania R. R., Philadelphia, February, 1930.

Specimens of Stone, Iron and Wood Bridges, Viaducts, Tunnels and Culverts of the U.S. Rail Roads, by Geo. Duggan, New York, Appleton, Wiley, and other publishers, 1850. Includes plans of many notable early works such as the Cascade Bridge and Starrucca Viaduct in the Erie, etc.

Steamboats

"Rise and Progress of American Engineering," *Trans. Am. Soc. Civil Engrs.,* Vol. 5 (1876), p. 73. A brief résumé.

Eminent Engineers, by Dwight Goodard, New York, Derry-Collard Co., 1905.

James Rumsey, Pioneer in Steam Navigation, by Ella M. Turner, Scottdale, Pennsylvania, Mennonite Publishing House, 1931.

Robert Fulton, Engineer and Artist, by H. W. Dickinson, London, John Lane, 1913. See also *John Stevens* by Turnbull.

Transportation by Water, by E. R. Johnson, G. G. Heubner, and A. K. Henry, New York, Appleton-Century Crofts, Inc., 1935.

Steam Conquers the Atlantic, by D. B. Tyler, New York, Appleton-Century Crofts, Inc., 1939.

Water Works

"The Central Square Water-works of Philadelphia," *Eng. News-Record,* May 14, 1903, p. 422. See also Stevenson noted above.

The Water Supply of New York, 1658–1895, by Edward Wegmann, New York, John Wiley & Sons, Inc., 1896. Includes the new Croton supply of 1885–1891.

A Memoir of the Croton Aqueduct, by Chas. King, New York, 1843.

Illustrations of the Croton Aqueduct, by F. B. Tower, New York, 1843.

History of the Introduction of Pure Water into the City of Boston, by H. L. Bradlee, Boston, A. Mudge and Son, 1868.

Manufactures

British Regulation of the Colonial Iron Industry, by A. C. Bining, Philadelphia, University of Pennsylvania Press, 1933.

History of the Manufacture of Iron in All Ages (and particularly in the United States from Colonial Times to 1891, also a short history of early coal mining in the United States), by James M. Swank, 2d ed., Philadelphia, American Iron and Steel Association, 1892.

**English and American Tool Builders,* by J. W. Roe, New York, McGraw-Hill Book Company, Inc., 1916.

**Leading American Inventors,* by George Iles, New York, Henry Holt and Company, Inc., 1912.

The Rise of Manufacturing in Connecticut, Publication 44, The Connecticut Tercentenary, New Haven, Yale University Press, 1935.

History of Manufactures in the United States, by V. S. Clark, New York, Peter Smith, 1949, Vol. 1, 1607–1860; Vol. 11, 1860–1893. Primarily an economic study but contains much information of engineering interest.

Early Engineers

**Lives and Works of the Civil and Military Engineers of America,* by Chas. B. Stuart, New York, D. Van Nostrand Company, Inc., 1871.

John Stevens, An American Record, by A. D. Turnbull, New York, Century Co., 1928.

"John Bloomfield Jervis, Civil Engineer," by J. K. Finch, *Trans. Newcomen Soc.* (London), Vol. 11 (1930–1931), p. 118.

Early Columbia Engineers (Renwick, Allen, Stevens, and Craven), by J. K. Finch, New York, Columbia University Press, 1929.

Eminent Engineers, by Dwight Goddard, New York, Derry-Collard Co., 1905.

LATER WORKS

Railroads

A Short History of American Railroads, by Slason Thompson, New York, Appleton, 1925

The Romance of the Rails, by Agnes C. Laut, New York, McBridge, 2 vols.

*The Beginnings of the New York Central Railroad, by F. W. Stevens, New York, Putnam, 1926.

*The Growth and Development of the Pennsylvania Railroad Company, by H. W. Scholter, Philadelphia, Allen, Lane and Scott, 1927.

*How We Built the Union Pacific Railroad, by G. M. Dodge, Washington, D.C., Government Printing Office, 1910.

*Trails, Rails and War: The Life of General G. M. Dodge, by J. R. Perkins, Indianapolis, Bobbs-Merrill Company. The story of the engineer of the Union Pacific.

*The Strategy of Great Railroads, by Frank H. Spearman, New York, Chas. Scribner's Sons, 1905. Tells the stories of some of the later railroad consolidations.

The Economic Theory of Railroad Location, by A. M. Wellington, New York, John Wiley & Sons, Inc., 1887. An American railroad classic.

Canadian Engineering

"Fifty Years of Canadian Engineering," by H. K. Wicksteed, *Eng. News-Record,* April 17, 1924, p. 661.

A History of the Canadian Pacific Railway, by H. A. Innis, Toronto, McClelland and Stewart, 1923.

Canada's Great Highway, by J. H. E. Secretan, London, John Lane, 1924. The Canadian Pacific Railroad, especially the later phases of its construction.

Sanford Fleming, Empire Builder, by L. J. Burpee, New York, Oxford University Press, 1915. The story of the "Father of Canadian Engineering."

The Life and Work of Sir Wm. Van Horne, by Walter Vaughn, New York, Century Company, 1920.

Bridges

"American Railroad Bridges," by Theodore Cooper, *Trans. Am. Soc. Civil Engrs., Vol.* 21 (1889). A most valuable study by an expert.

"American Iron Bridges," *Proc. Inst. Civil Engrs., (London),* Vol. 22 (1862). Reveals the battle between British and American engineers on the relative merits of their different designs.

Travaux publiques des États-Unis d'Amérique en 1870, by M. Malezieux, Paris, Dunod, 1875 (text and plans) and

Les Ponts de l'Amérique du Nord, by L. A. Comolli, Paris, Lefèvre,

1879 (text and plans). Not only offer valuable information but reflect the interest of European engineers in the remarkable American works of this period, as does also

Traité de la construction des ponts et viaducs, by M. R. Morandière, Paris, Dunod, 1888, 2 vols. A remarkable collection of plans of hundreds of important bridges.

The Bridges of the Rhine, by Karl Möhringer, Baden, 1931. A work in English describing the notable bridges of the Rhine.

**A History of the St. Louis Bridge,* by C. M. Woodward, St. Louis, G. I. Jones and Co., 1881. A remarkably complete and interesting story of the "granddaddy" of American steel arches.

"The American Railroad Viaduct, Its Origin and Evolution," by J. E. Griner and others, *Trans. Am. Soc. Civil Engrs.,* Vol. 25 (1891), p. 349.

"The Cantilever Bridge at Niagara Falls," by C. C. Schneider, *Trans. Am. Soc. Civil Engrs.,* Vol. 14 (1885), p. 499.

The Washington Bridge, by Wm. R. Hutton, New York L. Von Rosenberg, 1889. Over the Harlem at New York.

"The Niagara Railway Arch," by R. S. Buck, *Trans. Am. Soc. Civil Engrs.,* Vol. 40 (1898), p. 125.

Foundations

"Pneumatic Foundations," by General Wm. Sooy Smith, *Trans. Am. Soc. Civil Engrs.,* Vol. 11 (1873), p. 411. An important paper by an American pioneer in this process.

Hydraulic and Sanitary

Rivers and Canals, by L. F. Vernon-Harcourt, New York, Oxford University Press, 2d ed., 1896.

The Inland Waterways of England, by L. T. C. Rolt, London, George Allen and Unwin, Ltd., 1950. England's historic canals with interesting illustrations of lock and other surviving structures.

The Suez Canal, by C. W. Hallberg, New York, Columbia University Press, 1931. Mainly political and diplomatic history.

L'Isthme et le Canal de Suez, by J. Charles-Roux, Paris, 1901.

"Historical Review of the Development of Sanitary Engineering in the United States during the Last One Hundred and Fifty Years," *Trans. Am. Soc. Civil Engrs.,* 1928, p. 1208.

"History of Water Purification," by Geo. C. Whipple, *Trans. Am. Soc. Civil Engrs.,* Vol. 85 (1922).

The Water Supply of New York, 1658–1895, by Edward Wegmann, New York, John Wiley & Sons, Inc., 1896.

Report on the Filtration of River Waters for the Supply of Cities, as Practised in Europe, by Kirkwood (previously noted).

A History of the Jetties at the Mouth of the Mississippi River, by E. L. Corthell, New York, John Wiley & Sons, Inc., 1880. An outstanding American work.

Mechanical Engineering

"The American Mixed-flow Turbine and Its Setting," by A. T. Safford and E. P. Hamilton, *Trans. Am. Soc. Civil Engrs.*, Vol. 85 (1922), p. 1237. Offers a most complete history of the development of turbine design and theory.

A History of the Growth of the Steam-Engine, by Thurston. Previously noted (Chap. 4).

Engineering in American Industry, by C. N. Lauer, New York, Mc-Graw-Hill Book Company, Inc., 1924.

The Gas, Petrol and Oil Engine, by Dougald Clerk, New York, John Wiley & Sons, Inc., 1909. First published in 1888. Gives brief historical outline.

Fiftieth Anniversary Issue of the *J. Am. Soc. Mech. Engrs.*, Vol. 52, No. 4, April, 1930.

Electrical Engineering

Amber to Amperes, by Ernest Greenwood, New York. Harper & Brothers, 1930.

A Saga of the Seas, by P. B. McDonald, New York, Wilson-Erickson, 1937. Cyrus W. Field and the Atlantic Cable.

History of Electric Light, by Henry Schroeder, Washington, D.C., Smithsonian Institution, 1923.

History of the Incandescent Lamp, by J. W. Howell and Henry Schroeder, Schenectady, The Maqua Co., 1927.

"Our Debt to the Electricians of the Nineteenth Century," by Henry Crew, *Selected Papers, Soc. Promotion Eng. Education*, October, 1928.

Edison, His Life and Inventions, by F. L. Dyer and T. C. Martin, New York, Harper & Brothers, 1929, 2 vols. The authorized life.

Dynamo-Electric Machinery, by Silvanus P. Thompson, London, Spon and Chamberlain, 1902, 2 vols. Volume I gives a brief but excellent historical outline of dynamo development.

Electric Traction for Railway Trains, by Ed. P. Burch, New York, McGraw-Hill Book Company, Inc., 1911. Includes a 50-page historical outline.

Niagara Power, by Ed. Dean Adams, Buffalo, Niagara Falls Power Co., 1927, 2 vols. A pioneer American work.

George Westinghouse, by Col. Henry G. Prout, New York, American Society of Mechanical Engineers, 1921. See also Commemoration Forum Book, 1937.

The History of the Telephone, by H. N. Casson, Chicago, A. C. Mc-Clurg & Company, 1910.

*Beginnings of Telephony, by F. L. Rhodes, New York, Harper & Brothers, 1929. An exhaustive story of the maze of inventions, improvements, and legal battles over patents which characterized the development of telephony. Mr. Rhodes was an active member of the great group of researchers and engineers of the modern industry.

Wiring a Continent (The History of the Telegraph Industry in the U.S. 1832–1866), by Robt. L. Thompson, Princeton, Princeton University Press, 1947.

Mining and Metallurgy

Tunneling, Explosive Compounds and Rock Drills, by Henry S. Drinker, New York, Wiley, 1878. A classic in its field.

For iron and steel see earlier references: Scrivenor (Chap. 1), Swank (Early Works, Manufacturing).

*Sir Henry Bessemer, An Autobiography, London, Engineering, 1905.

The Iron Trade of Great Britain, by Jas. S. Jeans, London, Methuen & Co., Ltd., 1906.

Incredible Carnegie, by J. K. Winkler, New York, Vanguard Press, 1931.

The Inside History of the Carnegie Steel Co., by Jas. H. Bridge, New York, Aldine Book Co., 1903.

Aluminum, by J. W. Richards, Philadelphia, H. C. Baird and Co., 1896. Contains a brief review of early history.

Engineers

"Memoir of Albert Fink," Trans. Am. Soc. Civil Engrs., Vol. 41 (1899), p. 626. These memoirs (see Index to Trans.) include many outstanding engineers such as J. H. Linville, Vol. 59 (1907), p. 549. See also special articles in the Society's periodical, Civil Engineering, "George S. Morison," and others.

The Roeblings, by Hamilton Schuyler, Princeton, Princeton University Press, 1931.

The Builders of the Bridge (the story of John Roebling and his son), by David B. Steinman, New York, Harcourt, Brace and Company, Inc., 1945.

Reminiscences of General Herman Haupt, privately printed, 1901. Describes the interesting Civil War and other works of this colorful personality.

CHAPTER 7. THE NEW ENGINEERING

Engineering Science

There are numerous papers on the history of various phases of engineering science, but the actual conditions of practice are best secured from the various technical journals of the day, especially from the discussions of papers dealing with specific works. The actual steps in the development of engineering science are reflected in some of the outstanding books of the period 1800–1860. For example,

G.C.F.M. De Prony (1755–1839), *Architecture hydraulique* (The Art of Elevating Water by Different Machines, etc.) Paris, Didot Fils, 1790.

L.M.H. Navier (1785–1836) *Résumé des leçons . . . sur l'application de la méchanique . . .* , Paris, 1826.

Henry Mosley (1801–1872), *A Treatise on Hydrostatics*, 1830, and *The Mechanical Principles of Engineering and Architecture, 1843.*

Wm. J. M. Rankine (1820–1872) *Applied Mechanics,* 1858.

Manual of the Steam Engine, 1859.

Civil Engineering, 1862.

Albin J. Weisbach (1806–1871), *Lehrbuch der Ingenieur und Maschinenkunde,* 1854.

Handbuch der ingenieur-wissenschaft, by Max Becker, 1857. Began in one or two volumes and was later expanded into a small library.

Mechanics of Materials

A History of the Theory of Elasticity and of the Strength of Materials, by Todhunter and Pearson, New York, Cambridge University Press, 1893. This is the classical work in this field (three volumes) but deals solely with theory and so does not reflect current practice.

"A History of the Flexure Formula," by H. F. Moore, *J. Eng. Education,* 1930.

Life of Sir William Fairbairn, by Wm. Pole, London, 1877.

Structural Analysis

"One Hundred Fifty Years Advance in Structural Analysis," by H. M. Westergaard, *Trans. Am. Soc. Civil Engrs.,* Vol. 94 (1930), p. 226.

A Work upon Bridge Building, by Squire Whipple, Utica, New York, 1847. The first published work on truss analysis. See also an independent but later publication:

The General Theory of Bridge Construction, by Herman Haupt, New York, 1851.

Engineering Thermodynamics

A History of the Growth of the Steam Engine, by Robt. H. Thurston, Ithaca, Cornell University Press, 1939. Originally published in 1878. See Chap. VII on "Thermodynamics."

"Our Progress in Mechanical Engineering," by Robt. H. Thurston, *Trans. A.S.M.E.,* Vol. 2 (1881), p. 415.

"A Résumé of Mechanical Engineering Since James Watt," by Wm. D. Ennis, Selected Papers, *Soc. Promotion Eng. Education,* No. 6, 1929.

Hydraulics

See references in Chap. 3 under "Hydraulics" for Pitot, Belidor, and Chézy. The work of the French expert Darcy is best reflected in his various publications (in French) :

The Public Fountains of Dijon, 1856.

Experiments on the Flow of Water in Pipes, 1857, and a posthumous work on "Open Channels" published in 1865.

See *Mémoirs de l'Academie des Sciences,* Vol. 19 (1865), for the studies of Henri E. Bazin (1829–1917).

Among the American classics in this field are

A General Formula for the Flow of Water in Rivers and Other Channels, by Gauguillet and Kutter, translated by Herring and Trautwine, New York, John Wiley & Sons, Inc., 1891.

Lowell Hydraulic Experiments, by Jas. B. Francis, 1855.

*"Great hydraulic engineers of New England's classic period," *Eng. New-Record,* Vol. 107 (1931), p. 475.

CHAPTER 8. MODERN ENGINEERING I: TRANSPORTATION

The Engineering Profession

There are a number of books covering various aspects of the engineering profession, some popular and descriptive, others of a more analytical character. Among others see,

The Profession of Engineering, by D. C. Jackson and W. P. Jones, New York, John Wiley & Sons, Inc., 1929. A series of papers by some seven engineering leaders.

Building an Engineering Career, by C. C. Williams, New York, McGraw-Hill Book Company, Inc., 2d ed., 1946. Largely descriptive.

The Professional Engineer, by Esther L. Brown, New York, Russell Sage Foundation, 1936.

The Engineer, by John Hays Hammond, New York, Charles Scribner's Sons, 1921. A small book in the Vocational Series by a famous American mining engineer.

The Young Man and Civil Engineering, by George F. Swain, New York, The Macmillan Company, 1922. Also a "Series" book by an outstanding leader in engineering education.

So You Want to Be a Chemist? by Herbert Coith, New York, McGraw-Hill Book Company, Inc., 1943.

Addresses to Engineering Students, edited by Waddell and Harrington, Kansas City, Missouri, The Authors, 1911. An earlier selection by a famous consulting partnership.

Also current publications of the Engineers Council for Professional Development.

General Note—Modern Engineering

The references to "Later Works" under Chap. 6 include a number of works which deal, in part at least, with 20th century developments. Several general works summarizing recent trends are noted later under Chap. 14. There are, however, relatively few more detailed studies covering 20th century developments in specific fields of engineering. The student will find it necessary to turn to the technical and professional publications of the period for details of many specific works. Knowing the year in which a plant or work was constructed or put in operation, one can usually find numerous references by consulting *The Engineering Index,* an annual publication. An attempt has been made in the following bibliography to give an indication of the character of material available rather than to supply an exhaustive listing; in fact, a reasonably complete bibliography would require several volumes.

A valuable general summary, survey, and analysis will be found in

*Technological Trends and National Policy, Report of the Subcommittee on Technology to the National Resources Committee, Washington, D.C., Government Printing Office, 1937. Part III of this report gives brief reviews of 1. Agriculture; 2. The Mineral Industries; 3. Transportation; 4. Communication; 5. Power; 6. The Chemical Industries; 7. Electrical Goods Industries; 8. Metallurgy; and 9. The Construction Industries.

A number of textbooks also contain, in introductory chapters, brief historical outlines which are of interest and value.

TRANSPORTATION

The literature of railroads is so vast that only a few of the more general works can be noted. A number of these, dealing with both United States and Canadian works, have already been noted in Chap. 6 under "Railroads" and "Canadian Engineering." In addition see:

Historic Railroads, by R. S. Holland, Philadelphia, Macrae-Smith. Includes notes on the Trans-Siberian, Florida Keys, Andean, and other notable projects.

For recent improvement in railroad transportation, see:

Railroads of Today, by S. K. Farrington, Jr., New York, Coward-McCann, 1949. One of several books by this author dealing with modern railroad operation.

Transportation: Principles and Problems, by T. C. Bingham, New York, McGraw-Hill Book Company, Inc., 1947. Deals primarily with railroad economic problems, especially regulation and rate making, also covers the development of transportation in the United States.

See also current papers in technical journals such as "Railroad Improvements of Two Decades," by C. A. More, *Eng. News-Record,* May 30, 1929, p. 864. A special issue of the *Railway Age* (May 16, 1931) was devoted to a review of locomotive development, and there have been numerous other papers. The Association of American Railroads, Washington, D.C., has been an active and constructive force in encouraging equipment standards and similar joint actions leading to greater interchangeability of equipment, etc., and publishes yearly a statistical review of railroad operations.

Highways

The literature on modern highway building is voluminous, and there are a number of excellent texts, but current problems are discussed in many scattered papers in various technical journals. For example,

"History and Development of Road Building in the United States," by Thomas H. MacDonald, *Trans. Am. Soc. Civil Engrs.,* Vol. 92 (1928), p. 1181.

Canals

Rivers and Canals, by L. F. Vernon-Harcourt, New York, Oxford University Press, 1896, 2 vols.

The Suez Canal, by C. W. Hallberg, New York, Columbia University Press, 1931.

"Advances in Waterways Engineering During a Half Century," by W. M. Black, *Trans. Am. Soc. Civil Engrs.,* 1929, p. 191.

Four Centuries of the Panama Canal, by W F. Johnson, New York, Henry Holt & Company, 1906. Covers the earlier history of this undertaking.

The Panama Canal, 2 vols., The International Engineering Congress (held in San Francisco in 1915.) Describes the actual building of the canal.

William Crawford Gorgas, His Life and Work, by his wife and B. J. Hendrick. A stirring story which, however, does not give due credit to the other workers who actually built the canal.

An Engineer's Recollection, by John F. Stevens, reprinted from the *Eng. News-Record,* 1935. Gives, very briefly, an account of "Early Days at Panama" and "Sea Level vs. Lock Canal."

Theodore Roosevelt's Letters to His Children, New York, Charles Scribners' Sons, 1923. Gives some interesting human sidelights on the Panama Canal.

Harbors and Docks

Harbours and Docks, Their Physical Features, History, Construction, Equipment and Maintenance, by L. F. Vernon-Harcourt, New York, Oxford University Press, 1885.

Harbour Engineering, by Bryson Cunningham, London, Chas. Griffin & Co., 1908. The same author contributed a series of descriptions of European harbors to *The Engineer* (London).

See also "Advance in Waterways Engineering" by General Black previously noted (Canals).

A History of the Jetties at the Mouth of the Mississippi River, by E. L. Corthell, New York, John Wiley & Sons, Inc., 1880.

The Office of the Chief of Engineers of the Army, by W. S. Holt, a Service Monograph of the Institute for Government Research published by The Johns Hopkins Press, Baltimore, 1923. Outlines the early history, activities, and responsibilities of the Corps.

Aviation

A History of Aeronautics, by E. C. Vivian, London, W. Collins Sons, 1921. Includes a bibliography.

A History of Aircraft, by F. A. Magoun and E. Hodgins, New York, McGraw-Hill Book Company, Inc., 1931.

The Wright Brothers: Fathers of Flight, by J. R. McMahon, Boston, Little Brown & Company, 1930.

Our Wings Grow Faster, by G. C. Loening, New York, Doubleday & Company, Inc., 1935. A personal story by a pioneer designer.

CHAPTER 9. MODERN ENGINEERING II: MATERIALS

General

*History of American Mining, by T. A. Rickard, New York, McGraw-Hill Book Company, Inc., 1932. Does not include all areas but is a most interesting and authoritative work.

Interviews with Mining Engineers, by T. A. Rickard, San Francisco, Mining and Scientific Press, 1922. Stories of the men of metals.

*Our Mineral Civilization, by Thos. T. Read, Baltimore, The Williams & Wilkins Company, 1932. A brief outline of the role of metals and minerals in modern life.

Man and Metals (a History of Mining in Relation to the Development of Civilization), by T. A. Rickard, New York, McGraw-Hill Book Company, Inc., 1932.

*Minerals Yearbook, published annually by the Bureau of Mines, U.S. Dept. of the Interior, Washington, D.C., Government Printing Office. An invaluable source of information on and summary of trends in all branches of the mineral industry.

Seventy-five Years of Progress in the Mineral Industry, 1871–1946 (including proceedings of the 75th Anniversary Celebration and World Conference on Mineral Resources, March, 1947), edited by A. B. Parsons, New York, The American Institute of Mining and Metallurgical Engineers, 1949. Includes historical outlines of Mining Geology, Metal Mining, Ore Dressing, Smelting and Leaching, Iron and Steel and Nonferrous Metallurgy, Coal, Petroleum, Nonmetallic Production, and Statistics.

Metal Magic (the Story of the American Smelting and Refining Company), New York, Farrar, Straus & Co., Inc., 1949.

Swank's *History of Iron in All Ages* covers early operations in the United States. Later data are widely scattered in the multitude of reports of the Bureau of Mines but are summarized annually in the *Minerals Yearbook.*

The Story of American Coals, by W. J. Nicolls, Philadelphia, J. B. Lippincott Company, 1904.

Petroleum

There is, of course, a tremendous bibliography on petroleum. We note here only a few books of special interest from the historical viewpoint.

The Petroleum Industry, by Josephine Perry, New York, Longmans, Green & Co., Inc., 1946. A brief semipopular story in the series "America at Work."

The Earlier and Later History of Petroleum, by J. T. Henry, Philadelphia, J. B. Rodgers Co., 1873. An early history of the oil industry.

*Done in Oil, by David D. Leven, New York, The Ranger Press, 1941. This is a large volume of over 1,000 pages, well illustrated, describing technical details, and giving statistical and economic data. Chapter I outlines briefly the history of the industry.

About Petroleum, by J. G. Crowther, New York, Oxford University Press, 1938. An introduction to the great treatise on *The Science of Petroleum,* Oxford University Press, 1938, 4 vols.

Petroleum Comes of Age, by A. A. Lawrence, Tulsa, Oklahoma, Scott-Rice Co., 1938.

See also Tarbell's *History of Standard Oil* noted in text.

Iron and Steel

See earlier references (Chap. 6), especially Swank's *History of Iron in All Ages;* also Scrivenor in Chap. 1.

The Romance of Steel, the Story of a Thousand Millionaires, by H. N. Casson, New York, A. S. Barnes and Company, 1907.

Handbook of Mining in the Lake Superior Region. Prepared for a meeting of the American Institute of Mining and Metallurgical Engineers, August, 1920. A most interesting historical outline and description of the mining operations in this famous area.

Copper

The Copper Mines of the World, by W. H. Weed, New York and London, The Hill Publishing Co., 1907.

The Copper Mines of Lake Superior, by T. A. Rickard, New York and London, The Engineering and Mining Journal, 1905. See also the *Hand-*

book of *Mining in the Lake Superior Region,* noted under "Iron and Steel." Rickard's *History of American Mining* has brief descriptions of Lake Superior, Butte, Arizona, and other operations.

The Story of Copper, by Watson Davis, New York, Century Company, 1924. A general outline.

Modern Copper Smelting, by D. M. Levy, London, Charles Griffin & Co., Ltd., 1912.

Aluminum

Aluminum, by J. W. Richards, Philadelphia, H. C. Baird & Co., 1896. Covers the early history of this metal.

Lead and Zinc

Lead, The Precious Metal, by O. C. Harn, New York, Century Company, 1924. A semipopular story, primarily concerned with the many uses of lead.

Lead and Zinc Mining and Milling in the United States, by Jackson, Knaebel, and Wright, *Bull.* 381, U.S. Bureau of Mines, Government Printing Office, Washington, D.C., 1935.

Tin

Tin: Its Mining, Production, Technology and Applications, by C. L. Mantell, New York, Reinhold Publishing Corporation, 2d ed., 1949.

Sulfur

The Stone That Burns, by Wm. Haynes, New York, D. Van Nostrand Company, Inc., 1942. The story of the American sulfur industry.

Gold

The Gold Mines of the World, by J. H. Curle, London, George Routledge & Sons, 1905. This book offers primarily a check list and earlier evaluation of properties. It has passed through several editions and includes a number of most interesting pictures.

The Gold Rushes, by W. P. Morrell, New York, The Macmillan Company, 1941. An outline of gold discoveries throughout the world with many references.

The Saga of the Comstock Lode, by G. D. Lyman, New York, Charles Scribner's Sons, 1934.

The Diamond Mines of South Africa, by Gardner F. Williams, New York, 1902 and 1906.

The Gold Mines of Southern Africa, by Owen Letcher, Johannesburg and London, 1936.

Canadian Mining

Free Gold, The Story of Canadian Mining, by Arnold Hoffman, New York, Rinehart & Company, Inc., 1947. A colorful and romantic story by a participant.

Chemical Industries

Creative Chemistry, by E. E. Slosson, New York, Century Company, rev. ed., 1930. See especially the chapters on the coal-tar products.

This Chemical Age, by Wm. Haynes, New York, Alfred A. Knopf, Inc., 1942. The subtitle: The Miracle of Man-made Materials.

Men, Money and Molecules, by Wm. Haynes, New York, Doubleday & Company, Inc., 1936. The story of the chemical business.

Chemical Pioneers, by Wm. Haynes, New York, D. Van Nostrand Company, Inc., 1939. The founders of the American chemical industry.

British Chemical Industry: Its Rise and Development, by Sir G. T. Morgan and others, New York, Longman's Green & Co., Inc., 1938.

Twenty-five Years of Chemical Engineering Progress. A series of papers, edited by S. D. Kirkpatrick and published as the 25th anniversary volume, American Institute of Chemical Engineers, New York, D. Van Nostrand Company, Inc., 1933.

Special Industries

Raw Materials from the Sea, by E. F. Armstrong, Brooklyn, Chemical Publishing Company, Inc., 1946. A story of the remarkable magnesium development of World War II.

DuPont, by W. S. Dutton, New York, Charles Scribner's Sons, 1942. The 140-year history of this famous company, founded in 1802.

The World's Struggle with Rubber, by J. C. Lawrence, New York, Harper & Brothers, 1931. Describes the pre-World War II difficulties in natural rubber production and marketing.

CHAPTER 10. MODERN ENGINEERING III: POWER

General

"Power the Source of Modern Civilization," by George A. Orrock, *Eng. News-Rec.,* February 7, 1929, p. 217. An outstanding paper by a veteran leader (affectionately and widely known as Uncle George) of the power industry.

The 50th Anniversary Issue of *Mech. Eng.* (ASME), published in April, 1930, contains a number of reviews of developments in power and its applications, including an interesting paper on "Central Stations" by Mr. Orrock.

"Fifty Years of Progress in Steam Turbines," *Nat. Engr.,* Vol. 51 (1947), pp. 572 and 872. There are numerous papers dealing with specific plants, such as "The State Line Plant," *Elec. World,* Vol. 2 (1929), p. 871; "The Deepwater Plant," *Power Plant Eng.,* November 15, 1929. Similarly there are papers covering specific developments, such as that reviewing use of higher steam pressures, *Power,* May 28, 1929, p. 854.

Water Wheels

"The American Mixed-flow Turbine and Its Setting," by A. T. Safford and E. P. Hamilton, *Trans. Am. Soc. Civil Engrs.,* Vol. 85 (1922), p. 1237. A very complete and well-illustrated study.

"The development of the Hydraulic Reaction Turbine in America," by H. B. Taylor, *Eng. Mag.,* March, 1910, p. 841.

"Ten Years of Evolution of Hydro-electric Units," *J. Western Soc. Engrs.,* October, 1915.

Hydro-electric Plants

A bibliography on earlier plants will be found in *Hydro-electric Power Stations,* by Lof and Rushmore, New York, John Wiley & Sons, Inc., 1917, p. 757. See also references for Chap. 6, "Later Works," "Electrical Engineering." Among many special papers describing modern plants and their equipment, see "The Keokuk Plant on the Mississippi," *Eng. News-Record,* September 28, 1911, p. 355, and, for its electrical equipment, *Gen. Elec. Rev.,* 1914, pp. 85 and 375.

"Caribou (High head) Development," *Elec. World,* August 26, 1909, p. 471, and *Eng. News-Record,* March 23, 1922, p. 472. "Conowingo," *Trans. Am. Soc. Civil Engrs.,* Vol. 93 (1929), p. 970. "Rocky River" (a unique pumped storage plant), *Trans. Am. Inst. Elec. Engrs.,* October, 1928, p. 1100.

For a summary of world's water power resources, see *Water Power Engineering,* by H. K. Barrows, New York, McGraw-Hill Book Company, Inc., 3d ed., 1943.

Transmission

For early d-c installations, see *Jour. Inst. Elec. Engrs. (London),* Vol. 51 (1913), p. 640. For later reviews, *Elec. World,* April 25, 1914, and September 21, 1929.

Lighting

A History of the Incandescent Lamp, by J. W. Howell and Henry Schroeder, Schenectady, New York, The Maqua Co., 1927.

Internal-combustion Engines

See 50th Anniversary Issue of *Mech. Engr.,* April, 1930, previously noted.

Evolution of the Internal-combustion Engine, by Edward Butler, London, Charles Griffin & Co., Ltd., 1912. An early review.

Combustion on Wheels, by David Cohen, Boston, Houghton Mifflin Company, 1944. A critical popular study of the Motor Age.

English and American Steam Carriages and Traction Engines, by Wm. Fletcher, New York, Longmans, Green & Co., Inc., 1904. Contains 250 interesting illustrations.

History of the Oil Engine, by A. F. Evans, London, Sampson, Low, Marston Co., 1932. A British study.

Diesel Engine Development and Application to Mobile Equipment in America, by H. L. Hamilton (a Newcomen Society address), Princeton, Princeton University Press, 1944.

"Those Who Cradled Diesel Industry," *Diesel Power,* Vol. 25 (1947), pp. 95 and 133.

Refrigeration, Ventilation, Heating

See paper by J. E. Starr in the 50th Anniversary Issue of *Mech. Eng.,* April, 1930, above noted.

CHAPTER 11. MODERN ENGINEERING IV: MANUFACTURES

*English and American Tool Builders, by J. W. Roe, New York, McGraw-Hill Book Company, Inc., 1916 and 1926. The standard and authoritative work on the rise of the machine tool.

History of Manufactures in the United States, by V. S. Clark, last ed., New York, Peter Smith, 1949, 2 vols. Emphasizes especially the relationship of economic conditions in the growth of American manufactures. See also *Manufacturing* in the series "Industries of America," edited by Malcolm Keir, New York, The Ronald Press Company, 1928.

My Life and Work, by Henry Ford (in collaboration with Samuel Crowther), New York, Doubleday, Page & Co., 1923.

Backgrounds of Power, by Roger Burlingame, New York, Charles Scribner's Sons, 1949. A recent popular story of the origins and rise of mass production with numerous extraneous notes and comments which appear to have little relationship to the subject.

*Principles of Scientific Management, by F. W. Taylor, New York, Harper & Brothers, 1911. See also the earlier papers of the same author published by the American Society of Mechanical Engineers, "A Piece Rate System, Being a Partial Solution of the Labor Problem," 1895, and "Shop Management," 1903.

The bibliography of labor-management relations is tremendous, but the general reader will find the two following small books particularly interesting:

*Human Leadership in Industry, by Sam A. Lewisohn, New York, Harper & Brothers, 1945. A brief survey by an author who has devoted many years of study to this problem.

The Social Problem of an Industrial Civilization, by Elton Mayo,

Cambridge, Harvard University Press, 1945. Outlines some of the essentials of an adaptive, industrialized society and emphasizes the fact that the worker must have a sense of well-being in his job and a desire to collaborate in the essential activities of his group. This thesis was developed earlier in *The Human Problems of an Industrial Civilization,* 1933, by the same author.

There are many books on particular industries, and several works descriptive of World War II production have also been published.

The Automobile Industry (Its Economic and Commercial Development), by R. C. Epstein, New York, McGraw-Hill Book Company, Inc., 1928. Illustrating finance and big business.

The Romance of the Reaper, by H. N. Casson, New York, Doubleday, Page & Co., 1908, and *Cyrus Hall McCormick, His Life and Work,* by the same author, Chicago, A. C. McClurg & Company, 1909.

Power and the Plow, by L. W. Ellis, New York, Doubleday, Doran & Co., 1911.

The Early History of the Typewriter, by C. E. Weller, La Porte, Indiana, 1921. The story of a typewriter pioneer, Christopher L. Sholes (1819–1890).

The Story of the Typewriter 1873–1923, Herkimer County Historical Society, Herkimer, New York, A. H. Kellogg Co., 1923.

Merchant of Alphabets, by Reginald Orcutt, New York, Doubleday & Company, Inc., 1945. The story of Ottmar Mergenthaler (1854–1899) and the linotype.

Power in the Textile Industry, by W. M. Vermilye (a Newcomen Society address), Princeton, Princeton University Press, 1938.

The Textile Industries of the United States, by W. R. Bagnall, Cambridge, Mass., The Riverside Press, 1893.

American Carpet Manufacture (A History and an Analysis), by A. H. Cole and H. F. Williamson, Cambridge, Harvard University Press, 1941.

A Century of Carpet and Rug Making in America, New York, The Bigelow-Hartford Carpet Co., 1925.

History of the Shoe and Leather Industries in the United States, by C. H. McDermott and others, Boston, J. W. Denehy & Co., 1920.

CHAPTER 12. MODERN ENGINEERING V: COMMUNICATIONS AND ELECTRONICS

For the telephone, see references for Chap. 6.

A History of Wireless Telegraphy, by J. J. Fahie, New York, Dodd Mead & Company, Inc., 1899. As indicated by the date of publication, this covers only the earlier work in this field.

Invention and Innovation in the Radio Industry, by W. R. MacLaurin, New York, The Macmillan Company, 1949. Not only a fascinating story of radio and television but an interesting study of the sequence of stages from research and invention to the later struggles of application, promotion, and organization through which basic discoveries are translated into practical, useful accomplishment and service. Contains a brief bibliography.

Among the biographies, see

Marconi, Pioneer of Radio, by Douglas Coe, New York, Julian Messner, Inc., Publishers, 1943.

Fifty Years of Electricity: the Memories of an Electrical Engineer, by Sir J. A. Fleming, London, The Wireless Press, 1921. By the famous inventor of the Fleming valve.

A Conqueror of Space, by Georgette Carneal, New York, Liveright Publishing Corp., 1930. The authorized life of Dr. Lee De Forest.

CHAPTER 13. MODERN ENGINEERING VI: CONSTRUCTION

General

A number of the references noted in Chap. 6 (Later Works: Bridges, Foundations, Hydraulics, etc.) will be found of interest in connection with the very brief summary of this chapter. There are a few survey papers in which the student will find valuable general impressions and viewpoints of leading engineers as well as brief notes of outstanding advances and important works. For example,

"A Half Century of Engineering and Construction Progress," a special 50th Anniversary issue of the *Eng. News-Record,* Vol. 92, No. 16, April 17, 1924, and a similar issue "Building a Great America," commemorating the 75th anniversary of this publication, September 1, 1949.

For more detailed information, however, and for many projects not noted in these more general surveys, one must turn to the few books dealing with special works and, in particular, to technical professional journals such as the *Trans. Am. Soc. Civil Engrs., Eng. News-Record, Western Construction News.* The *Index to Transaction* of the American Society of Civil Engineers and the *Engineering Index* are, of course, most useful in tracking down such data. A few references are given here as samples to illustrate the character of such information.

"Memoirs" of members are published annually in the *Trans. Am. Soc. Civil Engrs.,* which give interesting outlines of the careers of members of the profession. See *Index to Transactions.*

Construction Materials

There are several books which deal with engineering materials (such as *Engineering Materials,* by A. H. White, New York, McGraw-Hill Book Company, Inc., 1948), and the specifications of the American Society for Testing Materials (ASTM) are regarded as standard and widely quoted.

The literature of this subject is, of course, vast and includes materials from stone and concrete, timber, iron and steel, to paints and protective coatings. Yet there is little available on the history of materials of construction covering the successive stages in the improvement of their qualities and the forces and factors which have influenced their development, choice, and use. Some textbooks contain brief historical statements and there have been a few papers summarizing current practice but, in general, this story must be uncovered through an extended study of engineering works themselves, of the actual use of materials in construction.

Among the papers on concrete, for example, are such reflections on earlier experience and practice as:

"Concrete and Concrete-Steel in the United States," by Edwin Thacher, (International Engineers Congress, 1904) *Trans. Am. Soc. Civil Engrs.*, Vol. 54 (1905), Part E, p. 425.

"Historical Sketch of the Use of Concrete and Reinforced Concrete," *Trans. Am. Soc. Civil Engrs.*, Vol. 77 (1914), p. 393. The same publication, Vol. 87 (1924), carried a bibliography on cement and concrete.

One of the most interesting evolutions of concrete and concreting methods has been that connected with dam construction. This has not been brought together but may be followed by studying the successive changes in practice in the Kensico, Arrowrock, Paicoma, Diabolo, Chute à Caron, and Calderwood Dams which reveal the evolution from cyclopean to cobble to spouted and, finally, to a more dense, "dryer" mix required if porosity is to be avoided, deposited by bottom-dump buckets.

The use of alloy steels has resulted in a number of papers of historical interest such as

"Nickel Steel for Bridges," *Trans. Am. Soc. Civil Engrs.*, Vol. 63 (1909), p. 316. By a pioneer in this field, Gustav Lindenthal, and "A Study of Steel for Engineering Structures," *Trans. Am. Soc. Civil Engrs.*, Vol. 86 (1923), p. 1292.

The various industrial associations, such as the Portland Cement Association and the American Institute of Steel Construction, have published many pamphlets, usually of current but often also of historical interest Thus, *Cement and Concrete, A General Reference Book,* published in 1929 by the Portland Cement Association, reflects the practice at that time.

Bridges

There are several more general books on bridges:

History of Bridge Engineering, by H. G. Tyrell, Chicago, published by the Author, 1911. Provides a check list of earlier bridges, and briefly notes many famous works.

Bridges, by C. S. Whitney, New York, W. E. Rudge, 1929. Contains many beautiful illustrations.

Grandes Voutes, by Paul Sejourne, Bourges, V. Tardy, 1913. A monumental French work in six volumes, fully illustrated. The author was the engineer of the Luxemburg stone arch of 1898–1903, almost the last and certainly the most daring of all stone arches and the prototype of modern concrete arch bridges.

"The Continuous Truss Bridge . . . at Sciotoville," by Gustav Lindenthal, *Trans. Am. Soc. Civil Engrs.,* Vol. 85 (1922), p. 910.

"The Hell Gate Arch Bridge," by O. H. Ammann, *Trans. Am. Soc. Civil Engrs.,* Vol. 82 (1918), p. 852.

Suspension Bridges, by D. B. Steinman, New York, John Wiley & Sons, Inc., 1929.

"Wind Failures of Suspension Bridges," by J. K. Finch, *Eng. News-Record,* March 27, 1941.

Movable Bridges, by O. E. Hovey, New York, John Wiley & Sons, Inc., 1926.

Construction Methods

Here again the student must turn to the published descriptions of particular works if he wishes to follow in detail the evolution of construction methods. Some of the milestones in this field are noted in the text.

Shortly after 1900, H. P. Gillette published several books dealing with construction costs which refer to earlier works and methods: *Rock Excavation, Methods and Cost,* New York, M. C. Clark, 1904; *Earthwork and Its Cost,* New York, Engineering News Publishing Co., 1907; *Handbook of Cost Data,* New York, M. C. Clark, 1906.

An early textbook, *Foundations of Bridges and Buildings,* by Jacoby and Davis, New York, McGraw-Hill Book Company, Inc., 3d ed., 1941. Gives an extended bibliography.

In 1930 the American Society of Chemical Engineers issued a "Bibliography of Construction Methods and Plant," Manual No. 4.

Skyscrapers, by W. A. Starrett, New York, Charles Scribner's Sons, 1928. By a pioneer skyscraper builder.

'A Half Century of the Skyscraper," *Civil Engrs.* (Am. Soc. Civil Engrs.) Vol. 4 (1934) p. 634.

For Bank of the Manhattan Co., see *Eng. News-Record,* April 24, 1930, p. 691.

The Kensico Dam, plant, and methods attracted much attention. See *Eng. News,* May 20, 1915; *Eng. Record,* February 13, 1915; and *J. New Engl. Water Works Assoc.,* December, 1915.

Dams

Edward Wegmann's monumental volume, *The Design and Construction of Dams,* New York, John Wiley & Sons, Inc., first published in 1899 and revised in some seven subsequent editions, is a mine of information of historical interest.

The Western Construction News (San Francisco) published several tabulations of dam construction (see March 10, March 25, April 10, 1927, and February 10, 1929) which reveal interesting trends. The U.S. Bureau of Reclamation booklet *Dams and Control Works* of 1929 also gives brief data on the earlier works of this organization.

"Recent Practice in Hydraulic-fill Dam Construction," by J. D. Schuyler, *Trans. Am. Soc. Civil Engrs.*, Vol. 58 (1907), p. 196 (see also Vol. 50, p. 105) was a pioneer paper on a type of dam widely used in the West and later developed in Eastern practice. See *Trans. Am. Soc. Civil Engrs.*, Vol. 83 (1920).

"The Record of 100 Dam Failures," by Lars Jorgensen, *J. Elec.*, March 15, 1920, offers some interesting opportunities for study.

The part played by British Colonial engineers in this story should also be noted. See

The Irrigation Service (of Egypt), by P. M. Tottenham, Government Publication Office, Cairo, 1928.

Tunnels

See "Tunnel" references for Chap. 5.

"Description of Alpine Railroad Tunnels," *Trans. Am. Soc. Civil Engrs.*, Vol. 75 (1912), p. 751.

"Construction Methods for Rogers Pass Tunnel," *Trans. Am. Soc. Civil Engrs.*, Vol. 81 (1917), p. 448.

"Construction Methods on the Moffat Tunnel," *Trans. Am. Soc. Civil Engrs.*, Vol. 92 (1928), p. 63.

"Construction Methods on the Cascade Tunnel," *Trans. Am. Soc. Civil Engrs.*, Vol. 96 (1932), p. 915.

"The Shandaken Tunnel," *Trans Am. Soc. Civil Engrs.*, Vol. 92 (1928), p. 233.

"Mersey Tunnel," *Pro. Inst. Civil Engrs.* (*London*), Vol. 86 (1886), p. 40.

"A Brief Description of the Tunnels under the North and East Rivers, New York," *Trans. Am. Soc. Civil Engrs.*, Vol. 76 (1913), p. 1690.

The Subways and Tunnels of New York, by Gilbert, Wightman, and Saunders, New York, John Wiley & Sons, Inc., 1912.

Le Chemin de Fer Metropolitan de Paris, by A. Dumas, Paris, 1901. The official history of the first Paris subway.

"The Hudson River Tunnel," *Trans. Am. Soc. Civil Engrs.*, Vol. 9 (1880), p. 259; Vol. 11 (1882), p. 314. Early history.

"The New York Tunnel Extension of the Pennsylvania Railroad," *Trans. Am. Soc. Civil Engrs.*, Vol. 68 (1910) and Vol. 69 (1910) cover all phases of this great work.

"The Queens Midtown Tunnel," *Trans. Am. Soc. Civil Engrs.*, Vol. 109 (1944), p. 679.

Municipal Works

Such texts as *Public Water Supplies* by Turneaure and Russell, New York, John Wiley & Sons, Inc., 1940, not only describe but give many references to important works.

"Historical Review of the Development of Sanitary Engineering in the U.S. during the Past 150 Years," *Trans. Am. Soc. Civil Engrs.*, Vol. 92 (1928), p. 1208.

The Catskill Water Supply of New York City, by Lazarus White, New York, John Wiley & Sons, Inc., 1913.

Foundations

For the caisson-cofferdam process, see letter of J. V. Davis (engineer for the Hudson Terminal) *Eng. News-Record*, April 29, 1926, p. 703. The Federal Reserve Bank (1921–1922) was a later major work of this type. See *Eng. News-Record*, April 15, 1926, p. 598; also *Eng. News-Record* August 5, 1926, p. 206, for Barclay-Vesey (New York Telephone Co.) Building.

The great center anchorage of the Bay Bridge is described in numerous papers, including *Eng. News-Record*, Vol. 112 (1934), p. 431.

For the use of the sand-island plan at Suisun Bay, see *Western Construction News*, February 25, 1930, or *Railway Age*, Vol. 88 (1930), p. 1458.

"Open Foundation Plant and Methods on Manhattan Island," *Eng. News-Record*, Vol. 97 (1926), p. 816. Summarizes the trend toward open work and methods.

The bibliography in Jacoby and Davis has been noted (see "Construction Methods"). *Cofferdams*, by White and Prentis, New York, Columbia University Press, 1940, contains a bibliography, p. 259, while *Underpinning*, by the same authors and publisher, 1931, reviews the highly specialized techniques used in this work.

CHAPTER 14. ENGINEERING AND WESTERN CIVILIZATION

Some of the studies which should be consulted in connection with this and succeeding chapters are noted in the following list. When we turn to what social thinkers like to refer to as the "impact of engineering" in modern life, opinion, and viewpoint—or even just plain wishful thinking—color, if indeed they do not obscure, the major problems involved. The writer has, therefore, included in this and later lists some comments on the general character of the books noted.

The British economic situation is briefly and most effectively summarized in a chapter "The End of the 19th Century," in *The West at*

Bay by Barbara Ward, New York, W. W. Norton & Company, 1948, by the talented foreign editor of the London *Economist*. A booklet, *Technological Stagnation in Great Britain,* published by the Machinery and Allied Products Institute, Chicago, January, 1948, summarizes the findings of several recent special British reports including those on textiles and coal and also vital problems of management, labor, and taxation.

Technological Trends and National Policy (including the Social Implications of New Inventions), Report of the Subcommittee on Technology to the National Resources Committee, Washington, D.C., Government Printing Office, 1937. This is the most important general study, and Part III (already noted in Chap. 8) provides a most interesting general survey of engineering trends and developments. Part I develops the forecasting thesis and suggests government planning as a palliative for unemployment and overproduction. Part II is disappointingly brief. The contents are as follows:

Part   I. *Social Aspects of Technology*
Sec.   I. National Policy and Technology
Sec.   II. The Prediction of Inventions
Sec. III. Social Effect of Inventions
Sec.   IV. Resistance to the Adoption of Technological Innovations
Sec.   V. Unemployment and Increasing Productivity
Part   II. *Science and Technology*
Sec.   I. The Relation of Science to Technological Trends
Sec.   II. The Interdependence of Science and Technology
Part III. *Technology in Various Fields* (for contents, see Chap. 8)

Technology and Livelihood, by Mary L. Fleddérus and Mary Van Kleech, New York, The Russell Sage Foundation, 1944. Subtitled, "An Inquiry into the Changing Technological Basis for Production as Affecting Employment and Living Standards." The factual portion of this study is based almost entirely on the National Resources Report noted above. The authors comment: Technology must be analyzed in its entirety as setting new tasks of social organization for every community, for every nation, and for the whole world. . . . Understanding of the process of adjustment requires not only analysis of social consequences . . . but recognition of technology itself as a prime mover in social change." The authors are, however, not engineers and have fallen into error of assuming that technological progress requires the establishment of "optimum standards of living" and that "the organized utilization of productive processes for human life must become the major task in every community, from village to nation and world." In short, they seem to fail to realize that such "planned adjustment of productive capacity" would automatically eliminate the spirit of change and adventure from which stem the very technological advances such planning is supposed to adjust. Nevertheless, this book is well worth careful study.

Techonology and Society, by S. McKee Rosen and Laura Rosen, New York, The Macmillan Company, 1941. Subtitled, "The Influence of Machines in the United States." This is a more popular book and is based to a major degree on the results of the National Resources Report. It emphasizes the machine in our American economy and its overpowering social influence. The writers conclude that technological progress must be directed and "that such direction will necessitate wide extension of the function of government as a means of planning and controlling many of the results of technological change," a statement with which this writer would disagree.

Capitalism the Creator, by Carl Snyder, New York, The Macmillan Company, 1940. While the modern planning enthusiast would not even damn this book with faint praise but simply ignore it, there is much information and no little practical common sense in its 475 pages. The author leaves no doubt as to his position, but it is unfortunately not one that we can wholeheartedly accept. He argues eloquently that the capitalist system has, as we believe, been a vital factor in creating our wonderful country and our remarkable living standards and that it should be left severely alone to work out its beneficent effects. The endless tinkering and economic experimentation of the '30's are properly decried, but we find few attempts to analyze inescapable current problems or to suggest suitable remedies.

Prosperity, We Can Have It If We Want It, by Murray Shields and Donald B. Woodward, New York, McGraw-Hill Book Company, Inc., 1945. The authors state: "We have a suspicion that the economists of an earlier day, who dedicated themselves to the development of methods of achieving prosperity, were on the right track." This is a popular and interesting anti-New Deal study, which concludes that ". . . the government has forgotten how to think in terms of production as the chief employer of the people, since bureaus and agencies and departments of the government, once staffed, fight determinedly for their survival, since the nation's taste for handouts and subsidies and relief has been whetted by the easy policies of the past decade. . . . That people want to live permanently on relief and under the domination of government is a preposterous belief which can be had only by those who misread the nation's history and misunderstand the temper of our people."

Science and the Modern World (The Lowell Lectures, 1925), by Alfred North Whitehead, New York, The Macmillan Company, 1948. This is a "must" for all engineering students. The character of this remarkable study is best reflected in some quotations from the book itself:

"The thesis which these lectures will illustrate is that this quiet growth of science has practically recoloured our mentality so that modes of thought which in former times were exceptional are now broadly spread through the educated world" (p. 3).

"The greatest invention of the nineteenth century was the invention of the method of invention. A new method entered into life. In order to understand our epoch, we can neglect all the details of change, such as railways, telegraphs, radios, spinning machines, synthetic dyes. We must concentrate on the method in itself; that is the real novelty, which has broken up the foundation of the old civilization" (p. 141).

Chapter XIII deals with the "Requisites for Social Progress" and emphasizes both educational needs and the fact that adventure is an essential in modern life.

"It is very arguable that the science of political economy, as studied in its first period after the death of Adam Smith (1790), did more harm than good. It destroyed many economic fallacies, and taught how to think about the economic revolution then in progress. But it riveted on men a certain set of abstractions which were disastrous in their influence on modern mentality. It de-humanised industry" (p. 288).

"The prosperous middle classes, who ruled the nineteenth century, placed an excessive value upon placidity of existence. They refused to face the necessities for social reform imposed by the new industrial system, and they are now refusing to face the necessities for intellectual reform imposed by the new knowledge" (p. 299).

*Democracy and Progress, by David McCord Wright, New York, The Macmillan Company, 1948. This work came to the author's attention after the author's book was well in hand. Its basic thesis is the same as that here set forth. Professor Wright analyzes the economic and social problems of the present era of unparalleled physical power, coupled with social and political confusion, from the standpoint of an expert economist who possesses a keen understanding of the essentials for continued engineering progress. "It is extraordinary," he remarks, "how unfailingly the modern emphasis on law, on 'planning,' and on regulation turns our attention away from the solutions which, though difficult, are the only democratic ones; and directs it instead toward pseudo solutions which do not really solve the problem but only end it. The challenge which faces our society today is not to give security and stability. That could be easily done. The challenge is to give relative security and stability while retaining creativeness and freedom." Professor Wright's book should be read by all students of engineering.

CHAPTER 15. ENGINEERING AND ECONOMIC CHANGE I: AGRICULTURE

This story is summarized in *Technological Trends,* Part III, Sec. I (see Chap. 14). *Technology and Society* also covers the mechanization of agriculture with numerous illustrations of modern machines. See also references to Chaps. 10 and 11, such as *The Romance of the Reaper* and *Power and the Plow.*

A more recent book *The Road to Survival* by William Voght, New

York, William Sloane Associates, 1948, is a most thought-provoking study of the exhaustion of our agricultural lands not only through continued cropping without returns to the soil but also through our carelessness in aiding rather than seeking to minimize flood damage and soil erosion.

Another, but unfortunately extravagant, alarmist and not too reliable study along similar lines is *Our Plundered Planet,* by Fairfield Osborn, New York, Little, Brown & Company, 1948.

CHAPTER 16. ENGINEERING AND ECONOMIC CHANGE II: MANUFACTURING AND THE TECHNOLOGICAL SERVICES

The references already given, notably *Technological Trends* and *Technology and Livelihood* offer brief summaries. Lauer, *Engineering in American Industry* contains a number of valuable graphs but is, of course, now quite out of date (1923).

CHAPTER 17. ENGINEERING AND THE WORKER

Human Leadership in Industry, by Sam A. Lewisohn, New York, Harper & Brothers, 1945. This little book should be required reading for all engineering students. It makes clear that, in any economy from capitalistic to communistic, management and direction are essential. It offers many suggestions as to the essentials of effective supervision and management. See also references under Chap. 11.

CHAPTER 18. THE DISTRIBUTION OF TECHNOLOGICAL GAINS

Among the various organizations which publish, from time to time, reports of a fact-finding statistical nature on various economic problems is The National Bureau of Economic Research. While the United States has accumulated much important statistical information, we still lack complete, basic data in many areas. The variables entering such problems are numerous. It is frequently impossible to isolate or allow for them, and the results of the National Bureau studies are, thus, generally of value as indicating trends or as qualitative rather than accurately quantitative measurements. They are notable for their unbiased, objective viewpoint and are limited in accuracy only by available sources of information. We have already noted:

The Anatomy of Prices, by Frederick C. Mills, *Bull.* 80, September, 1940.

The Structure of Post War Prices, by Frederick C. Mills, Occasional Paper 27, July, 1948.

A brief paper, *The National Income and Its Distribution,* by Rev. Edward A. Keller, Director of the Bureau of Economic Research, University of Notre Dame, 1947, both tabulates and summarizes a large amount of statistical information on this subject and also gives many references to source material.

The most recent work in this field is *America's Needs and Resources,* by J. F. Dewhurst and Associates, New York, The Twentieth Century Fund, Inc., 1947. A monumental volume of 812 pages This has been summarized in an excellent popular form using picture-graphs under the title:

*U.S.A. Measure of a Nation, by T. R. Carskadon and Rudolf Modley, published for the Fund by the Macmillan Company, New York, 1949.

CHAPTER 19. TECHNOLOGICAL CHANGE AND CAPITAL GOODS

"America's Capacity to Produce, by Edwin G. Nourse and Associates, Washington, D.C., The Brookings Institution, 1934. This is the first of four most interesting and valuable studies, dealing with American production, consumption, capital formation, and income and economic progress, which it was hoped might furnish a basis for answering the basic question: "Could we not, within the limitations of our natural resources, our people, and our traditions, with only evolutionary modifications and readjustments to current conditions, restore and stabilize such a productivity of goods and services as would provide a general standard of living as high as that which we have known at the peaks of prosperity in the past? Could we not expect to improve on our best past performances until every citizen (barring physical or mental defectives) who cared to exert himself could maintain a material standard of living equal at least to that of the so-called "middle class" in the prosperous days before the collapse of 1929?"

One must recall that this study was made 15 years ago in the early years of the Decade of Depression and Doubt. Nevertheless this problem is still with us; it has been but temporarily lost to sight because of the war and the surge of postwar recovery. This study, therefore, still constitutes a most important current contribution to economic thought.

The authors go on to state that: "If such ample consumption is to be attained from our economic system, two general conditions must be met. (1) On the technical side, the equipment of plants, machinery, tools and materials . . . must be maintained and . . . enlarged to provide for expanding population and rising standards of living. (2) On the pecuniary side, there must be such a distribution of purchasing power among all the population groups that productive resources do not lie unused simply for lack of market while large numbers of people are deprived both of employment and of the goods and services which they need and desire." With these statements the writer of the present volume has no quarrel. They are, in fact, the two major theses which he has attempted to develop in this book.

From the standpoint of content also, *America's Capacity to Produce* offers some brief but most valuable and interesting summaries of past production (1900–1930) and the basic industrial characteristics of a group of selected industries, including: Agriculture, Coal and Coke,

Petroleum, Copper, Cement, Food Products, Textiles, Automobiles, Paper, and Iron and Steel and the services of Electric Power, Transportation, Merchandizing, and Money and Credit.

America's Capacity to Consume, by Maurice Levin, H. G. Moulton, and Clark Warburton, Washington, D.C., The Brookings Institution, 1934. The questions which this second study in the series covers are best set forth in the following excerpt:

"The hypothesis has frequently been advanced that the small incomes received by the masses of the population provide in the aggregate so meager a purchasing power for the potential output of our productive establishment as to be a potent source of economic difficulties . . . . In this second volume we turn to the flow of income arising out of our productive operations. It is this income which determines the capacity of the people to purchase the consumption goods which are annually produced, and also to provide the savings which are essential to the formation of new capital."

Part I deals with the national income and its increase over the first three decades of the present century, Part II with how those who receive this income dispose of it, and Part III with the relation of consumption to production.

The general conclusions of this study of the years 1900–1930 were: The masses of the people had very low standards of living and were able to make savings of negligible importance. The productive capacity of the United States was not adequate to turn out sufficient goods and services to satisfy the unfilled consumptive desires of the American people as a whole. Owing to the uneven distribution of the national income, the bulk of savings is made by a small fraction of the population. Finally, the increasing number of people in the higher income brackets had led to a diversion of the national income from consumptive channels into savings. It might be noted that we have gone far since 1930 in bringing about radical changes in these conditions.

The Formation of Capital, by H. G. Moulton, Washington, D.C., The Brookings Institution, 1935. This is an analysis of the process of capital formation and of the factors which govern the rate of growth of plant and equipment. The author notes: "The conclusions reached as to the forces which control the growth of capital will be found fundamentally at variance with traditional views on the subject."

He points out that, under primitive conditions, each individual apportions his labor between the creation of consumption and of capital goods, whereas, in a capitalistic society, the allocation of energy results from a multitude of individual decisions and is dependent upon the functioning of a complex financial and business mechanism. He insists that the demand for capital goods is derived from the demand for consumption goods. Hence, if new capital is to be created, there must be an increasing flow of funds through consumption channels as well as through savings channels.

Income and Economic Progress, by H. G. Moulton, Washington, D.C., The Brookings Institution, 1935. This final volume of this most interesting series reviews the preceding three studies and offers a summary of the general observations and conclusions stemming from them. As the author notes: "All the world loves a panacea." We always tend to over-simplification and to find in one idea the cure for all our economic and social ills.

The general conclusion resulting from these studies is that the major problem we face is that of securing and maintaining a widespread and increasing purchasing power among all our people. Part II, dealing with "Lines of Progress," discusses the role of taxation in bringing about a more uniform distribution of the profits of our economic life. The plan of raising money wages is also interestingly analyzed and discussed as is profit sharing. Finally the author argues most convincingly for "Distributing Income through Price Reductions" as the real key to a dynamic and progressive economic and industrial life. "There is one type of distribution reform which in our judgment outranks all others in its promise of attaining the goal we seek. This is in the gradual but persistent revamping of price policy so as to pass on the benefits of technological progress and rising productivity to all the population in their role of consumers." "The interest of the profitmaker," he notes, "coincides with the welfare of the consumer." This latter observation has also been put in the form: What, in the long run, is best for the American people will be best for American business.

Controlling Factors in Economic Development, by H. G. Moulton, Washington, D.C., The Brookings Institution, 1949. This is more general economic survey and study and is here noted for it brings up to date many of the matters discussed in the preceding series and also discusses some more recent problems not covered in the earlier studies.

The Bogey of Economic Maturity, by George Terborgh, Chicago, Machinery and Allied Products Institute, 1945. This "antistagnationist" analysis also has been published in a small, paper-covered summary form.

Dynamic Equipment Policy, by George Terborgh, New York, McGraw-Hill Book Company, Inc., 1949. Sponsored by the Machinery and Allied Products Institute, this study is especially valuable for the picture it presents of the major problems of keeping an industrial plant up to date. The procedures and analysis of specific replacement problems are summarized and illustrated by a number of examples in a small *MAPI Replacement Manual,* issued by the Institute in 1950.

CHAPTER 20. ENGINEERING AND RESEARCH

Profitable Practice in Industrial Research, edited by Malcolm H. Ross, New York, Harper & Brothers, 1932. This is a collection of several papers by the pioneers of American industrial research in which various phases of research—purpose, organization, methods, finances, etc.—are discussed.

The Genius of Industrial Research, by D. H. Killeffer, New York, Reinhold Publishing Corporation, 1948. This interesting—we were going to say, fascinating—book gives in considerable detail the stories, usually by the researcher himself, of a number of notable research discoveries, especially in the field of the chemical industries. The two basic methods of research—the Edisonian, of direct attack through repeated trials, and the Aristotelian, of development from a theory—are contrasted and analyzed. The values of both are discussed as is the evaluation of industrial research in general.

See also *The Endless Frontier,* by Dr. Vannevar Bush (Chap. 21).

CHAPTER 21. CONCLUSION

In writing this final chapter, we have drawn on many of the books to which we have referred in the bibliographies of Chaps. 15–20.

In addition we recommend: *The Endless Frontier,* a special report made to President Roosevelt by Dr. Vannevar Bush, then Director of the Office of Scientific Research and Development, July, 1945. This most careful and unbiased study and analysis by an author of outstanding experience and authority was condensed in the magazine *Fortune,* September, 1945.

Professor Hayek's brief book condemning government planning, *The Road to Serfdom,* has been noted in the text. Some of the dangers and difficulties of such planning, especially in connection with recent British experience, are strikingly set forth in *Ordeal by Planning,* by John Jewkes, London, Macmillan & Co., Ltd., 1948.

Alternative to Serfdom, by J. M. Clark, New York, Alfred A. Knopf, Inc., 1948, is a series of five lectures given by Professor Clark on the William W. Cook Foundation at the University of Michigan. The keynote of this book is that "the price of freedom is its responsible exercise." "Groups are numerous and varied," observes the author, "and every individual is a member of many. Our job of social salvation lies in reworking the relations of these groups and the individuals within them. . . . The democratic state has not found its place, nor how to do its job in the new world. Instead of being the organ of a unified society, with its functions and powers arising rather naturally from the constitution of the society it represents, it is groping desperately, precisely because it has no organized society back of it in respect to most things—only when the country is attacked overtly, by force of arms and by a foreign power. More dangerous threats to our social constitution, from within, do not unify , but divide us." Among other topics discussed are "Competition and Security" and "Toward a Society of Responsible Individuals in Responsible Groups."

On the world-wide side of this story, see *The Steep Places* by Sir Norman Angell, New York, Harper & Brothers, 1947. The author's keen mind and penetrating prose dissipate ideological fallacies and make clear the tremendous problems of human conduct we must face if we are to achieve by voluntary cooperation, instead of through force and compulsion, the unity which is essential in the modern world. "We hold within our hands the material means of preserving those freedoms we fought two wars to defend. . . . If, yielding to disruptive and divisive impulses, we fail in the necessary cooperations . . . we shall have been turned from the better course and from the means of salvation, by those baser forces of the human spirit which it has been the purpose of this book to render visible."

INDEX

Specific engineering plants, structures, or works are listed under such general headings as aqueducts, bridges, canals, dams, mines, power plants, railways, ships, tunnels, and water supplies.

A

Acid, fuming, 158
  hydrochloric, 155, 156
  nitric, 161
  sulfuric, 157, 158
Aerodynamics, 96, 112
Age, Pyramid, 11
Agricola, 28, 29, 149
Agricultural home economy, 248, 252, 253
  predictions of Malthus regarding, 40
Agricultural machinery, 80, 255, 256
  effect of, 254, 255
Agricultural products, consumption of, on farm, 257
  market for, 257, 258
  per city dweller, 255
  types of, 258, 259
Agricultural workers, number of, 254, 255, 264
  production of, per worker, 255, 257
  purchasing power of, 284–291
  work hours per week of, 261
Agriculture, 252–261
  American, decline in employment in, 254
  increased productivity of, 255, 256
  mechanization in, 255
  present status of, 258–261
  research in, 255
  British, 40, 41
  decline in, 60, 253
  effect of enclosure on, 41
Aid, federal and state, for highways, 109
Airplanes, early experiments with, 112
  effects of, on structural design, 95, 244

Airplanes, engines for, 114
  flight records of, 114
  jet-propelled, 115
  mail service by, 114
  strato-cruiser, 115
  Wright brothers and, 112–114
Airships, 114
Alcock, 114
Alexander the Great, 116
Alloy steels, 138, 139
  use of, in bridges, 231
Alpine, first FM station, 223
Alteneck, 84
Alternating current (a-c), vs. direct current (d-c), 95, 178, 191, 193
  problems of, 178, 191
Aluminum, discovery of, 144
  fabrication of, 145
  price of, 145
  production of, 144, 145
  use of, in bridges, 231
American Bell Telephone Co., 218
American Bridge Company, 137
American industry (*see* American manufactures)
American Institute of Chemical Engineers, 99
American Institute of Mining and Metallurgical Engineers, 98
American manufactures, in 19th century, 68
  spread of, 213–215
  in 20th century, 213–215
American Society of Civil Engineers, 98
American Society for Engineering Education, 101

375

ENGINEERING AND WESTERN CIVILIZATION

Brindley, James, 43, 49, 52
British birth rate, 60
British industry, 60
British labor, 61
Brown, C. E. L., 84
Brunel, Isambard K., 57, 58
Brunel, Mark I., 57, 58, 79, 205, 241, 242
Brush, William J., 152
Building construction, 233, 234
Buildings, notable, Chateau of Coucy, 24n.
  Chrysler, 233
  Empire State, 233
  Home Insurance, 233, 234
  Hudson Terminal, 243
  Manhattan Company, 232, 233, 243n.
  Masonic Temple, 233
  Metropolitan Life, 233
  Park Row, 233
  St. Paul, 233
  Singer, 233
  Tacoma, 233, 234
  Woolworth, 233
Bureau of Public Roads, 109
Bureau of Reclamation, 234, 257
Burr, Theodore, 69
Burr, William H., 69
Burt, William A., 135
Busch, Adolphus, 199
Butler, "Lazy Jim," 150
Butler, Nicholas Murray, 21, 203, 248
Butte, 139, 140
By-product coke ovens, 298

C

Cage construction, building, 233
Caissons, foundations of, French, 33, 37, 239
  modern, 239
  pneumatic, 58
Caloric theory of heat, 88
Canadian engineering, 106
Canadian mining, 154
Canalization of rivers, Coolidge on, 116
  in France, 34
  in Italy, 27

Canalization of rivers, of Ohio River, 116
  of Tennessee, 116
Canals, American, 72, 116
  British, 42–44, 49, 117
  French, 34, 117
  German, 117
  Italian, 27
  notable, Chesapeake and Ohio, 67, 71
    Chicago Drainage, 232
    Delaware & Hudson, 72
    du Midi, 34
    Erie, 67, 69n., 70–72, 116
    Grand Trunk, 44
    Liverpool and Manchester, 43, 44
    Pennsylvania, 71
  vs. railroads, 49, 72n., 117
  ship, Amsterdam, 118
    Corinth, 117
    Kaiser Wilhelm or Kiel, 118
    Manchester, 118
    Panama, 118–120, 234
    St. Mary's or Soo, 117, 135
    Suez, 117, 118, 232
Cannon, 24, 25
Capital, British, in 19th century, 60, 293
  early lack of, in United States, 60
  market for, 294
  need for increasing, 293
  present situation of, 280
Capital goods, 98, 292, 293
Capital, venture, 294
Capitalism the Creator, 202
Carlyle, Thomas, 28, 320
Carnegie, Andrew, 81, 135
Carnegie Steel Co., 74n., 81
Carnot, Sadi, 89
Cartels in Britain, 64
Carthaginians, 22
Cartwright, Edward, 45
Carty, John J., 216
Cast iron, development of, in Britain, 46
  in United States, 134
  modern production of, 138
  in steel making, 46, 137
  use of, in bridges, 48, 73
Castles, medieval, 22
Castner, H. Y., 144

378   ENGINEERING AND WESTERN CIVILIZATION